...some of the many
examples of harm caused by
attempting to apply evolution
to society's problems"

EVOLUTION'S
DANGEROUS IDEAS

—

Eugenics, Lobotomies, Using X-Rays to
Speed Up Evolution, and Other Dangerous
Ideas Inspired by Darwinism

JERRY
BERGMAN

Modern Science was founded and formed by Christian theists who challenged the 'natural philosophy' of the Greeks with Scriptural tenets and truths. What eventually emerged was the Scientific Revolution of the 13th-18th centuries that has benefited the world of today with the blessings of discovery, invention, and technology. However, in the early-to-mid-19th century, there arose an 'Evolution Revolution' to challenge the Biblical basis of Modern Science.

Indoctrinated Darwinists frequently equate "evolution" with "science," yet evolutionism only masquerades as science. As research scholar Dr. Jerry Bergman masterfully documents, "evolution" is nothing more than an atheistic philosophy of falsehoods and failures. Its history of hoaxes and horrors only trends toward dreadful disasters of deception, destruction, and death—*Evolution's Dangerous Ideas*. Bergman deals the deathblow to evolutionism, showing it to be both scientifically bankrupt and bogus; its only true legacy is bringing harm to humanity in the wake of cultural corruption and societal suicide.

It's time to return to true science rooted in morality and legitimacy, and to turn away from the sophistry and subterfuge of the pseudoscience, even anti-science, of "evolution." Bergman's research rips away evolution's mask, exposing its catastrophes for all to see, and sets us back on the path to scientific sanity—the sure science we can truly trust.

—David V. Bassett, M.S. Teacher and Author

Within the pages of a single book, Dr. Bergman exposes some of the most notorious, including some of the most dangerous, ideas that have been spawned by our culture's embrace of the morally bankrupt and erroneous claims of evolutionary naturalism.

The hoaxes, initiated either for monetary benefit or to buttress the failed ideas of Darwinism, expose not only the perpetrators, but also the almost blind willingness of the public at large to accept them. Examples of these are the Cardiff Giant and the Fiji mermaid, along with more blatant deceits such as the story of the Tasaday "primitives" and the work of Paul Kammerer.

Dr. Bergman also shows that acceptance of evolutionary theory has led to far reaching errors in the interpretation of actual scientific data. The changing stories of the Neanderthal people and of the extant   coelacanth fish are prime examples. Dr. Bergman also shows that evolutionary preconceptions were critical to the acceptance of phrenology, the "one gene – one trait" idea, the idea of blood type being linked to evolutionary hierarchy, and to the rejection of a pillar of scientific investigation, namely the essential postulate of cause and effect.

Furthermore, these pages expose the link between belief in Darwinism and harmful medical practices such as the overuse of x-rays and the use of frontal lobotomies for psychiatric care. All this notwithstanding, this book shows that the most wide ranging and destructive ideas derived from the acceptance of evolutionary thought have been policies adopted by various countries of the world, including the intellectual evolutionary racism in America which resulted in the Tuskegee experiments, and acceptance of eugenics whose intellectual offspring are abortion and genocide, most notably the Nazi holocaust.

I highly recommend this book in explanation to those who might wonder, "How could these things have occurred?"

—Kirk Toth M.S. Biology Editor

I have known of Dr. Jerry Bergman for decades, have read much of his writing, and very much value his exposés. I will comment briefly on five of the 17 chapters in his book, *Evolution's Dangerous Ideas*. In "Using Dangerous X-Rays to Speed Up Evolution," we learn that H.J. Muller was given the 1946 Nobel Prize for stating that increasing the mutation rate by radiation speeds up "evolution." The facts are, however, that zero "new information" is added and often there is loss (the opposite of what evolution needs). In "The Tall Tale of the Cardiff Giant and Evolution," Dr. Bergman documented that reading Darwin influenced the anti-Christian George Hull to become an atheist. This reading was a major motivation to carry out the hoax, namely to make Christians look foolish." In the chapter titled "Proving Evolution by Fraud: The Paul Kammerer Case," Dr. Bergman noted that Kammerer spent decades researching and publishing his findings for the once-popular 'acquired characteristics' evolutionary theory. His peers eventually uncovered solid evidence that Kammerer faked much of his evidence. When he was later exposed, he took his own life with a gun.

In "The Fiji Mermaid Evolution Hoax," we learn that the hoax was promoted by the circus great P.T. Barnum. It turns out it is a good example of how non-scientists have reinforced Darwinism in the public's mind by forging evidence. In "The Worst Blunder: Rejecting The Law of Cause and Effect in Cosmology," Dr. Bergman correctly observed that the idea that everything, or anything, can exist for no reason is not rational. One of the oldest lines of reasoning for a creator, and for many people the most convincing, is the Law of Causality. A simple everyday example is when a mother discovers wet mud tracks on the living room floor, she does not need to personally see the culprit to deduce what has occurred. The mud is enough proof to conclude that someone has traversed on her floor with muddy shoes. Likewise, the existence of the creation is itself sufficient to prove a Creator.

—**Paul G. Humber, speaker, author, and educator**, has a master's degree from the University of Pennsylvania. He taught math at Haverford School, a private college preparatory day school founded in 1884, for 24 years. He is currently Director, CR Ministries (Philadelphia, PA, USA)

Acknowledgments

Bryce Gaudian, David Bassett, Kirk Ktoth MA, Biologist, Douglas B. Sharp, BS; Mike Oard, M.S., Bryce Gaudian, Kitty Foth-Regner, Ellen Myers, M.A., Dr. David Herbert, Wayne Frair, Ph.D., Emerson Thomas McMullen, Ph.D., Steven E. Woodworth, PhD., Professor David J. Oberpriller, Bolton Davidheiser, Ph.D., John Woodmorappe, M.A., Ian Taylor, M. S.; Steven E. Woodworth, PhD, Bryce Gaudian, Bert Thompson, Ph.D., Clifford Lillo, MA, Robert Kofahl, Ph.D., Jody Allen R.N., and Professor Aeron Bergman, M.A, for their feedback on earlier drafts of this work.

cántaro
publications

www.cantaroinstitute.org

Evolution's Dangerous Ideas: Eugenics, Lobotomies, Using X-Rays to Speed Up Evolution, and Other Dangerous Ideas, Inspired by Darwinism
by Jerry Bergman

Published by Cántaro Publications, a publishing imprint of the Cántaro Institute, Jordan Station, ON.

Book design by Steven R. Martins

Library & Archives Canada

ISBN 978-1-990771-57-6

Printed in the United States of America

Table of Contents

Introduction

THIS IS THE SECOND BOOK to support the fact that Darwinism has caused enormous harm in society. The first book covered how Darwinism fostered scientific racism. This book covers 17 of the most harmful ideas and hoaxes committed in the name of evolution, often concocted to support Darwinism. These few examples of the many available illustrate how Darwinism has misled scientists, researchers, and the general public. Most were birthed by Darwinism and several were a direct result of the Darwinian worldview indoctrination. Two were awarded the Nobel Prize, and several resulted in enormous harm to a large number of innocent people. Some caused financial harm, and a few caused harm to health. In some extreme cases death has resulted, such as among frontal-lobotomy patients. This book is the 12th volume I have written documenting the harm to society caused by Darwinism. I have two more books ready to further document this thesis. In short, it is beyond question that Darwinism has caused an enormous amount of harm to humanity.

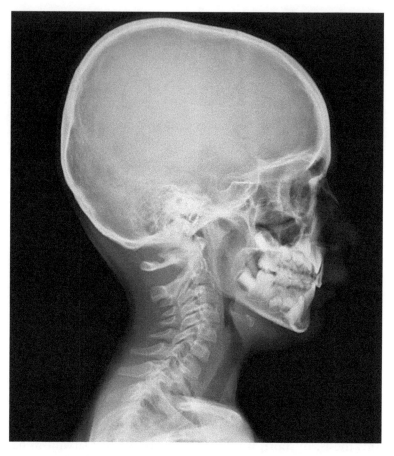

An example of a head profile x-ray showing the detail this technique is able to image. From Wikimedia commons.

Source: https://commons.wikimedia.org/wiki/File:Medical_X-Ray_imaging_WYJ07_nevit.jpg.

1

Using Dangerous X-Rays to Speed Up Evolution

MUTATIONS ARE BELIEVED by evolutionists to be the main source of new genetic information required for evolution. Mutations are changes in the DNA code caused by mutagens, including carcinogens such as tobacco smoke, and radiation such as cosmic rays. The importance of mutations as the source of new genetic information was believed to be so significant that the 1946 Nobel Prize was presented to H. J. Muller for his discovery that increasing the mutation rate by radiation would speed up evolution. Although still regarded as the bedrock of evolution, the experimental evidence has since documented that actually significant genetic *degeneration* is caused by radiation, not new *information* to enable evolution to progress. It is, consequently, not a significant source of the variation that is critical for Darwinian evolution. Falsifying the conclusion that mutations produce significant levels of new, potentially useful, genetic variety falsifies the core of evolutionary theory.[1]

Protein: The Core of the Body

Evolutionary theory postulates that natural selection preserves beneficial genetic additions and helpful changes. All human body organs, including skin and muscles, plus enzymes and hormones, are constructed primarily of protein. The genetic code used to produce this protein is constructed of deoxyribonucleic acid (DNA). Evolution requires new genetic variety which is then pruned by natural selection. It also eliminates the deleterious genetic changes. DNA both builds animal bodies and is the hereditary material passed on to future generations. As acknowledged by one of the leading evolutionists of the last century, Theodosius Dobzhansky, gene changes caused by mutagens, known as mutations, are the major source of evolutionary diversity.[2] Professor Sniegowske added: "mutation is the ultimate source of the genetic variation… mutations are accidents, and accidents will happen… Indeed, mutations are accidents."[3] In short, random mutation is the raw material required for natural selection because it is the source of the genetic variety that drives evolution.

The Discovery of Mutations

When Darwin developed his theory of evolution, he was unable to propose a viable mechanism that produced genetic variety from which natural selection could select. The problem he faced was *not* "survival of the fittest" which is what his famous

---

1. Sniegowski, Paul D., et al., 2000. The evolution of mutation rates: Separating causes from consequences. *BioEssays* 22(12):1057-1066.

2. Sadava, David E., et al., 2006. *Life, Vol. II: Evolution, Diversity and Ecology*, 8th Edition. San Francisco, CA: W.H. Freeman, p. 571.

3. Sniegowski, et al., 2000, p. 1064.

book is about, but the **arrival** of the fittest. Around 1900, Dutch botanist Hugo de Vries (1848-1935) theorized that new species were not formed by slow changes that produced continuous variations in life as Darwin taught. Rather, they were caused by the sudden appearance of new genetic variations, an alteration he named "mutations". De Vries also proposed that mutations are heritable and, therefore, are passed down to successive generations.[4] His observation was eventually united with natural selection, forming the revised evolutionary theory called Neo-Darwinism.

Roentgen Discovers X-Rays

In 1895, German physics professor Wilhelm Roentgen discovered X-rays. X-rays are a highly ionizing form of radiation that is most familiar from its medical application. Within months of the publication of Roentgen's paper detailing his discovery, X-ray applications ranged from medical use in hospitals to shoe stores where they were used to help determine how well shoes fit the customers' feet.[5]

American scientist Dr. Hermann Joseph Muller (1890 –1967) knew evolutionists believed that "gene mutations formed the chief basis of organic evolution, and therefore of most complexities in living things."[6] In the 1920's, working

4. de Vries, Hugo. 1909. *The Mutation Theory: Experiments and Observations on the Origin of Species in the Vegetable Kingdom*, Volume 1. Chicago, Illinois: The Open Court Publishing Company; 1910. *The Mutation Theory: Experiments and Observations on the Origin of Species in the Vegetable Kingdom*, Volume 2. Chicago, Illinois: The Open Court Publishing Company.
5. Shapiro, Gilbert. 1986. *A Skeleton in the Darkroom: Stories of Serendipity in Science*. San Francisco, CA: Harper & Row.
6. Muller, Hermann J. 1927. Artificial transmutation of the gene. *Science*. 66(1669):84-87, July 22.

with fruit flies, Dr. Muller discovered that X-rays could *increase* the mutation rate in living organisms by as much as a factor of 100. He soon theorized that he could drastically speed up evolution by using radiation to artificially create large numbers of new mutations. His experiments involved placing fruit flies in petri dishes, turning on his X-ray tube, then mating the flies that survived. Lastly, he attempted to measure and evaluate the number of mutations in the offspring.[7]

The excitement that this discovery produced in the scientific community was enormous. As a result, Muller was awarded the Nobel Prize in Physiology in 1946 "for the discovery of the production of mutations by means of X-ray irradiation." In his Nobel lecture Muller wrote:

> Not only is this accumulation of many rare, mainly tiny changes the chief means of artificial animal and plant improvement, but it is, even more, the way in which natural evolution has occurred, under the guidance of natural selection. Thus the Darwinian theory becomes implemented, and freed from the accretions of directed variation and of Lamarckism that once encumbered it.[8]

When Muller confirmed that large numbers of new mutations can deliberately be caused by X-rays, he formally proposed that they be used to irradiate animals and plants to increase the evolution rate. In short, X-rays were an important means which humans could use to change "the hereditary ma-

---

7. Muller, 1927.
8. Muller, Hermann J. 1946. "The Production of Mutations," Nobel Lecture—December 12, 1946. Reprinted in *Nobel Lectures, Physiology or Medicine 1942-1962*. Amsterdam, Netherlands: Elsevier Publishing Company, pp. 154-172, p. 162.

terial" to speed up evolution [9] His synthesis of natural selection with mutations produced the latest evolutionary theory, called Neo-Darwinism.

Using X-Rays to Speed Up Mutation Rates

One of the many articles that described evolutionists' excitement using Professor Muller's experiments to speed up evolution documented the importance of mutations, stating that evolutionary changes

> can be produced 150 times as fast by the use of X-rays as they can by the ordinary processes of nature. This means that man may someday force the production of new and desirable plant and animal varieties far more rapidly than he has hitherto been able to.[10]

The headline of this article explained the reason for the excitement, namely the "New Discovery Speeds Up Evolution: Science Prize Winner Makes Discovery Believed by Many to Have Immense Practical and Scientific Significance."[11] Yet another headline enthusiastically proclaimed "Scientist Creates New Forms of Life: Dr. H. J. Muller Says Study of Mutations Shows Striking Changes are Possible. Works with Fruit Flies. U. S. Geneticist, Now in Russia, Produces Many Varieties of

---

9.   Lönnig, Wolf-Ekkehard. 2005. Mutation breeding, evolution, and the law of recurrent variation. *Research Signpost 37* 661(2):45-70, January, p. 47.

10. Thone, Frank. 1928. New discovery speeds up evolution: Science prize winner makes discovery believed by many to have immense practical and scientific significance. *Scientific American* 138(3):235, March, p. 235.

11. Thone, 1928, p. 235.

Insect With X-Rays."[12]

The X-ray dose that Muller exposed his test animals to was so intense that only 11 percent of the animals survived. These few survivors were then allowed to breed. When the first generation hatched from their eggs, Muller bred the second generation, then a third. He soon saw what he considered amazing results:

> Mutations such as he had often seen in un-X-rayed stock turned up, together with a number of brand new ones. All told, he figures that he has produced at least 100 distinct gene mutations, genes being the carriers of hereditary qualities, and that the raying has speeded [sic] up the process over 15,000 percent. In the end, the rays will be applied to sheep and cattle, wheat and fruit.[13]

Muller the Eugenicist

Muller was a eugenics supporter, at least when he was younger, as he documented in his book titled *Out of the Night: A Biologist's View of the Future*, written in support of the technique. In this book he described how mutations, combined with eugenics, could be used to create a superior race and, as a result, a better future for all of humankind. Thorne added that, assisting or forcing nature so that new traits

> will be produced faster than at the old rate, has for centuries been the breeder's dream. Until recently, however, there was not even a hint of hope that this dream might be realized, because nobody knew what made mutations happen; nobody knew their mechanism. And until that was known, man lacked a handle to

---

12. *The New York Times*, 29 March 1936.
13. Thone, 1928, p. 235.

take hold of it in his effort to push nature along a bit.[14]

Muller was awarded not only the Nobel Prize for his mutation research, but also the prestigious Darwin-Wallace Medal in 1958 and the 1955 Kimber Genetics Award, presented by the U. S. National Academy of Sciences. As an active atheist and anti-creationist, Muller also served as President of the *American Humanist Association* from 1956 to 1958.[15]

Achieving the Breeder's Dream Fails

Now that evolutionists knew how to produce new mutations, they believed they could finally achieve the breeder's dream of producing new genetic variety. The goal was to speed up the rate of evolution by artificially increasing the mutation rate. Muller reasoned that if

> mutations always follow when accidents happen to the chromosomes in the course of nature, why not arrange a few such accidents, and thus get your desired hastening of the mutation process? Professor Muller decided to use heavy doses of X-rays. He chose the little flying creature we find on fruit when it begins to spoil, known variously as fruit-fly, vinegar-fly and pomace-fly. It has the advantage that it breeds very rapidly.[16]

Muller recognized the fact that mutations could be harmful, especially if high doses of radiation were used. Nonethe-

---

14. Thone, 1928, p. 235.
15. Linskens, H.F. 1982. Review of: *Genes, Radiation and Society: The Life and Work of H.J. Muller* (1981) by E.A. Carlson. *Theoretical Applied Genetics* 63(3):200, September 1, p. 200; Carlson, Elof Axel. 2011. Speaking out about the social implications of science: The uneven legacy of H.J. Muller. *Genetics* 187(1):1–7, January.
16. Thone, 1928, p. 235.

less, he felt that he could control the level to effectively evolve animals and plants, while concurrently avoiding most of the deleterious effects. This method, called mutation breeding, at first produced "an enormous euphoria … among biologists in general and geneticists and breeders in particular that the time had come to revolutionize the 'old' method of recombination breeding by the entirely new branch of mutation breeding."[17] Muller was optimistic about his discovery because he was convinced that what he called the 'invisible mutations,' those that cause minor non-lethal changes, "were the basis of the origin of all life-forms, including man."[18] One author, writing contemporaneously with Muller, after claiming that we are the product of millions of years of evolution, wrote: "Until recently it was thought that our species had stopped evolving far in the past." He then added that sophisticated, complex, modern high-tech X-ray technology has now allowed us to not only speed up, but also to direct our own evolution.[19] This irresponsible claim ignores the evidence and is worse than naive.

The Mutation Breeding Theory Now Discredited

Research soon confirmed the view accepted today, namely that mutations rarely produce beneficial changes.[20] We now also recognize that any method that produces DNA mutations commonly causes deleterious birth or developmental defects, as well as disease, especially cancer.[21] It was for this reason that

17. Lönnig, 2005, p. 48.
18. Lönnig, 2005, p. 48.
19. Max, D.T. 2017. Beyond human. *National Geographic* 231(4):40-63, April.
20. Sanford, John. 2014. *Genetic Entropy*, 4th Edition. Lansing, NY: FMS Publications.
21. Gurley, LaVerne Tolley, and William J. Callaway. 1992. *Introduction to Radiologic Technology*, Third Edition. St. Louis, MO: Mosby-Yearbook.

the use of X-ray machines in shoe stores to determine shoe fit is now banned. Doctors recognize that the risk-benefit ratio for medical use of X-rays must have potential benefits that outweigh the risks before an X-ray is taken. Muller also knew this, but because mutations were the only known source of significant new genetic variety, he reasoned that mutations must be the source of most of the raw material that caused evolution.[22] As an atheist, he had no other choice.

Muller and other X-ray experimenters even tried to treat germ cells with "heavy doses of X-rays" to induce the occurrence of "true gene mutations."[23] This process produced several hundred new mutant genes whose offspring were followed up for three or more generations. An analysis of the results concluded that lethal mutations "greatly outnumbered the non-lethals, producing a visible morphological abnormality," a finding that was repeatedly found in other X-ray research.[24]

The fact is, "although on very rare occasions a mutation can produce an improvement in a living thing, mutations are random changes unrelated to an animal's needs except by chance."[25] An example of the rare mutation that produces beneficial effects is a dominant gene mutation which allows expression of the recessive gene, conferring to the organism a beneficial trait in certain limited circumstances.[26]

---

22. Muller, 1927, pp. 86-87.

23. Muller, Hermann J. 1936. *Out of the Night: A Biologist's View of the Future*. New York, NY: Vanguard.

24. Muller, 1927, p. 85.

25. Halacy, Daniel S., Jr. 1966. *Radiation, Magnetism, and Living Things*. New York, NY: Holiday House.

26. Behe, Michael. 2019. *Darwin Devolves: The New Science About DNA*. New York, NY: Harper-One, pp. 170-195.

Mutations Cause Disease

Given our present knowledge about ionizing radiation from the experimental evidence, Muller's optimism and conclusions were grossly naïve, actually dangerous. His theory was accepted for decades, largely because evolutionists had no other viable method to produce new genetic variety. This is why machines in shoe stores allowing customers to use low-dose X-rays to evaluate shoe fit were not banned in the Western world until the late 1960s.

Unfortunately, the clear evidence in Muller's day that radiation was dangerous was largely ignored. One of the many well-documented examples involved Thomas Edison's assistant, Clarence Dally. After spending eight years helping to develop X-ray technology, Dally lost most of his fingers, then his hand, next his arm below his elbow, and finally his life from cancer. He died in 1904 as a result of his X-ray exposure. After this, Edison refused to be involved in X-ray technology, even refusing to have an X-ray when he was ill.

Mutation Repair Systems

A major problem with mutations is that, due to "contamination of the genome by very slightly deleterious mutations: why have we not died 100 times over?"[27] One reason is that humans possess several mechanisms that repair the vast number of mutations that regularly occur in our genome.[28] Exposure to mutagens causes problems because repair is not 100 percent ac-

---

27. Kondrashov, Alexey S. 1995. Contamination of the genome by very slightly deleterious mutations: Why have we not died 100 times over? *Journal of Theoretical Biology* 175(4):583-594.

28. Bergman, Jerry. 2006. The elimination of mutations by the cell's elaborate protein quality control system: A major problem for Neo-Darwinism. *CRSQ* (*Creation Research Society Quarterly*) 43(2):68-74.

curate and, eventually, the body becomes swamped with them, causing disease and death.

One summary of the results of years of research on speeding up the rate of new mutations concluded that most mutational breeding programs "failed, especially in the early days of over optimism, to produce anything useful."[29]

This finding of failure was not due to any lack of effort to document mutations. Of the thousands of tests, "only a very small fraction of induced mutants (certainly less than 1%) has ever been found suitable to enter yield trials and eventually only 1% of those evaluated passed the official tests and obtained approval for commercial utilization."[30] To enter a yield trial the mutant must be proven promising enough to be formally researched in a large animal population. Those mutations that proved beneficial were usually because the mutation damaged a dominant gene, thus allowing the recessive gene to be consistently expressed. The improvement was not because the mutation produced a new and better "more evolved" gene that in some way improved the animal or plant.

The end of this line of research, as Professor Lönnig stressed, was that "according to all the evidence achieved so far by experimental investigations (and later also by careful considerations in theoretical genetics), there is absolutely no future for mutation breeding in animals – not to speak of severe ethical problems involved in the artificial mutagenesis of birds, mammals and other animals capable of feeling pain."[31] Even mutational

29. Simmonds, Norman William. 1979. *Principles of Crop Improvement.* London, UK: Longman Publishing Group.
30. Micke, A. 1976. Induced mutations in cross-breeding. *IAEA* (International Atomic Energy Agency), 1 - 4. Wien (Vienna, 13-17 October 1975).
31. Dobzhansky, Theodosius. 1941. *Genetics and the Origin of Species.* New

breeding of plants produced a ratio of useful to useless mutations estimated to be less than around 1 to 100,000.[32]

Scientists now have documented that over 99.9 percent
of all mutations are near-neutral, mildly detrimental, or deleterious. *Near-neutral* means that they do not directly cause
disease, but accumulate, causing aging and, eventually, disease
and death. All carcinogens cause cancer by producing mutations that affect cell-division regulation. Over 5,000 genetic
diseases, such as sickle-cell anemia, are known to be caused
by mutations. It is estimated that 10-20 percent of all preg-
nancies result in miscarriages, and the actual number may be
much higher. Many miscarriages are not formally *classified* as
such because the loss occurs very early in the pregnancy, sometimes even before the woman knows she is pregnant.[33] By far
the most common reason for a miscarriage is DNA damage.
This is evidence documenting the fact that the human DNA is
now enormously corrupt compared to the original creation.[34]

York, NY: Columbia University Press.

32. Gottschalk, W., and G. Wolff. 1983. *Induced Mutations in Plant Breeding.* New York, NY: Springer-Verlag; Broertjes, C., and A.M. Van
Hartenvan. 1978. *Application of Mutation Breeding Methods in the Improvement of Vegetatively Propagated Crops.* [An interpretative literature
review.] London, UK: Elsevier Science.

33. Frost, Julia, et al., 2007. The loss of possibility: Scientisation of death
and the special case of early miscarriage. *Sociology of Health and Illness*
29(7):1003-1022.

34. Qi, H., et al. 2018. High resolution global chromosomal aberrations
from spontaneous miscarriages revealed by low coverage whole genome
sequencing. *European Journal of Obstetrics & Gynecology and Reproduc-
tive Biology* 224:21-28; Goddijn, M., and N. Leschot. 2000. Genetic
aspects of miscarriage. *Best Practice & Research Clinical Obstetrics &
Gynecology* 14(5):855-865.

Only Rare Organisms Thrive on Radiation

A rare few organisms appear to thrive on radiation, such as the fungus *Cryptococcus neoformans*. This organism uses the pigment that causes human skin color, melanin, to obtain energy for growth.[35] Researchers tested the response from gamma radiation given off by rhenium-188 and tungsten-188 on three different fungi species. The result was that all three, *Cladosporium sphaerospermum*, *Cryptococcus neoformans*, and *Wangiella dermatitidis*, grew faster in the presence of radiation.[36]

Researchers found that irradiated melanin increased their capacity to reduce a compound central to NADH (nicotinamide adenine dinucleotide) by a factor of four compared to non-irradiated melanin.[37] NADH has a central role in the chemical process that generates useable energy in all life-forms. This finding fits the fact that melanized microorganisms are commonly the dominant species in soils contaminated with radionuclides. Humans are protected against both UV and solar radiation by melanin, which causes what is called "skin tanning".

Outer space does not protect life on Earth from certain harmful ionizing radiation, thus requiring another protection system. Melanin not only helps explain the resistance of melanized fungi to ionizing radiation but also the fact that it

35. Dadachova, Ekaterina, and Arturo Casadevall. 2008. Ionizing radiation: How fungi cope, adapt, and exploit with the help of melanin. *Current Opinion in Microbiology* 11(6):525-531.

36. Ledford, Heidi. 2007. Hungry fungi chomp on radiation. *Nature*, https://www.nature.com/news/2007/070521/full/070521-5.html

37. Dadachova, E., et al. 2007. Ionizing radiation changes the electronic properties of melanin and enhances the growth of melanized fungi. *PLoS One*, doi:10.1371/journal.pone.0000457.

can decompose certain radioactive materials.[38] However, no evidence exists that the radiation helps the organism to survive by causing mutations.

The Mutation Rate in Humans

The mutation rate in humans has been documented to result in "at least one new mutation ... in each round of cell division, even in cells with unimpaired DNA repair and in the absence of external mutagens. As a result, every child is born with an estimated 100 to 200 new mutations that were not present in the parents."[39]

It was once believed that most mutations were in the so-called "junk" DNA that lacked functions, and thus were assumed to be harmless. However, it has now been experimentally documented that the vast majority of DNA has a function. Because of this, the mutational load caused by mutagens contributes to the degeneration of the genome, eventually causing genetic meltdown and extinction. In short, 'evolution' is true, but going backward. Both individuals and populations are **devolving** downward, a process called genetic entropy, not evolving upward as Darwinists claim.[40] Mutations in individuals not only cause disease, such as cancer, but all of the other effects of aging.

---

38. Mirchink, T.G., G.B. Kashkina, and I.D. Abaturov. 1972. Resistance of fungi with different pigments to radiation. *Mikrobiologiia* 41(1):83–86; Saleh, Y.G., M.S. Mayo, and D.G. Ahearn. 1988. Resistance of some common fungi to gamma irradiation. *Applied Environment Microbiology* 54(8):2134–2135.

39. Meisenberg, Gerhard, and William Simmons. 2006. *Principles of Medical Biochemistry*. Philadelphia, PA: Mosby, p. 153.

40. Sanford, 2014.

Summary

Ironically, most Darwinists ignore the well-documented science and assume that mutations are the major source of genetic variety from which natural selection can select.[41] In fact, it is still almost universally believed that "mutation is the ultimate source of new genetic variation within populations," thus is the foundation of evolution.[42] The fact is, mutations are lethal to Darwinism.[43] Evolution requires a source of new genetic information, and without it evolution cannot occur.[44] In spite of over a century of effort, Darwinists have not been able to propose a better explanation for the source of new genetic variety. All of their attempts to "speed up evolution" have not only failed, but in the end have been documented to be unequivocally harmful.

Actually, the history of the attempts to further evolution by using radiation to produce mutations documents the fact that mutations cannot be the source of the enormous variety required to fuel evolution.[45] No means exists of producing significant amounts of *new* genetic variety. Rather, mutations are a major cause of disease, including cancer and birth defects.[46] Science has now been forced to invest in an enormous amount

---

41. Bergman, Jerry. 2022. *The Three Pillars of Evolution Demolished: Why Darwin Was Wrong.* Bloomington, IN: WestBow Press (A Division of Thomas Nelson and Zondervan Press).

42. Wade, Michael. 2005. "Evolutionary Genetics." *Stanford Encyclopedia of Philosophy*, https://plato.stanford.edu/entries/evolutionary-genetics/#pagetopright.

43. Bergman, Jerry. 2002. Why mutations are lethal to Darwinism. *CRSQ* 38(4):181-189.

44. Bergman, 2002.

45. Sanford, 2014.

46. Charlesworth, Brian. 2012. The effects of deleterious mutations on evolution at linked sites. *Genetics* 190(1):5-22, January.

of research to ameliorate the results of diseases caused by the accumulations of mutations that have occurred since Adam.

Dutch botanist Hugo de Vries who proposed tat mutations is the answer to the source of genetic variety. Published in *Popular Science Monthly* August 1905.

Adolf Hitler the Leader of the Third Reich and the man who, more than any other, began WWII and the attempt to exterminate all European Jews. From Wikimedia commons.

Source: https://commons.wikimedia.org/wiki/File:Bundesarchiv_Bild_183-S33882,_Adolf_Hitler_retouched.jpg

2

Why the Most Educated Nation Produced the Holocaust

AFTER WWII ENDED, a major concern was understanding what caused a war that cost the lives of an estimated 50–56 million military personnel and civilians, with an additional estimated 19–28 million deaths from war-related disease and famine. Historians have documented that towards the end of the war, when the Nazis had to make the choice between either winning the war or killing Jews, destroying the Jews was the priority.[1]

One claim is that Hitler hated Jews because he had some very bad past experience with them. Actually, according to the documented evidence, Hitler's experiences with Jews were consistently positive. When Hitler lived in the Männerheim Bri-

---

1. This claim was well-documented in the 2022 6 hour Ken Burns PBS documentary *The U.S. and the Holocaust.*

gittenau hostel in Brigittenau, Vienna, a number of Jews lived there with whom he was on excellent terms. Most of his paintings were sold by Jewish dealers that Hitler was also on good terms with. One of the most loyal buyers of his paintings in Vienna was the Jew, Samuel Morgenstern. Hitler even expressed his admiration for Rothschild for sticking to his religion, even though this meant he could not use the German courts to settle valid grievances.

Throughout most of 1918, the Jew Lt. Hugo Gutmann (1880–1962) served as Adolf Hitler's direct superior. Gutmann later recommended Hitler for the award of the Iron Cross First Class (a decoration rarely awarded to persons of Hitler's low Gefreiter rank). The decoration was presented to Hitler in August 1918 by the regimental commander, Major von Tubeuf.[2] Hitler wore this medal throughout the remainder of his career, including while serving as Führer of Nazi Germany. In 1938, Gutmann was arrested by the Gestapo, but released as a result of the SS personnel who knew his history.[3] Gutmann, due to Hitler's intervention, received a full pension from Nazi Germany which he lived on until the end of the Second World War.

The Jew Eduard Bloch (1872–1945), was Hitler's family physician when they lived in Linz until 1907. Bloch had a special fondness for the Hitler family. When Hitler's mother, Klara, was dying of breast cancer, Bloch billed the family at a reduced cost, sometimes even refusing to bill them outright. In 1908, Hitler wrote to Bloch, assuring him of his gratitude for the loving care given to his mother when she was ill, a reverence that Hitler expressed with gifts. One gift was a valuable large

2. Kershaw, Ian. 2008. *Hitler: A Biography*. New York, NY: W.W. Norton & Company, p. 59.
3. Weber, Thomas. 2010. *Hitler's First War.* Oxford, UK: Oxford University Press, pp. 344 ff, September 16.

wall painting which, according to Bloch's daughter, Gertrude (Trude) Kren (born 1903 in Austria; died 1992 in the U. S.), was lost. As late as 1937, Hitler was concerned about Bloch's well-being and called him an Edeljude ("noble Jew").

When the Nazis annexed Austria in 1938, the 66-year-old Bloch wrote to Hitler asking for protection. In response, Hitler awarded Bloch special protection and personally intervened to ensure his safety.[4] Bloch stayed in his house with his wife undisturbed until the formalities for his emigration to the United States were completed. Without any interference, they were able to sell their family home at market value, highly unusual considering the distress sales of emigrating Jews at the time and Nazi expropriation of Jewish assets through the Reich Flight Tax. Moreover, the Bloch's were allowed to take the equivalent of 16 Reichsmarks out of the country. The usual amount allowed to Jews was a mere 10 Reichsmarks.[5]

Bloch lived in the United States until his death in 1945 from stomach cancer.[6] Many more examples could be cited. Furthermore, I was unable to find a single example of a negative experience Hitler had with Jews. The reasons for Hitler's determination to eliminate Jews includes the fact that he was fully convinced that they were, except for the Edeljudes, an inferior race and had to be exterminated in the Nazi's goal of producing a superior race based on Darwinism.[7] In this goal

4. Cowley, Jason. 2002. The search for Dr. Bloch. *Granta*, 79. October 1; retrieved April 24, 2007.
5. Hamann, Brigitte. 2008. *Hitlers Edeljude: Das Leben des Armenarztes Eduard Bloch*. Munich, Germany: Piper Verlag, p. 427.
6. Álvarez, Jorge. 2020. "Eduard Bloch, the Jewish doctor whom Hitler helped to leave Germany in 1940." *LBV Magazine*, English Edition, April 3; retrieved March 17, 2022.
7. Cawthorne, Nigel. 2022. *The Evil Madness of Hitler: The Damning Psychiatric Profile*. London, UK: Arcturus Publishing, p. 164.

he had the support of academia, the "intelligentsia." Before the war, Germany boasted more Nobel laureates in science than any other nation, including the United States. The Holocaust was designed and carried out by well-educated professional people in the most educated nation on Earth. How and why this happened is the subject of this chapter.

One assumes that intelligent people would recognize that their inhumane racists actions were based on a belief that was without scientific support. Unfortunately, Germany, as well as much of the Western world, was not exempt from the power that a non-Biblical worldview can have over even academically gifted individuals. A major reason why Nazi ideology was embraced by intelligent people was because the German educational system had inculcated Darwinian and social Darwinian ideas into students for years prior to the Holocaust.[8] All levels of German education, from preschool to college, aggressively indoctrinated students in eugenics. This played a crucial role in propelling the Germans toward the evolutionary racist ideology that ultimately lead to their justification of the Holocaust horrors.

While educational censorship prevented the facts from being expressed, the foremost reason why Nazi ideology birthed and spread horrendous consequences was because German leaders and "the intelligentsia" fueling the educational systems rejected the Genesis creation account. Therefore, they rejected the belief that all mankind was created in the image of God and descended from one couple—Adam and Eve. As is true of orthodox communism, no alternative explanations were per-

---

8. United States Holocaust Memorial Museum (Washington, D.C.). 2020. "Final Solution": In Depth. *Holocaust Encyclopedia.* https://encyclopedia.ushmm.org/content/en/article/final-solution-in-depth, December 8.

mitted. Comply or else.

As historian Stephen Hicks asserts, the "list of intellectuals who supported the Nazis long before they came to power .... represents a 'Who's Who' list of powerful minds and cultural leaders."[9] Nazi eugenics goals, based on the myth of superior-inferior human races, were central to the Holocaust and, in the end, ultimately lead to the atrocities of WWII.[10] An important step toward the Nazi Holocaust was

> Charles Darwin's *Origin of Species* [which] profoundly undermined the Biblical basis of understanding human groups by declaring that human beings had evolved ... over hundreds of millennia, and by suggesting that races had evolved by a process of adaptation. ... Darwin offered the prospect of understanding the human race biologically, and it was a [sure] step for certain of his followers to invoke natural selection and survival of the fittest as the basis of human behavior and racial characteristics. In the United States there were early Darwinists who appealed to the theory in support of white superiority. ... In Germany, however, Darwinism took a rather different direction: calls for social intervention that would control selection in order to avoid the degeneration of human groups.... beyond this lay the promotion of the superiority of the Germanic peoples... and the need to combat Christianity.[11]

A leading historian of Nazi Germany, Edwin Black, doc-

9. Hicks, S. 2010. *Nietzsche and the Nazis*. Rockford College, IL: Ockham's Razor Publishers, p. 9.
10. Burns, Ken, et al. 2022. "The U.S. and the Holocaust." New York, NY: PBS (Public Broadcasting System).
11. Cornwell, J. 2003. *Hitler's Scientists: Science, War, and the Devil's Pact.* New York, NY: Viking Press, p. 76.

umented that the Nazi government's eugenics goals dictated how people would live and die. In short, "Hitler's regime was one of totalitarian aspirations. The Nazi system was built on ideology and terror... and institutional Darwinism."[12] The Nazi physicians "would become the unseen generals in Hitler's war against the Jews and other Europeans deemed inferior. Darwinian-influenced doctors created the science, devised the eugenic formulas, wrote the legislation, and even hand-selected the victims for sterilization, euthanasia, and mass extermination. Black shirts and Brown shirts would inflict the horror—but white coats directed it."[13] American psychiatrist and Harvard associate, Robert Lifton, records the horrors of Nazi medical techniques, concluding that it was the doctors in Auschwitz that ordered, supervised, and sometimes carried out the murder of over a million persons in that camp.[14] Lifton called Auschwitz "the racial cure" for the problems of Germany.[15] Researchers Annas and Grodin further commented that Nazi physicians also "became leaders in the National Socialist Party and were honored for their work.... The Nazi theory, based on a social Darwinist view of genetics and racial purity, meshed perfectly with the Nazi ideology".[16]

Actually, the Nazi nurses (most of whom were women) directly killed many more persons than did the Nazi physicians.[17]

12. Childers, T. 2001. *A History of Hitler's Empire,* 2nd Edition. Chantilly, VA: The Great Courses, p. 22.

13. Black, E. 2009. *Nazi Nexus: America's Corporate Connections to Hitler's Holocaust.* Washington, D.C.: Dialog Press, p. 35.

14. Lifton, R.J. 1986. *The Nazi Doctors: Medical Killing and the Psychology of Genocide.* New York, NY: Basic Books, p. 18.

15. Lifton, 1986, p. 145.

16. Annas, G., and M. Grodin (editors). 1992. *The Nazi Doctors and the Nuremberg Code.* New York, NY: Oxford University Press, p. 15.

17 Benedict, S., and L. Shields. 2014. *Nurses and Midwives in Nazi*

As Darwin opined in his *Descent of Man,* women were inferior to men. German women were forced to follow the commands of the 'superior' men and believed they had to carry out the killings as directed. By refusing to do so they could face sterilization, persecution, torture, or internment. The German system (once again, based on evolution) had indoctrinated enough of their women to willingly carry out the work associated with 'racial purity'/'racial cleansing.'

The physicians' social Darwinist core belief was that certain individuals, or groups of people, were genetically superior to others. The Nazis wholeheartedly embraced this idea, and for this reason social Darwinism was central in bringing about the Holocaust. Furthermore, they made "widespread use of the Darwinian term 'selection,' [and] the Nazis sought to take over the functions of nature (natural selection) and God… in orchestrating their own 'selections,' their own version of human evolution … the resulting 'racial and social' biology could make vicious forms of anti-Semitism seem intellectually respectable to learned men and women."[18]

The result was a "biocracy" where the state was the means to apply biological Darwinism to the entire territory that was controlled by Germany. There were so many doctors that were influential in the Holocaust and Nazism that a separate trial was held for them at Nuremberg. Twenty of the 23 persons tried for war crimes at this trial were medical doctors.[19] Exclud-

Germany: The "Euthanasia Programs." New York, NY: Routledge Publishing; McFarland-Icke, R. 1999. *Nurses in Nazi Germany: Moral Choice in History.* Princeton, NJ: Princeton University Press.

18. Lifton, 1986, p. 17.
19. Vollmann, J., and R. Winau. 1996. Nuremberg Doctors Trial: Informed consent in human experimentation before the Nuremberg Code. *The British Medical Journal* 313(7070):1445-1447, p. 1445.

ing seven of the 23 tried at Nuremberg (acquitted only because the court did not find 'enough' evidence to convict them), all others were sentenced to life imprisonment, or death by hanging. Most were committed Nazis, completely committed to the Nazi eugenics program.[20]

Psychological Evaluations of Leading Nazis

Many leading Nazis, such as Adolf Hitler, Joseph Goebbels, and Heinrich Himmler committed suicide before, or very soon after, Germany surrendered. The leading Nazis still alive were subjected to the Nuremberg war-criminal trials. Prior to the Nuremberg trials, psychiatrists were brought in to determine the dominant beliefs of the Nazi leaders, so as to better understand what fueled their destructive ideology.

The psychological testing and evaluations were driven by the scientific community's desire to determine the motivation for the Nazi war crimes because their crimes called into question the very nature of humankind. Thus, there was an urgency to conduct detailed psychological examinations on living Nazi leaders as soon as feasible.

The leading psychiatrist charged with examining the head Nazis was an American, Columbia University-trained, Lt. Colonel Dr. Douglas Kelley. The principal psychologist was American Lt. Dr. Gustave Gilbert, also Columbia University-trained. These doctors evaluated 21 of the high-level Nazi leaders on trial for war crimes.

From these interviews, it was determined that the reasoning the Nazi leaders used to justify the Holocaust was the belief that the people who succeeded in society thrived due to their superior genes. The people who lived in less-developed cul-

20. Annas and Grodin, 1992, p. 106.

tures were less capable due to their inferior genes.[21] They also believed that even a taint of an inferior race carried a genetic proclivity to disease and cultural inferiority. They believed that, similar to how humans cull inferior animals to improve the breed, so too must we remove inferior humans from society to achieve the same goal.

The leading Nazis also believed that race was in the blood. Having bad blood was similar to typhoid carriers who passed the bad blood to their offspring. Since no one can change their genetics by education, or any other environmental improvement, the inferiority in the blood was believed beyond reform or redemption. The only solution was that the inferior genes must be bred out of society. This ideology was summarized by the Nazi slogan "Blut und Boden" ("blood and soil") which was Nazi Germany's ideal of a racially defined national body ("blood") united with a settlement area ("soil"). Harvard University government and social studies professor, Daniel Goldhagen, has extensively documented that the primary goal of Hitler and the Nazi Movement was to annihilate the "bad blood," especially the Jews.[22] The fact is, "Hitler was not primarily interested in conquest; conquest was but a means to an end. The ultimate objective was the realization of Nazi ideology based on racial superiority in which the Jews—and other groups, including the Roma—would be killed."[23]

21. Dimsdale, J. 2016. *Anatomy of Malice: The Enigma of the Nazi War Criminals.* New Haven, CT: Yale University Press, pp. 13-14.

22. Goldhagen, D. 1996. *Hitler's Willing Executioners.* New York, NY: A.A. Knopf, p. 86.

23. Holmes, M. 2022. *From the Treaty of Versailles to the Treaty of Maastricht: Conflict, Carnage and Cooperation in Europe, 1918 – 1993.* New York, NY: Routledge Publishing, p. 34.

WWI's Precursor to the Holocaust

The deaths that resulted from WWI, plus the national humiliation and severe inflation that resulted from Germany's loss of the war, enraged many Germans. This rage, coupled with Darwinian indoctrination that their suffering was due to the acts of "sub-humans," resulted in a desire for vengeance against the Jewish, Roma, Slavic and other minorities who many Germans believed contributed to Germany's defeat. A major problem after WWI was that not enough food existed to share with these so-called "useless eaters and vermin." This influenced Hitler's vision

> . . . to obliterate all of the undesirables and to provide the purified Aryan nation with the freed-up space and confiscated resources so that a resurgent Germany could rule the world in security and plenty. With a strong leader, he believed that Germany would march from humiliation to triumph and complete its manifest destiny by expanding into a fruitful land that had been cleared of all nondesirables. It was an intoxication that swept the nation.[24]

This ideology produced the fertile philosophical ground that led to the acceptance of social Darwinism, which dominated the leadership of the Nazi Party intelligentsia. The German intelligentsia consisted of scholars, academics, teachers, journalists, and literary writers. In the early 1900s, eugenics was widely accepted, not only by the German intelligentsia, but also by the intelligentsia of the West as a whole. For these and other reasons it was the well-educated that supported Nazism and Nazi goals, even though their racist ideas were not only morally wrong, but would lead to the largest mass murder

---

24. Dimsdale, 2016, p. 14.

in recorded history. Nazi historian, Professor Stephen Hicks, observed that even before the Nazis came to power,

> German intellectuals were among the world leaders in eugenics research. In 1916 Dr. Ernst Rudin, the director of the Genea-logical-Demographic Department of the German Institute for Psychiatric Research, established a field of psychiatric hereditary biology based on eugenics theory. Rudin became the president of the International Federation of Eugenic Organizations, the world's leader of the eugenics movement. ... By the time the Na-zis came to power, eugenics was an established part of German intellectual life. One striking indication of this is that German Universities had twenty-three official professors of Racial Hy-giene. National Socialism held that the state should take over where natural selection left off.[25]

In short, one of the main causes of the Holocaust was the "racial hygiene" worldview, and evolution in general, which German academics widely believed at this time.[26]

Hitler Becomes a Darwinist

While still living in Vienna, around 1907, Hitler embraced "a crude hackneyed Darwinism."[27] This Darwinism would form the foundation of his racist philosophy, especially his views on Lebensraum. The concept of Lebensraum ("living space") referred to "settler colonialism" which was deemed the unde-niable right of the superior race.[28] This Lebensraum belief was

---

25. Hicks, 2010, pp. 36-37.
26. Dimsdale, 2016, pp. 12-13.
27. Low, A. 1996. *The Men Around Hitler: The Nazi Elite and Its Collabo-rators*. Monograph. New York, NY: Columbia University Press, p. 3.
28. Low, 1996, p. 3.

central to Germany's invasion of Russia. Hitler was also among those who read the works of the leading Darwinist in Germany, Professor Ernst Haeckel. Hitler then selected the social Darwinist ideas which he found in Haeckel and other German Darwinists.[29] Haeckel was "a towering figure in German biology, an early Darwinian, and was also a racist."[30]

Gottfried Feder was the founder of the original German Workers' Party, which later changed its name to the National Socialist German Workers' Party, abbreviated as the Nazi party. The name change was to express its core value more accurately, namely socialism. When Hitler first heard the anti-capitalist views of Feder he said they changed his life.[31] Feder greatly influenced Hitler's more aggressive opposition to Jews. The party platform was written by Feder, Hitler, and a politician named Anton Drexler. Drexler had written a 40-page anti-Semitic, anti-socialist, anti-capitalist pamphlet titled *My Political Awakening*, which also greatly influenced Hitler.[32]

Hitler's opposition to Jews was based on beliefs that he accepted from Feder, Drexler, and others. These included the idea that many of society's problems were due to "the world domination of the Jews," and that Jews were the major threat to German society.[33] The exact contributions of these two men is unknown, but we know they had a major influence on Hitler.

29. Remak, J.H. 1990. *The Nazi Years: A Documentary History*. Long Grove, IL: Waveland Press, p. 3.

30. Lifton, 1986, p. 125.

31. Dornberg, J. 1982. *Munich 1923*. New York, NY: Harper & Row, p. 344.

32. Kershaw, I. 2010. *Hitler: A Biography*. W.W. New York, NY: Norton & Company, p. 75.

33. Cawthorne, N. 2022. *The Evil Madness of Hitler*. London, England; Arcturus Publishing, p. 18.

Hitler had few original ideas, choosing rather to assimilate the ideas of other intellectuals and run with them.[34]

Rudolf Hess and Karl Ernst Haushofer Influence Hitler

University of Munich professor Karl Ernst Haushofer (1869–1946) was one of the most important originators of the ideas that culminated in WWII.[35] In 1919, Haushofer met a university student named Rudolf Hess, one of the original founders of the Nazi Party. Both Haushofer and Hess naively accepted Darwin's worldview and successfully implemented it into the German Nazi policy.

In 1923, Adolf Hitler and Rudolf Hess were part of the failed attempt to overthrow the German government. When Hitler and Hess were imprisoned for their part in the coup they were visited by Professor Haushofer. During the summer and fall of 1924, Haushofer spent many Wednesdays holding seminar-style lectures with the two inmates. As a result, Hitler later claimed that "Landsberg was my university [education] at state expense."[36] Furthermore, at this time Hitler read "the second edition of the first great German eugenic text, *Foundation of Human Heredity and Racial Hygiene*, which had been published in 1921." This text was written by three leading German academics, professors Erwin Baur, Eugen Fischer, and Fritz Lenz.[37] *Human Heredity* was very well-received in academic circles and became the standard textbook on racial hygiene (racism) in Germany, both before and after the Nazi Party ruled Germany.

34. Kershaw, I. 2000. *Hitler: Profiles in Power*. Oxfordshire, England: Routledge Publishing.
35. Low, 1996, pp. 25-32.
36. Herwig, H.H. 2016. *The Demon of Geopolitics: How Karl Haushofer "Educated" Hitler and Hess.* New York, NY: Roman & Littlefield, p. xiv.
37. Black, 2003, p. 270.

From these and other eugenicists, Hitler codified the central place of eugenics in his book *Mein Kampf*, which became the bible of both the Nazi Movement and Nazi Germany. In that book he stressed his goal of removing by whatever means possible, or enslaving, the inferior races, including Jews, Slavic people, and Romani. In the end, Hitler's main priority was genocide, not conquest.[38] He also made clear that he had no qualms about using brutality to achieve Nazi goals, stating that a

> pogrom is a splendid thing, but nowadays it has lost a good deal of its Medieval effectiveness.... How would it profit us to eradicate the Jewish population of Munich when the Jews in the remainder of the country, as it is now, still control money and politics? In all of Germany there are more than a million Jews. What do you want to do? Kill all of them during the night? That would, of course, be the best solution, and if that were done then Germany would be saved. But that isn't possible. ...the world would attack us instead of thanking us as they really should do. The world has not understood the Jewish question for the simple reason that they are ruled by the Jews. ... The Jewish question is a chain, and Germany must tear this chain if it does not want to die.[39]

Nazi Leaders Had High IQs

The world was shocked by the fact that a highly educated, culture-rich nation such as Germany could be the source of the worst sadistic war crimes in history, including genocide. The

---

38. Holmes, 2022.
39. Bryant, M. 2022. "Intimations of Genocide in Mein Kampf." Chapter 8 in Michalczyk, J.J., et al. 2022. *Hitler's 'Mein Kampf' and the Holocaust: A Prelude to Genocide.* New York, NY: Bloomsbury Academic, pp. 131-132.

evaluations of the psychologists described above included evaluating Nazi leaders' intellectual capacity, which demonstrated that they all possessed significantly above-average IQ's. The average IQ of the 21 Nazi leaders was 128, nearly two standard deviations above the average IQ of 100.[40] The conclusion was that these men possessed a higher IQ than 97 percent of the general population.

Hitler's second in command, Hermann Göring, scored 138 on his IQ test, or above 99.4 percent of the population. Hitler's chief administrator over German-occupied Netherlands, Seyss-Inquart, scored 141, which was above 99.7 percent of the population. Seyss-Inquart spearheaded the deportation and murder of tens of thousands of Jews. The inescapable facts of his involvement in genocide led to his conviction of crimes against humanity and his execution in 1946.

Joseph Goebbels

One man whose ideas were critically important in Hitler's Nazi program was Nazi propagandist, Dr. Joseph Goebbels. His IQ will remain a mystery because he committed suicide along with his wife, after murdering their six children in the last days before the war ended. Goebbels was

> the most brilliant and educated of all the Nazi politicians. ... he was one of the most powerful of the very top Nazis—perhaps number two or three after Hitler. ... He received a wide-ranging classical education by attending five universities in Germany, eventually receiving a Ph.D. in literature and philosophy from Heidelberg University in 1921. During his graduate days he absorbed and agreed with much of the writings of communists

40. Dimsdale, 2016.

Karl Marx and Friedrich Engels, especially their searing condemnation of capitalism.[41]

As true Darwinists, the Nazis recognized that "The major battle is between different racial and cultural groups with different biological histories ... between Germans—with their particular biological inheritance and cultural history—[and] all other racial cultures."[42] To enforce their position in the race battle, Point 23 of the Nazi Party platform calls for strict censorship of all newspapers and Point 24 puts limits on religions that do not agree with Nazi goals. Later, these same rules became central to the suppression of creationists in the American academia, as documented by Bergman.[43]

Nazi Race Studies Programs

Race studies programs in German schools taught which races were superior and which were inferior, how to identify them, and why this information was of central importance to the overall health of German society. Consequently, the better-educated Germans were the most likely to be indoctrinated into accepting Nazi racial ideology, and thus supported the imple-

41. Hicks, 2010, p. 18.
42. Hicks, 2010, p. 19
43. Bergman. J. 2008. Revised version, 2012. *Slaughter of the Dissidents: The Shocking Truth About Killing the Careers of Darwin Doubters.* Southworth, WA: Leafcutter Press, (Revised 2nd Edition published in 2013); 2016. *Silencing the Darwin Skeptics: The War Against Theists.* Southworth, WA: Leafcutter Press; 2018. *Censoring the Darwin Skeptics: How Belief in Evolution is Enforced by Eliminating Dissidents.* Southworth, WA: Leafcutter Press; 2019. *Evolution is the Doorway to Atheism.* Southworth, WA: Leafcutter Press; 2022. How Darwin was the basis of Lebensraum (or Darwinism, Friedrich Ratzel, and the implementation of 'Lebensraum'). *Journal of Creation* 36(4):64-66; 2023. Teaching Darwinism to children: How children's books indoctrinate children in Darwinism. *Answers Research Journal* (in press).

mentation of this ideology. As Bavarian Minister of Education, Dr. "Hans Schemm, declared in 1934, "National Socialism is nothing but applied biology," an idea that he incorporated into the curriculum programs which he developed or supported.[44] Biology, especially evolutionary biology, had enormous prestige in the Third Reich and was used to give the Nazi eugenic worldview a scientific veneer.

It achieved this goal by providing what they believed was incontrovertible proof of the validity and importance of Nazi racist goals and plans.[45] Race instructions that were developed by the medical profession became the central topic in biology teaching. Furthermore, certain "racially" oriented disciplines, including genealogy, population genetics, race hygiene, anthropology, and Darwinian evolution "were critical resources for National Socialism because they appeared to provide scientific validation for the eugenicist and racist doctrines enshrined by the party."[46]

Leading Scientists Support Eugenics

Listed below are some leading German intellectuals who not only accepted, but actively supported, Hitler and the Nazi race ideals. Arthur Moeller van den Bruck was a cultural historian, philosopher, and writer, best known for his 1923 book, *Das Dritte Reich* (*The Third Reich*), which promoted German nationalism. University of Greifswald professor Dr. Carl Schmitt

---

44. Haas, Francois. 2008. German Science and Black Racism. *FASEB Journal.* 22(2):332-337. P. 332.

45. Bäumer-Schleinkofer, Ä. 1995. *Nazi Biology and Schools.* Translated by Neil Beckhaus. Berlin, Germany: Peter Lang GmbH Internationaler Verlag der Wissenschaften.

46. Harrington, A. 1996. *Reenchanted Science: Holism in German Culture from Wilhelm II to Hitler.* Princeton, NJ: Princeton University Press, p. 175.

was one of the most-respected legal minds in Europe and the author of many important academic books. He was a German jurist and political theorist who provided much intellectual support for, and was actively involved in, the Nazi movement. Soon after he joined the Nazi Party, Greifswald supported the burning of books by Jewish authors along with "un-German" and "anti-German" material, while calling for a much more extensive purge to even include authors influenced by Jewish ideas.

The 1912 Nobel laureate in literature, dramatist and novelist Gerhart Hauptmann, was also a committed Nazi. He described his meeting with Hitler as the "greatest moment of my life."[47] Hauptmann was a founding member of the eugenics organization, "The German Society for Racial Hygiene." German historian and philosopher of history, Dr. Oswald Spengler, was the author of the bestselling two-volume set titled *The Decline of the West*, which was widely read and endorsed by many acknowledged German and international intellectuals.

University of Freiburg professor Martin Heidegger, "widely considered one of the most influential thinkers of the twentieth century," joined the National Socialist German Workers Party in 1933.[48] Heidegger organized and supervised several militaristic organizations consisting of university students and faculty working for Nazism.

Heidelberg University professor of theoretical physics Philipp Lenard was awarded the 1905 Nobel Prize for his important discoveries involving cathode rays. Lenard was an an-

---

47. Hicks, 2010, p. 9.
48. Palmer, T. 2016. Martin Heidegger: Philosopher of Nazism and other collectivist cults, https://fee.org/articles/martin-heidegger-philosopher-of-nazism-and-other-collectivist-cults.

ti-Semite and an active proponent of the Nazi ideology. He actively supported Adolf Hitler in the 1920s and was Hitler's "Chief of German Physics" during the Nazi era. His loyalty to the Nazi beliefs motivated him to dismiss Albert Einstein's science contributions as inferior "Jewish physics."[49]

University of Munich professor Johannes Stark was awarded the Nobel Prize in physics in 1919 for his discovery of the Doppler effect and the splitting of spectral lines in electric fields.[50] He joined the Nazi Party in 1930 and was a committed Nazi until World War II ended. After the war, his Nazi support was considered so significant that he was sentenced to four years in a labor camp by the German de-Nazification court.

Many Highly Intelligent Persons Were Leading Nazis

These and many other intellectuals believed that Nazism was based on uncontroversial scientific evidence. They also believed that Nazism was noble and the ultimate hope of humanity. Furthermore, in harmony with Darwinism, they believed that peace makes people soft and, in contrast, war makes people vigorous and strong. Strong people, in contrast to weak people, are also willing to fight, and even die for, their ideals.

Many leading German scientists were supportive of eugenics which, in the 1920's and 1930's, was widely considered "settled science" in biology. Eugenics is defined in reference books as "The study of methods of improving the quality of human populations by the application of genetic principles."[51]

49. Wheaton, B.R. 1978. Philipp Lenard and the photoelectric effect, 1889-1911. *Historical Studies in the Physical Sciences* 9:299–322.

50. *The New York Times*. 1957. "Johannes Stark, German Physicist; Nobel Prize-Winner in 1919 Dies--Was Sentenced to 4 Years as a 'Leading Nazi'," 22 June 1957, p. 15.

51. Hine, R. 2015. *A Dictionary of Biology*. New York, NY: Oxford Univer-

Consequently, Nazism, and thus Hitler, enjoyed a great deal of support from not only the scientific establishment but from those who supported academia and science in general. Rudolf Hess, Hitler's Deputy Fuhrer, declared in 1934 that "National Socialism is nothing but applied biology."[52]

The Nazis also had the support of the worldwide eugenics movement which consisted of numerous professors. The Nazi eugenics program was based on research by American eugenicists, especially Harry Laughlin. Laughlin was awarded an honorary doctorate in 1936 from the University of Heidelberg for his work on the "science of racial cleansing."[53] Furthermore, once the Nazi Party came to power, the worldwide scientific prestige of Germany facilitated the ruthless and inhumane spread and application of eugenics and racist ideas. Hitler brazenly made his racist anti-Semitism his first goal for the war.[54]

Many leading German educators also accepted the belief that science supported Nazi race theories. In 1933, "race studies" teaching was required throughout the entire German Reich. Consequently, racism was taught in German schools from 1935 until the war ended in 1945.[55] During this time, German school final examinations included racism as one area in which questions had to be answered correctly. No one was exempt from these tests which promoted Nazi dogma, and school-age children's acceptance thereof was monitored.

sity Press, p. 209.
52. Michalczyk, J. 2022, p. 32.
53. McDonald, J. 2013. Making the world safe for eugenics: The eugenicist Harry H. Laughlin's encounters with American internationalism. *The Journal of the Gilded Age and Progressive Era* 12(3):379–341.
54. Goldhagen, 1996, p. 86.
55. Bäumer-Schleinkofer, 1995, p. xiii.

Nazism and Darwinism: The Party of the Well-Educated

When the Nazis came to power in 1933, 51% of the party members were from the professional classes. A large number of teachers were members of the Nazi Party and were required to take an oath of "absolute fidelity to Adolf Hitler." In a similar vein, in the United States today, the lower courts have consistently ruled that public school teachers are not allowed to present information against Darwinism, even information published in mainline academic journals. The obvious result is that many students believe Darwinism as solid science.

Professor Stephen Hicks has concluded: "The Nazis had also achieved great success with older students, those of university age. Before Hitler came to power, Nazi student groups existed at universities all over Germany." Thus, *before* the Nazis took control of the government in 1933, "it was common for students to come to classes wearing brown shirts and swastika armbands, and in many cases, it was the most intelligent and idealistic university students who were the most active and outspoken supporters of National Socialism. These students were supported by many of their professors."[56]

When the Nazis took power, all Jews and others persons deemed racially objectionable were prohibited from holding academic positions. This policy resulted in hundreds of tenured Jewish professors, including Nobel laureates, being fired.[57] The next step was book burning. Dr. Goebbels explained that any book which was deemed subversive to "our future or strikes at the root of German thought" should be destroyed. Book burnings began on May 10, 1933, only a few months after the Nazis assumed power that year.

---

56. Hicks, 2010, p. 32.
57. Hicks, 2010, pp. 29, 31-32.

Massive University Book Burnings Begin

In an open square across from the University of Berlin, roughly 20,000 books were burned in a huge bonfire. At the event, Goebbels spoke to 40,000 cheering students and professors.[58] Professor Hicks added that the book burnings "were not instigated by the Nazi Government. Nor were they instigated by non-intellectual thugs. The book burning was instigated by university students. The Nazi Party's *student* organization conceived and carried out book burning all across the country— book bonfires burned brightly that night in every German university city. The professors had taught their students well."[59]

Factors Contributing to WWII

Germany's defeat and loss of their colonies and land, plus the humiliation of the treaty of Versailles, resulted in much resentment by the German people. These factors screamed for a resolution, but did not demand war as the solution. Nonetheless, WWII and the Holocaust were two events which, although intertwined, were separate. WWII could have occurred without the Holocaust, but the European Holocaust (outside of Germany) would not have occurred except for WWII. Germany was able to extend the Holocaust only into countries that it controlled. In fact, war was a pretext to achieve the Nazi's main goal, which was the extermination of the Jews and other "inferior" races. Toward this goal, "Hitler's Germany mobilized all of its resources: bureaucratic, military, legal, scientific, economic, and intellectual."[60] To make things worse, several major Ameri-

---

58. Hicks, 2010, p. 33.
59. Hicks, 2010, pp. 33-34.
60. Bergan, D. 2016. *War and Genocide: A Concise History of the Holocaust.* New York, NY: Rowman & Littlefield Publishers, p. viii.

can corporations supported Nazi Germany and eugenics.[61]

The genocidal killing of Jews in Germany and the conquered nations produced much opposition to both the war and Hitler. A large number of persons, including high-level generals, were angry at the massive, senseless executions of Jews and others in the countries Germany controlled. Initially, many Ukrainians, Estonians, Latvians, Lithuanians, along with both Western and Eastern Europe, considered the Germans as liberators from the Soviet Union. Hundreds of thousands of non-Germans fought, either voluntarily or under the influence of others, for the Nazi cause.[62] Then, when the genocidal killings began, people formerly in favor of German rule turned against the Nazis. This fact was exploited by the Soviets and other countries. The end result was that Nazism eventually failed militarily.

Thus, without the Holocaust, the likelihood is that German war successes would have been significantly increased. Without social Darwinism as a central part of the Nazi program WWII might have had a very different outcome. Close to six million persons would have been part of the productive labor force. Many would have been part of the German Army, Navy, and Luftwaffe (Air Force) instead of being killed in the camps or executed in the field. Many scientists, craftsman, and skilled laborers would have been added to the Nazi war machine. Jews as a whole served very honorably in WWI, proving their un-questionable loyalty to Germany, as well as their bravery and fighting skills. Close to 300,000 Jews served in World War I, among them were 25,000 Jewish officers. Many Jewish Misch-

---

61. Black, 2009.
62. Böhler, J., and R. Gerwarth. 2017. *The Waffen-SS: A European History*. New York, NY: Oxford University Press.

linge (those of mixed Jewish descent) also served in WWII.[63]

Some historians conclude that if Germany had not been handicapped by eugenics and racism, they would have achieved most of the territory and cooperation necessary to rule most of Europe.[64] The main reason they invaded Russia was the Nazi firm commitment to the idea of Lebensraum, the belief that superior races had not only the right, but the obligation, to overtake land inhabited by inferior races. The Nazi goal in Russia was to kill as many Slavs as necessary to control the country, and then make the rest slaves.[65]

One example of this Lebensraum program is the 900-day-long siege of Leningrad from 1941 to 1944 that claimed the lives of one million of the city's inhabitants, mainly through cold and hunger. This number was greater than all American casualties in all of the U. S. wars combined. Historians have classified the siege of Leningrad as a genocide due to the systematic starvation and intentional destruction of the city's civilian population, whom the Nazis regarded as an inferior race.[66] In short, evolutionary racism—the racial views and events adopted by the Nazis—was one, if not the major, reason Germany lost the war.[67]

63. Rigg, B.M. 2002. *Hitler's Jewish Soldiers: The Untold Story of Nazi Racial Laws and Men of Jewish Descent in the German Military.* Lawrence, KS: University Press of Kansas.

64. Alexander, B. 2001. *How Hitler Could Have Won World War II: The Fatal Errors That Led to Nazi Defeat.* New York, NY: Three Rivers Press/Random House.

65. Hund, W.D., et al. 2011. *Racisms Made in Germany.* Münster, Germany: LIT Verlag, p. 25.

66. Bidlack, R., and N. Lomagin. 2012. *The Leningrad Blockade, 1941–1944: A New Documentary History from the Soviet Archives.* Translated by Schwartz, Marian. New Haven, CT: Yale University Press, pp. 1, 36.

67. Overy, R. 1997. *Why the Allies Won.* New York, NY: W.W. Norton &

Darwinian Eugenics and Nazism

The Nazi Movement's foundation was in the Darwinian eugenics movement. Dawson College professor *Gabriel Tordjman observed:* "The *Nazi movement's* ideology actually was a mixture of *eugenics,* social Darwinism, racism, antisemitism and the Aryan myth."[68] Hitler had studied many eugenic publications and made it clear in his outline for the Nazi Movement, *Mein Kampf,* that the application of eugenics was central to his war goals.[69] Hitler also believed that war and struggle were natural to human society because it strengthened humans by eliminating the weak—ideas cultivated from his evolutionary worldview that included "survival of the fittest."

Thus, the intellectual core of Nazism was social Darwinism. Ironically, the main reason Nazism failed was due to its Darwinian core—which was the main driving force behind Lebensraum.[70] If the Nazis had never begun the war on Jews, Slavic people, and other non-Aryans, and never invaded Russia, they would have been more likely to have achieved their more limited goals, such as dominance of most of Europe.

The Central Importance of the Extermination of the Jews

One of the best examples showing that the extermination of the Jews was of central importance to Nazism was that, toward

Company, pp. 284, 313, 330, 326.

68. Tordjman, G. 2022. *Darwin's Tea Party: Biological Knowledge, Evolution, Genetics and Human Nature.* Montreal, Canada: Les Editions JFD, p. 254.

69. Michalczyk, J.J., et al. 2022. *Hitler's 'Mein Kampf' and the Holocaust: A Prelude to Genocide.* New York, NY: Bloomsbury Academic.

70. Murphy, D. 1997. *The Heroic Earth: Geopolitical Thought in Weimar Germany, 1918-1933.* Kent, OH: The Kent State University Press, p. 198.

the end of the war, when faced with the choice to either move supplies to the troops in Russia, or ship the Jews to the concentration camps, extermination of the Jews was the priority. Hitler believed that killing Jews was more important than losing the war. If they lost the war, at least they would have exterminated the Jews. The genocide of the Jews was the culmination of a decade of German policy under Nazi rule and the core goal of the Nazi dictator, Adolf Hitler.[71] Hitler, against the advice of his generals, even moved the war from Britain to the East because, compared to Britain, an enormously greater number of Jews lived in the East.

Not only Hitler, but the Nazi elite, including Heinrich Himmler, (the Reichsführer-S.S. and the principal architect of the Holocaust), and Reinhard Heydrich, prioritized genocide over winning the war. Leading Hitler scholar, Oxford University professor Martin Holmes, has documented that when German forces occupied

large swathes of Poland, Ukraine and Russia, the top priority was the murder of the Jews in those areas. The logistical needs of German forces to hold on to and administer the territory they now occupied was a secondary consideration. ...this genocidal policy was highly labor intensive. It required troops who were previously fighting on the Eastern Front or engaging in military duties throughout occupied Europe to engage in rounding up the Jews, transporting them across vast distances and murdering them on an industry scale—some six million of them in all. It required large numbers of troops, as well as German civilians, to be involved in the running and maintenance of the concentration camps. ...the Holocaust required the railway network to be

---

71. Burns, 2022.

used for the murder of the Jews, ahead of the logistical supply of German troops in battle, irrespective of the fact that the tide of the war had turned against the Axis forces on the Eastern front from December 1941. Every train taking the Jews to the death camps was a train not transporting troops to and from the front. Because of Hitler's prioritization on the Final Solution over military victory, the German army became steadily less able to defeat the Russians.[72]

Consequently, in the end, they lost the war but managed to murder the vast majority of Jews in the East.

Parallels Between Academe's Support of Nazism and for Evolution

Parallels exist between academia's support of eugenics and Nazism in Europe during the last century, and academia's support of Darwinism today. The well-educated scientists in America have accepted evolution for largely the same reasons that it was accepted in Nazi Germany. A survey by Professor Edward J. Larson and journalist Larry Witham published in the world's leading science magazine, *Nature*, found that 93 percent of the members of the National Academy of Sciences (NAS)—America's most elite body of academic scientists—are agnostics or atheists. Less than seven percent believe in a personal God.[73] Gallup polls consistently reveal that 80 percent of Americans believe in some form of creationism, in contrast to only three percent of leading science academics.[74]

72. Holmes, 2022, pp. 84-85.
73. Larson, E.J., and L. Witham. 1997. Scientists are still keeping the faith. *Nature* 386(6624):435–436, https://www.nature.com/articles/386435a0, p. 997.
74. Newport, F. 2014. In U.S., 42% believe creationist view of human origins, https://calvinchimes.org/2018/12/07/evolution-debate-

The latest Pew poll found that 97 percent of the academic scientific community accepted unguided evolution as the explanation for not only human origins, but for all biological diversity. Tragically, the same is largely true of Christian colleges. Fully 63 percent of biology professors belonging to institutions associated with the Council of Christian Colleges and Universities (CCCU) accept evolution as the origin of all life. Only six percent taught the creation model, and just 13 percent taught that evolution was an inadequate explanation for the origin of humans.[75]

The leftist bias in academia today is enormous. One study, which gathered information from 12,372 professors across the United States, found that college professors donated to Democratic Party causes over Republican ones at a rate of 95-to-1.[76] The ratio between Democrat and Republican donations was most pronounced in the areas of sociology, English, and anthropology. A recent Harvard Institute of Politics study found that only 35 percent of young Republicans feel comfortable sharing their political views on American campuses.[77] In recent years, American college faculty have also faced problems for holding right-leaning political beliefs.

Another important parallel with Nazi Germany is the re-

continues-amongst-christian-biology-profs/,
https://news.gallup.com/poll/170822/believe-creationist-view-human-origins.aspx.

75. Polanski, J. 2018. Evolution debate continues amongst Christian biology profs. *Chimes*, December 7.

76. Spencer, N. 2020. College professors donate to Democrats over Republicans by ratio of 95-to-1: Study. *Washington Examiner*, January 23.

77. Turley, Jonathan. 2019. Harvard Study: Only 35 Percent Of Young Republicans Feel Comfortable Sharing Their Views On Campus, https://jonathanturley.org/2019/11/20/harvard-study-only-35-percent-of-young-republicans-feel-comfortable-sharing-their-views-on-campus/.

quirement that evolution be the dominant worldview in all American public schools. The new biology textbooks no longer soft peddle evolution but ensure that evolution is covered in detail.[78] A clear example of this is the recent modification of biology textbooks to include evolution *throughout the entire book,* instead of just the last chapter, or only one section, as was once common.[79] This change was done to deal with the problem of instructors deliberately skipping the evolution section. This change was made to frustrate the efforts of teachers who were not advocates of evolution, forcing the evolution concept to be taught. As a result, students are indoctrinated into believing evolution is an established fact of science — similar to the indoctrination that occurred in classrooms in Nazi Germany.[80]

The course syllabi, as well as both state and local requirements, ensure that evolution is covered in detail.[81] Furthermore, evolution is now included in other academic areas, including literature, history, psychology, and philosophy. Programs which train teachers to teach evolutionism more effectively, such as the Teachers Institute for Evolutionary Science (TIES), are yet another example.[82] TIES has done presentations in hundreds of schools. A century ago, Europe's educational system advocated eugenics, Germany pushed Nazism, and today the United States pushes human evolution through court decisions and pressure from academia.

78. Kitchner, P. 1982. *Abusing Science: The Case Against Creationism.* Cambridge, MA: MIT Press, pp. 3, 177.

79. Bergman, Jerry. 2023. *The Methodist Darwin Syndrome: Consequences of Adopting Darwinian Theology.* Lansing, MI: Looking Glass River Publishing,

80. Black, 2009.

81. Vazquez, B. 2021. *On Teaching Evolution.* Reno, NV: Keystone Canyon Press.

82. Vazquez, 2021.

Even worse than indoctrinating our students in evolution as the Nazis did, the American courts have made it clear that *information opposed to evolution cannot be covered* in public school classrooms. When courts have ruled on what should be taught in science classrooms, they have consistently mandated the "evolution only" position. The courts did not base their conclusion on observable science, but rather on their secular worldview. Because most students listen to, and trust, the teaching of respected instructors, they accept it as valid. If repeatedly exposed to *evolutionary conclusions* in their many different classes, (which are then promoted by the news and entertainment media), most students will accept evolution as the only valid worldview.

As was true in Nazi Germany, social pressure against non-evolutionary theories dominates academia, as Shuichi Tezuka (pseudonym) demonstrated when he opined, "Young Earth creationism is widely understood as contrary to the scientific method and is the subject of much well-deserved criticism from science educators. ... [because it is responsible for] encouraging the distrust of established scientific conclusions."[83] Shuichi Tezuka also refers to the creation worldview as "Science denialism."

The Importance of High I. Q. Nazis

People with high IQ's are important influencers of societal thought and belief. Nazis with high IQ's shaped the thought of many Germans in the 1920s and 30s. Charles Darwin reportedly possessed an IQ of 140, and his fellow evolution advocates often possessed high IQ's as well. American psychologist

83. Tezuka, S. 2021. Cognitive creationism compared to young-Earth creationism. *Controversial Ideas* 1(1):3, doi: 10.35995/jci01010003., p. 3.

Catharine Cox found the mean IQ of scientists to be 164.[84] High-IQ persons are often emotionally tied to a philosophy (e. g., Nazism or evolutionism) even though such a philosophy not only lacks supporting evidence but is contrary to the evidence. IQ tests measure the knowledge-understanding aspect of a person, but not their wisdom. As true believers, evolutionists enthusiastically promote their view to a trusting, less-informed public. High-IQ individuals are thus major influencers of societal thought and belief today, just as were Darwin and his Nazi disciples.

Operation Paperclip

The level of talent that the German scientists and medical professionals possessed was so high that, in spite of their Nazi involvement, after the end of World War II the United States intelligence program brought in over 1,600 German scientists, engineers, and technicians from the former Nazi Germany to the U. S. They were given high-level jobs with the government.[85] America could not have achieved the enormous success in its space program without their expertise and talent. Furthermore, after 1947 some United States Intelligence Officers utilized so-called "ratlines" to move certain Nazi strategists, scientists, and medical professionals to the United States and other nations, particularly in South America.[86] Russia was also

---

84. Walberg, H.J., S.P. Rasher, and K. Hase. 1978. IQ correlates with high eminence. *Gifted Child Quarterly* 22(2):196–200.

85. Lasby, C. 1971. *Project Paperclip: German Scientists and the Cold War.* New York, NY: Atheneum; Jacobsen, A. 2014. *Operation Paperclip: The Secret Intelligence Program that Brought Nazi Scientists to America.* New York, NY: Little, Brown and Company.

86. Phayer, M. 2008. *Pius XII, The Holocaust, and the Cold War.* Bloomington and Indianapolis, IN: Indiana University Press; Phillips, P. 1978. *Strange But True.* London, England: Phoebus Publishing Company.

able to obtain 150 leading German scientists to work for their space program.[87]

Summary

Prominent scholars and scientists played leading roles not only in Hitler's rise to power, but also in the war to exterminate the Jews.[88] Some of the most highly educated people in the world supported a political party whose beliefs resulted in the worst Holocaust in history. Professors and educators in general were very active and effective in indoctrinating the people in Nazi Germany into the eugenics and the "inferior-race" belief. The problem of indoctrination into Darwinism that occurred in Nazi Germany by the educated elite still plagues the world today. No longer is the indoctrination focused on Darwinian racism, but it is now the *total* Darwinian evolutionary world-view. This worldview has replaced theism with functional athe-ism and an intolerance for the Christian worldview and its val-ues. Intelligent, highly educated people can fall into accepting unfounded ideas. Communism creates a culture where people embrace whatever the government or the "intelligentsia" or "academia" tells them they should believe.

Both Darwinian racism and Darwinian evolution promote beliefs that have caused an enormous amount of suffering.[89] In spite of the overwhelming evidence that has falsified the evolutionary worldview, it is widely accepted by the brightest individuals in America, and is maintained by most people in secular academia via aggressive indoctrination and censorship.

Parallels between Nazi Germany and the evolutionary es-

---

87. Cornwell, 2003, p. 424.

88. Weinrich, M. 1999. *Hitler's Professors: The Part of Scholarship Against the Jewish People.* New Haven, CT: Yale University Press.

89. Bergman, 2019.

tablishment are numerous and well-documented. Both the Nazis and the evolutionists have dominated the universities. They have convinced the vast majority of educated people to accept their worldview, and have ensured that only their philosophical narrative is taught as scientific fact. Evolutionists hold to a worldview that is irrational, just as was the Nazis' racism that once dominated the Nazi Movement. They have both successfully manipulated mainline media to practice aggressive censorship. In both cases, they have accepted an ideology that is not only harmful but woefully lacking in valid supportive evidence. There is overwhelming demonstrated scientific fact *against* their worldview. The Darwinian core is also one of the main drivers of intolerance in universities today.[90]

Most people, no matter what their IQ, have certain things in common. This includes a sense of right and wrong, national pride, love of family, and a need to seek justice. Biology had enormous prestige in the Third Reich and was effectively used to support the Nazi worldview. Likewise, Darwinism has achieved a high level of scientific respectability by providing what appears to be irrefutable scientific evidence for this worldview.

Darwinian racism has been overturned, and Darwinism too will eventually be overturned due to the steady accumulation of evidence contrary to this worldview. The late University of Umea Professor of Embryology Søren Løvtrup wrote: "I believe that one day the Darwinian myth will be ranked the greatest deceit in the history of science. When this happens many people will pose the question: how did this ever happen?"[91]

---

90. Bergman, 2008, 2012, 2013, 2016, 2018.
91. Løvtrup, S. 1987. *Darwinism: The Refutation of A Myth*. London, En-

The root causes of all atrocities in our world are based on worldviews counter to the Biblical worldview. Only Truth can "gird up" an individual/people group/educational system/country to "make you free."[92] Intelligence on its own can damage or destroy a society, culture, country, and the individual. Intelligent people only "fall" for ignorant ideas when they uncritically believe what they are taught in their educational systems and by their governments. All Christians should be Bereans[93] and know what Scripture teaches to support our worldview.

gland: Croom Helm, p. 422.
92. John 8:32.
93. Acts 17:10-11.

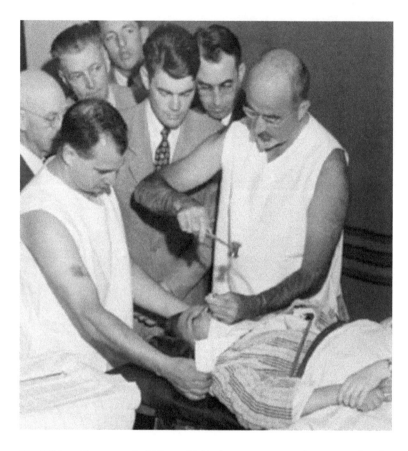

Dr. Walter Freeman (1895 – 1972) demonstrating the transorbital technique that he developed. Illustration from Citizens Commission on Human Rights International.

Source: https://www.reddit.com/media?url=https%3A%2F%2Fi.redd.it%2Funhimw0qdsi01.jpg

3

The Darwinian Mental Health Holocaust: Frontal Lobotomies

THE DARWINIAN WORLDVIEW has birthed the idea that undesirable aggressive behaviors were due to the influence of the primitive reptile brain that we inherited from our ancient reptilian ancestors. The proposed solution to this undesirable aggressive behavior was to reduce the reptile brain's influence by surgically separating the more primitive brain from the more advanced part, a practice called "lobotomy" . The procedure was widely used for several decades, not only in America and Europe, including Sweden, but also in Japan. Its proponents were leading academics, including Yale University Professor of Neurosurgery, Dr. William Scoville.[1] Although a few lobotomies were successful, in the long run they often did far more harm than good, and no small number were lethal. Furthermore, the procedure often had to be rep-

---

1.   Scull, Andrew. 2019. *Psychiatry and its Discontents*. Oakland, CA: University of California Press, p. 134.

licated, sometimes four or five times. All total, "Tens of thousands of lobotomies were performed in the United States from 1936 onward,"[2] and only in the 1970's did the practice finally end. The development of various effective psychotropic drugs, plus an unacceptable number of surgical failures, are what eventually forced its abandonment.

Lobotomy Based on Evolutionary Belief

The frontal lobotomy psychosurgery treatment was based on the evolutionary belief that, as the brain evolved in our direct ancestors, the newer sections, including the frontal cortex, evolved on top of the older brain parts. These "lower order" brain parts were "not vestigial" but rather were the "neurobiological traces of our evolutionary past."[3] This "lizard brain" controlled the "involuntary, emotional, and instinctual behavior in humans, and ... housed [the source of] violence as well as emotions—a claim with profound social and political implications."[4] The evolutionarily older brain sections in humans were eventually called the 'reptile brain.'[5] The frontal lobes were considered the "most recently evolved and especially human part of the brain."[6] Frontal lobotomies were an attempt to surgically separate the frontal lobes, especially the very front sections, from the underlying 'less evolved' brain parts. The term lobotomy comes from the Greek *lobos*, referring to the

2. Scull, 2019, p. 136.
3. Johnson, Jenell. 2016. *American Lobotomy: A Rhetorical History,* Ann Arbor, MI: University of Michigan Press, p. 110.
4. Johnson, 2016, p. 110.
5. Johnson, 2016, pp. 109–110; MacLean, Paul. 1973. *A Triune Concept of the Brain and Behaviour*. Toronto, Canada: University of Toronto Press.
6. Sternburg, Janet. 2015. *White Matter: A Memoir of Family and Medicine*. Portland, OR: Hawthorne Books, p. 143.

lobes of the brain, and *tomos*, meaning to cut.

The procedure was also known as frontal leukotomy or leucotomy from the Greek for 'white,' because the connecting fibers between the two brain parts that were surgically separated were located in the so-called 'white matter.' Supposedly the "reptile brain" was responsible for 'more primitive' behaviors such as uncontrolled aggression, and generally irrational, emotional behavior. This surgical procedure was done to reduce the undesirable 'reptile' behavior.[7]

The Triune Brain Concept

The 'triune brain' (or "triple brain") concept was also popular among Darwinists for decades. The 'triune brain' model, most recently advanced by Paul MacLean, proposed that the "forebrain comprises three separately-evolved, and to some degree independently-functioning, cognitive systems."[8] It proposed that humans inherited three brain levels which are (1) the innermost brain (the reptilian brain), next (2) the paleo-mammalian complex (the limbic system), and lastly, (3) the more-evolved outer layer (the neo-mammalian complex) which is the higher-level brain called the neocortex.[9] These

> "systems were subdivided according to an evolutionary hierarchy, whereby the anatomically oldest structures... governed the most 'primitive' body functions, such as respiration, blood pressure, and so on, while the newest structures... were assumed to

7. Comer, R. 2013. *Abnormal Psychology*. New York, NY: Worth Publishers, p. 52.
8. Sagan, Carl, 1977. *The Dragons of Eden*. New York, NY: Random House, p. 256.
9. Harth, Erich. 1982. *Windows on the Mind*. New York, NY: William Morrow & Company, p. 116; MacLean, 1973, pp. 7-9.

govern 'higher' functions such as thought and voluntary movements.... the "frontal lobes [were] evolutionarily the highest brain structure."[10]

Furthermore, these "three basic brains show great differences and chemistry... it is a wonder that nature was able to hook them up and establish any kind of communication among them."[11]

Each of these "three quite different mentalities," have their own memory, motor abilities, and emotion control.[12] The triune brain theory postulates that these three structures were sequentially added to the forebrain during the course of evolution. Each brain "corresponds to a separate major evolutionary step."

Shock Therapy

Austrian-Jewish neurophysiologist Manfred Joshua Sakel (1900-1957) invented insulin shock therapy in 1927. He postulated that schizophrenia and similar disorders resulted from injuries that damaged "the phylogenetically younger brain pathways so as to allow the older, more primitive pathways to dominate."[13] To treat the problem, Sakel taught that the clinician must reduce the influence of the primitive reptile brain.

Thus was born the era of surgical lobotomy, which only finally ended in the late 1970s.[14] In its heyday, "many of the era's

10. MacLean, 1973, p. 7.
11. MacLean, 1973, p. 7.
12. Sagan, 1977, p. 55.
13. Valenstein, Elliot. 1986. *Great and Desperate Cures: The Rise and Decline of Psychosurgery.* New York, NY: Basic Books, p. 57.
14. Miguel, Faria, 2013. Violence, mental illness, and the brain—A brief history of psychosurgery: Part 2—From the limbic system and cingulo-

most important medical figures—neurosurgeons, neurologists, psychiatrists, physiologists, and others—lent their support" to the procedure.[15] This history illustrates the fact that medicine sometimes drew as much from cultural ideas, such as evolution, as it did from clinical experience, clinical trials, and animal or laboratory experimentation. Another important treatment included the many attempts "to treat mental disorders by the removal of one or another of a patient's endocrine glands," a procedure that was also widely practiced until recently.

The motivations for these procedures were influenced by the evolutionary theory of rudimentary organs, plus ignorance of the importance of these organs, partly the result of the widespread belief that they were vestigial.[16]

The Evolution of the Brain According to Darwinism

The Darwinian teaching is that the most 'primitive' brain section consists of the spinal cord, hind brain, and mid-brain, containing the basic machinery to run the body's physiology. This brain section is closer to that of a fish or an amphibian than to a reptile. The next layer, the reptile brain, or the *R-complex* [for Reptilian-complex], is surrounded by the limbic system, the center of emotions. Last is the *neocortex* which, according to evolution, is the most recent evolutionary accretion.[17] Furthermore, "it would be astonishing if the brain components beneath the neocortex were not to a significant extent

tomy to deep brain stimulation. *Surgical Neurology International* 4(75), http://europepmc.org/article/PMC/3683171.

15. El-Hai, J. 2005. *The Lobotomist: A Maverick Medical Genius and His Tragic Quest to Rid the World of Mental Illness*. New York, NY: Wiley, p. 4.

16. Valenstein, 1986, p. 34.

17. Sagan, 1977, p. 56.

still performing as they did in our remote ancestors."[18]

Sagan concluded that the "concept of the triune brain is in remarkable accord with the conclusions drawn independently from studies of the brain."[19] It is not surprising that the lobotomist would draw on this idea to both support and justify lobotomy practice. As we will document, triune brain theory played a critical role in lobotomy theory.[20] Even in everyday language we draw on the reptilian brain inference, as is obvious in the expression "a cold-blooded killer." A person is called a "reptile killer because looking into their eyes is like looking into the eyes of a cold blooded reptile."[21] Sagan concluded his discussion of the triune brain by adding, the triune brain may be a metaphor but it is a "metaphor of great utility and depth."[22]

The Reptilian Brain Complex

The structures derived from the floor of the human fore-brain during early fetal development were labeled the "reptilian brain complex". The term derives from the belief of comparative neuro-anatomists that reptile fore-brains were dominated by those structures which controlled raw animal emotions. It was proposed that this claimed 'reptilian brain' was responsible for the instinctual behaviors involved in physical aggression, emotional outbursts, agitation, dominance, territoriality, and, in short, reptile-like personality traits.

History of Psychosurgery

18. Sagan, 1977, p. 60.
19. Sagan, 1977, p. 57.
20. Sagan, 1977, p. 52.
21. Martin, Ronald. 2018. *Murder at Pope's Cafeteria*. Morrisville, NC: Lulu Publishing Services, p. 83.
22. Sagan, 1977, p. 79.

On 13 September 1848, a 25-year-old railroad worker named Phineas Gage was struck in the head with a 43-inch-long iron tamping bar used to break up large rocks. The pointed three-cm (1.25 in)-diameter bar was driven completely through his head, destroying much of his brain's left frontal lobe.[23] Specifically, the iron bar entered the left side of his face, continuing upward behind the left eye, then proceeded through the left side of the brain, and exited from the frontal skull bone.

Considering the major damage that the bar caused, it was amazing that Mr. Gage survived the accident. The injury's effects on his personality and behavior were dramatic. Overall, he became less aggressive, and far more placid and introverted.[24] In short, he was emotionally flat; both his positive and negative emotions were lost.[25] Shown pictures of enormous beauty or sickening horror, his response was usually the same: little emotion, even when measured by heart rate, galvanic skin measurements, or other techniques.

A few years later, French surgeon and committed Darwinist, Paul Broca, concluded, partly on the basis of the now famous Gage case, that the prefrontal lobes (the portion at the very front of the frontal lobes) must be the part of the brain that separated humans from lower animals during evolution.[26] Broca was fascinated by evolution and its implications for brain study. He once remarked, "I would rather be a transformed ape

23. Fleischman, J. 2002. *Phineas Gage: A Gruesome but True Story About Brain Science*. Boston, MA: Houghton Mifflin.
24. Donald, G. 2017. *The Accidental Scientist: The Role of Chance and Luck in Scientific Discovery,* London, UK: Michael O'Mara Books, p. 130.
25. Fleischman, 2002, p. 67.
26. Valenstein, Elliot. 1991. Chapter 27: "The Prefrontal Area and Psychosurgery," *Progress in Brain Research* 85:539–554, p. 540.

than a degenerate son of Adam."[27]

The result of Broca's insight was that mental illness researchers attempted to surgically separate the parts of the brain that they believed had recently evolved from the parts they believed we inherited from our ancient reptilian ancestors. If Broca and others involved in this history had accepted the creation account that the human brain was created perfect, it is unlikely they would have concluded that separating brain sections by a surgical lobotomy could ameliorate various post-Fall problems. Lobotomy was even proposed as a way of achieving social control of certain elements of the population, such as political discontents.[28]

Early Application of the Reptile/Triune Brain Theory

One of the first persons to attempt to apply the theory of the reptilian brain to humans was Professor Gottlieb Burckhardt. He attempted to replicate Phineas Gage's accident in six schizophrenia patients who were confined at the Neuchâtel asylum in Switzerland. Although all six were deemed incurable, Burckhardt declared the experiment a success because the four survivors were greatly improved or even cured.[29] His report on the results that were presented at an 1889 Berlin medical confer-

27. Brabrook, E.W. 1881. 'Memoir of Paul Broca (1881),' *The Journal of the Anthropological Institute of Great Britain and Ireland* 10:242–261; Sagan, Carl. 1979. *Broca's Brain*. New York, NY: Random House, p. 6.

28. Garner, Roberta, and Black Hawk Hancock. 2014. *Social Theory: Continuity and Confrontation: A Reader*, 3rd Edition. Toronto, Canada: University of Toronto Press. p. 367; Mark, Vernon, and Frank Ervin. 1970. *Violence and the Brain*. New York, NY: Medical Dept., Harper & Row, pp. 26-37, 91.

29. MacLean, P.D., 1990. *The Triune Brain in Evolution: Role in Paleocerebral Functions*. New York, NY: Springer Publishing; Stone, James L. 2001. Dr. Gottlieb Burckhardt—The Pioneer of Psychosurgery. *Journal of the History of the Neuroscience* 10(1):80.

ence, was so favorable that it influenced others to attempt to replicate his procedure. As a result of his research, Professor Burckhardt is now considered the founder of psychosurgery, the use of surgery to treat psychiatric problems.

Opposition to Reptile Brain Theory

Some evolutionists even proposed that the problem was not the reptile brain, but the putatively more-evolved, "higher-level" brain, called the prefrontal cortex. Evolutionists contend that humans have the most-evolved frontal lobes in the entire animal kingdom. They reasoned that aggression and other mental problems emanated from these lobes and, consequently, the mental problems they produce could be ameliorated by separating the frontal lobes from the rest of the brain. This would reduce the influence of the most-evolved part of the brain.[30] After all, Darwin reasoned that humans were one of the most aggressive of all animals. Consequently, some practitioners proposed surgical treatments based on this *opposite* theory—that the *frontal lobes* are the problem, and not the so-called, primitive "less-evolved" brain parts beneath them. And although the brain was considered "the most important aspect of evolution," the "quest to pin down the exact moment on the evolutionary continuum when 'man' first appeared" has been unsuccessful.[31] This argument illustrates the tenuousness of the reptile brain theory.

Professor Egas Moniz

One person who replicated Burckhardt's work was Portuguese

30. El-Hai, 2005, p. 14.
31. Pressman, Jack D. 1998. *Last Resort: Psychosurgery and the Limits of Medicine (Cambridge Studies in the History of Medicine)*. New York, NY: Cambridge University Press, pp. 36, 56.

surgeon Egas Moniz (1874–1955), Clinical Professor of Neurology at the University of Lisbon.[32] Moniz was also inspired by a presentation at the London Neurological Congress given by Yale physiologist John Farquhar Fulton and his psychologist colleague, Carlyle Jacobsen. The two scientists reported their frontal lobotomy experiments on chimps involving surgically isolating the connections between the prefrontal brain lobes and the rest of the brain.[33]

Both Yale professors were very familiar with the Gage case described above. Professor "Fulton was intrigued by this notion that one of the most primitive structures and one of the most recently advanced might in fact be directly connected."[34] He attempted to sever the connection between the reptile brain, which included the thalamus, and the higher most-evolved brain, the frontal or neo-mammalian area.

Professor Fulton was primarily interested in brain evolution based on his belief that evolution had added newer brain structures to older, more primitive systems, (later called the "reptile brain"), that controlled fighting, self-protection, aggression, sexual behavior, and other basic survival instincts.[35]

The researchers claimed that the surgery produced monkeys that were much calmer, more cooperative, even passive. The monkeys previously resisted being restrained, and had exhibited 'frustrational behavior' if not rewarded due to failing to perform appropriately in the various experiments they were forced to endure. After the surgery, the monkeys no longer re-

32. Alexander, Franz, and Sheldon Selesnick. 1966. *The History of Psychiatry*. New York, NY: Harper & Row, p. 284.

33. Donald, G., 2013. *When the Earth Was Flat: All the Bits of Science We Got Wrong*, London, UK: Michael O'Mara Books, p. 133.

34. Pressman, 1998, p. 518.

35. Pressman, 1998, p. 67; MacLean, 1973, p. 14.

sisted, and remained friendly and alert.[36]

From what he learned by reading the work of the Yale professors, including Fulton, Moniz introduced a surgical operation he called *prefrontal leukotomy* in 1936. The surgery involved cutting the brain's 'white matter' connecting fibers. After his initial experiments, he attempted to use the procedure in treating schizophrenia and other psychotic mental conditions. At this time, no other treatment existed that could ameliorate the major symptoms of these baffling, debilitating diseases.

The treatment, later called *prefrontal lobotomy*, consisted of incisions that destroyed the connections between the prefrontal region and other brain parts. Moniz first used the technique on a female patient. He drilled holes in her head, then poured alcohol into the holes to destroy the white fibers connecting the frontal lobes to the rest of her brain.

Although Moniz concluded that the operation was a success, he later abandoned this crude technique and instead used a knife to sever the connection between what evolutionists declared was the "more-evolved" frontal cortex and the "primitive" brain parts behind it. In 1936, Moniz published his findings in several leading medical journals. He later traveled to London to present his results at a conference involving the general medical community.

In the words of one observer, Moniz was skilled at "presenting the unpalatable in such a way as to make it attractive" by referring to his "butchery as psychosurgery."[37] Moniz then proceeded to use his crude hacking procedure on a variety of mental patients, all of whom he declared to be improved.[38] Al-

36. Valenstein, 1990, p. 541.
37. Donald, 2017, p. 134.
38. Valenstein, 1991, p. 539.

though he published one monograph and at least 13 articles on his results in scholarly journals, he never did a proper long-term scientific follow-up study on his patients. For this and other reasons, his claims were, at best, irresponsible. Today, we realize that most of his patients replaced one set of symptoms for another set. Specifically, they replaced their aggression and irritability with a sluggish, disoriented, even moribund, countenance. Some were reduced to vegetative states, and others died of cerebral hemorrhaging or other complications.[39]

Dr. Walter Freeman Takes the Lead

Yale Medical School graduate, Dr. Walter Freeman, Professor at the George Washington University School of Medicine, (where he taught for 30 years), and a physician at St. Elizabeth's Hospital in Washington, D. C., soon learned of Moniz's allegedly wonderful results. Freeman had been asked to review Moniz's monograph, which sold him on the lobotomy theory technique.[40] It set him on a course that would define his life's work.

After reading the monograph, Freeman began his aggressive campaign in the name of science to lobotomize what ended up being several thousand Americans. His first victim was Alice Hammatt, who was treated in 1936 after she was given the choice of being locked-up in an asylum for the remainder of her life, or being lobotomized. Not unexpectedly, she chose the operation. This turned out to be a bad choice.

Freeman soon experimented with a faster lobotomizing procedure, namely the use of an actual ice pick and a few mal-

---

39. Kang, L., and Pedersen, N. 2017. *Quackery: A Brief History of the Worst Ways to Cure Everything.* New York, NY: Workman Publishing, p. 158.
40. Sternburg, 2014, pp. 45-46.

let taps to break through the top of the eye socket. He then moved the ice pick back and forth in the opening to the brain, thereby attempting to sever the connection between part of the frontal cortex and the rest of the brain. This method, called a *transorbital lobotomy*, was originally developed by Italian psychiatrist Dr. Amarro Fiamberti (1894-1970). Freeman eventually used the transorbital lobotomy on thousands of patents. Among its advantages was not having to bore a hole through the thick skull bone, but only having to puncture a small hole behind the eyeball, a location where the skull-bone tissue was very thin.

All methods described thus far were not only somewhat crude, but often affected very different parts of the brain. Freeman concluded that a more-promising area deserving focus was "the exploration of the central vegetative [evolutionarily primitive] centers in the interbrain."[41] Freeman had hoped that the transorbital method would lend some consistency to what then was a very imprecise hit-and-miss procedure.

Another major advantage was that the ice pick lobotomy could be done by anyone with a strong stomach, and, even better, could be done anywhere. Freeman carried his ice pick in his pocket, using it on one occasion to perform a lobotomy in a motel room. The "ice pick lobotomy was a cheap outpatient procedure which became a common psycho-surgical choice in state hospitals across the country."[42]

The 1949 Nobel Prize Awarded for the Procedure

Amazingly, the 1949 Nobel Prize in Physiology or Medicine

41. Pressman, 1998, p. 75.
42. Vertosick, Jr., Frank T. 1997. Lobotomy's Back. *Discover Magazine* 18(10):66-72., p. 70.

was given to Egas Moniz "for his discovery of the therapeutic value of leucotomy in certain psychoses"—a treatment that was then considered "one of the most important discoveries ever made in psychiatric therapy."[43] The award was one more evidence that, in its heyday from the 1920s to the 1950s, lobotomy was "very much in the mainstream in psychiatry," uncritically and enthusiastically supported and performed in leading university hospitals in countries around the world.[44]

Lobotomy was also used to treat the criminally insane, and was even used to 'cure' certain political dissidents.[45] In 1943, the Veterans Administration approved lobotomies for veterans suffering from mental illness or war trauma. In the end, close to 2,000 persons were lobotomized.[46] Reportedly, Veterans Administration Hospitals around the country vied for Dr. Freeman's services for which he was handsomely compensated.

The use of lobotomies began to decline only in the mid- to late-1950s but were still occasionally used well into the 1980s.[47] Although critics of the technique always existed, opposition eventually became fierce because of the many failures and decidedly mixed results. A few patients did fairly well; most others did not.

Most importantly, phenothiazine-based neuroleptic (anti-psychotic) drugs, such as chlorpromazine, became widely available. These drugs were, as a whole, much more effective than psychosurgery. They also had the advantage that medicine therapy could always be terminated if the results were prob-

43. Valenstein, 1991, p. 539.
44. Valenstein, 1986, pp. xi, 4.
45. Sternburg, 2015.
46. Phillips, Michael. 2013. "An Operation's Champion and the Vets Left Behind." *The Wall Street Journal*, December 13, pp. 1a, 16a.
47. Vertosick, 1997, p. 68.

lematic. The results of psychosurgery were not reversible and, once the harm became obvious, usually little could be done to repair the damage. Thus, the surgical treatment method was soon superseded by the chemical treatment method. During the 1940s and 1950s, lobotomies were performed on close to 50,000 patients in the United States, and around 17,000 in Western Europe, including 4,500 in Sweden.[48]

The Failures Add Up

Freeman's most famous case was 23-year-old Rosemary Kennedy, the oldest sister of former American President, John F. Kennedy. She underwent a prefrontal lobotomy in an attempt to control her sometimes extreme emotional outbursts, which may have resulted partly from the family's failed attempts to control her behavior. To help her have a more peaceful and productive life, psychiatric experts recommended the lobotomy procedure to her father, Joseph Kennedy. After the surgery, Rosemary was left with the mental capacity of a toddler, unable to walk, form a sentence, or even follow simple directions. Although she was able to relearn some basic skills, she never recovered. Instead, the surgery left her mentally and physically incapacitated for the rest of her life.

Freeman Finally Banned

Freeman was finally banned from operating only in 1967, after one of his long-term patients died from a brain hemorrhage following her third Freeman lobotomy. The total number of persons lobotomized by Freeman alone was estimated at close

---

48. Comer, 2013, p. 358; Anonymous. 2007. The rise & fall of the prefrontal lobotomy. *ScienceBlogs,* scienceblogs.com/neurophilosophy/2007/07/24/inventing-the-lobotomy, July 24..

to 3,500.[49] Very few Freeman-type lobotomies were performed in the United States after 1967.   Most of those lobotomized were women and children as young as four.[50] How many of these died prematurely from the operation is unknown, but the number is significant, estimated by Comer as many as 45,000 persons.[51]

Common serious problems included severe hemorrhaging, brain seizures, loss of motor control, partial paralysis, enormous weight gains, and major intellectual and emotional malfunction.[52] If a major blood vessel was damaged or severed, it could cause death, as it did in close to five percent of the treatments.[53]

The sometimes-severe adverse effects of the procedure were known from the beginning of lobotomy's use. Even the early research by Yale professor Fulton and his colleague Jacobsen reported their monkey subjects often losing both ambition and their drive to succeed in the various tasks in which they were involved. Almost all patients were seriously affected mentally, some very adversely as was Rosemary Kennedy and the two lobotomized relatives whom Janet Sternburg discusses in detail in her family history.[54]

The fact is, the dangerous lobotomy fad "was ultimately created by highly educated physicians—in many instances, able men who had contributed significantly to medicine earlier in their careers."[55] Freeman even published a textbook on his lobotomy technique with one of the most prestigious scientific

49. Donald, 2017, p. 139.
50. El-Hai, 2005, pp. 174–175.
51. Comer, 2013, p. 458.
52. Comer, 2013.
53. Valenstein, 1986, p. 252.
54. Sternburg, 2015.
55. Valenstein, 1986, p. 5.

publishers in his day.[56] This, in spite of the fact that the procedure was based "on the flimsiest of theories, and on completely inadequate evidence."[57] Nonetheless, the support of the press was critical in its widespread acceptance:

> Outside the medical profession itself, lobotomy was promoted by the popular press. Magazines and newspapers, whose readers numbered in the millions, popularized each new 'miracle cure' with uncritical enthusiasm, while commonly overlooking its shortcomings and dangers. These popular accounts created enormous interest in lobotomy among patients and their relatives, many of whom had abandoned hope, and they sought out the physicians mentioned in the articles with the desperation of a drowning person reaching for anything to stay afloat.[58]

In view of the widespread support for the procedure, awarding it a Nobel Prize is less ironic than it first appears, but in view of the damage it has caused, it has created credibility problems for both science and medicine.

Growing Opposition to the Procedure

A major reason for the eventual opposition to the technique, besides the high failure rate and the fact that better chemical treatment techniques became available, was that regardless of where or how the cuts were made the results were often fairly similar.[59] If a reptile brain area existed that could be separated from the more evolved brain, and if this was the basis for the

56. Freeman, Walter, and James Watts. 1950. *Psychosurgery in the Treatment of Mental Disorders and Intractable Pain,* 2nd Edition. Springfield, IL: Charles C. Thomas.
57. Valenstein, 1986, p. 62.
58. Valenstein, 1986, p. 5.
59. Anonymous, 2007.

therapeutic results claimed, the cuts would need to have been made specifically in the area connecting the two.

Only humans had large prefrontal lobes and, evolutionists reasoned, as humans evolved from some ape-like creature which had fairly-small frontal lobes, the solution to mental illness must be related to this difference.[60] The fact that it did not seem to matter much where the cuts in the cerebrum were made was clearly inconsistent with the entire evolution-based concept that justified lobotomy.

The researchers also found that the positive effects of treatment were often only temporary, and most of the patients relapsed in time, documenting the belief that the damage caused by the treatment was either being repaired or other parts of the brain were taking over the functions lost by the treatment.[61] Another problem was that the exact same protocol helped some patients but hurt others.

Brain researchers also increasingly concluded that the separate parts of the cerebral cortex are like a symphonic orchestra; each part contributes to the whole, but the music can still sound great even when some parts are missing.[62] In the case of a hemispherectomy (removal of half of the brain, which can sometimes be the only option for severe epileptic seizures), if completed when the patient is very young, the remaining hemisphere can largely compensate for the half that is removed, often causing only minor issues with walking.[63] Furthermore,

60. Vertosick, 1997, p. 71.
61. Valenstein, 1991, p. 544.
62. Robbins, Jim. 2008. *The Brain is Like a Symphonic Orchestra*. New York, NY: Grove Press. .
63. Carson, B.S., et al. 1996. Hemispherectomy: A hemidecortication approach and review of 52 cases. *Journal of Neurosurgery* 84(6):903–911, https://www.jstor.org/stable/2841526; Eileen, P.J., et al. 1997. Why

children born with only a half or less of the cerebral cortex can often almost totally compensate for the loss. This has been documented by twin studies in which one has a normal brain, and in the other a large percent of the cerebral hemisphere was missing.[64]

These observations do not deny that some specific brain parts are critical for certain functions, such as Broca's area being responsible for controlling motor functions involved with speech production. People who have damage to this brain area can generally understand words but struggle to assemble and express them at the level required to effectively communicate.

New brain research on the hemispherectomy procedure was critical in demolishing both the triune brain and reptile brain theories, as well as the core idea behind lobotomy procedure. One major problem was that the theory did not fit with evolutionary studies of animal brains: "there are only four surviving orders of reptiles, and none is considered representative of the forerunners of mammals."[65] Removal of specific structures, such as by stereotactic surgery with gamma radiation to ablate a cancerous pituitary, is accomplished with a high level of precision to treat a very specific area and condition. In contrast, damage to the cerebrum as done by a lobotomy was, for the reasons noted above, often worse than just a failure of the

---

Would You Remove Half a Brain? The Outcome of 58 Children After Hemispherectomy--The Johns Hopkins Experience: 1968 to 1996. *Pediatrics* 100(2):163–171.

64. Presentation on unique aspects of the human brain at Stony Brook University Professor of Neurosurgery Michael Egnor, M.D. Christian Scientific Society meet April 2017 features human exceptionalism, https://uncommondescent.com/human-evolution/christian-scientific-society-meet-april-2017-features-human-exceptionalism/.

65. MacLean, 1973. pp. 8-9.

treatment to help the client adjust.[66]

The Procedure Ended

The triune and reptile brain theories lost favor with most comparative neuroscientists in the post-2000 era.[67] The reasons include the fact that efforts to localize the reptile brain failed, and the hoped-for results of psychosurgery never materialized.[68] Even though the evolutionary assumption was generally retained, it was not surprising that the focus of treatment became successful health improvements for those suffering from mental illnesses.[69]

In "due course, Moniz and his Nobel prize-winning leucotome were quietly dropped from the introductory pages of psychiatry textbooks and consigned to the museum that housed the whips, chains, dunking chairs, and magic amulets of yore."[70] Meanwhile, the damage done to countless patients before the procedure was finally abandoned was profound. Today the history of lobotomy, and the enormous harm it has caused, is largely ignored, or only briefly covered, in the standard histories of psychology and psychiatry.[71]

66. Jagannathan, J., C.P. Yen, N. Pouratian, E. Laws, and J. Sheehan. 2009. Stereotactic radiosurgery for pituitary adenomas: A comprehensive review of indications, techniques and long-term results using the Gamma Knife. *Journal of Neuro-Oncology* 92(3):345–356.

67. Kiverstein, J., and Miller, M. 2015. The embodied brain: Towards a radical embodied cognitive neuroscience. *Frontiers in Human Neuroscience* 9(237):1–11, pp. 1–11.

68. Donald, 2012.

69. Franks, David D. 2006. *Handbook of the Sociology of Emotions*, Chapter 2: "The Neuroscience of Emotions," pp. 38-62. New York, NY: Springer.

70. Pressman, 1998, p. 402.

71. Alexander and Selesnick, 1966, p. 284; Sahakian, William. 1968. *History of Psychology*. Itasca, IL: Peacock Publishers; Schultz, Duane. 1969.

After Freeman's surgical privileges were removed, he transferred his case files to his van and took cross-country trips at his own expense, one lasting six months, to do follow-ups on former patients and present papers at professional meetings.[72] He estimated that he followed up on several thousand patients.[73] Freeman's assessments of the results of his technique, Vertosick claimed, "proved vague and unconvincing."[74] Some people were happy with the results, or they claimed that they were, but all too many were not.[75] Luke Dittrich called Yale Professor Dr. Scoville "a moral monster—ambitious, driven, self-centred and willing to inflict grave and irreversible damage on his patients in his search for fame."[76]

Conclusions

The leading scientists involved in developing the lobotomy procedure accepted evolution, and experimental evidence seemed to show that a part of the brain was important in expressing so-called primitive emotions. Consequently, their view of reality through their "evolution glasses" predisposed them to conclude that severing certain brain connections would produce a large reduction in these primitive emotions. Furthermore, the few lobotomy successes confirmed in their minds their evolutionary conclusions. In the end, as many as 45,000 persons were lobotomized, producing what neurologist Frank Vertosick called "a mental health holocaust."[77]

A History of Modern Psychology. New York, NY: Academic Press.

72. Sternburg, 2014, p. 178.
73. Valenstein, 1986, pp. 276-280.
74. Vertosick, 1997, p. 71.
75. Sternburg, 2014, p. 178.
76. Scull, 2019. p. 136.
77. Vertosick, 1997, pp. 68, 70.

Lobotomy is now a very embarrassing part of medical history. As we look back on this history one must wonder how and why it was ever widely accepted by both scientists and physicians.[78] Part of the reason was the incorrect assumptions that resulted from their brain-evolution belief. As a result, "Aside from the Nazi doctor Joseph Mengele, Walter Freeman ranks as the most scorned physician of the twentieth century."[79] The fact is, the "living brain has a surreal fragility; the porcelain surface is laced with arteries that began as thick cords, but branch into fine threads."[80]

The Darwinian Approach Resurrected

A newer, more refined procedure using advanced procedures, called a *cingulotomy*, uses electrodes to destroy a coin-sized area of the frontal lobes called the cingulate gyrus. A 1996 trial, using MRI guidance, was conducted by Harvard Medical School specialists on 34 patients with totally intractable severe anxiety/depression resulting from a variety of (non-schizophrenic) causes. The research, as reviewed by neurosurgeon Frank Vertosick, found that only around 1/3 improved.

Ironically, the procedure is based on the theory that the cingulate gyrus, a thin ribbon of brain tissue, is "a conduit between the limbic region, a primitive area involved in emotional behavior, and the [evolutionarily advanced] frontal lobes." Consequently, the cingulate technique "can trace its intellectual heritage right back to the chimps Beckey and Lucy," and even to Freeman himself.[81] This procedure requires future research and a long-term follow-up to determine its efficacy.[82]

---

78. Kang and Pedersen, 2017, pp. 145–150.
79. El-Hai, 2005, p. 1.
80. Vertosick, 1997, pp. 70-71.
81. Vertosick, 1997, p. 72.
82. Vertosick, 1997, p. 68.

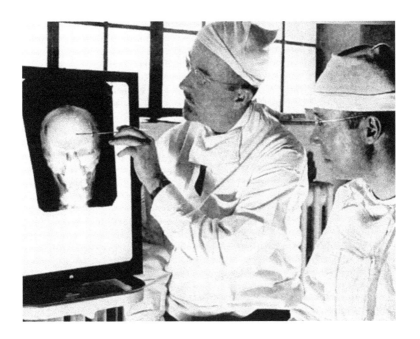

Dr. Walter Freeman (1895-1972), left, and Dr. James W. Watts study an X-ray before a psychosurgical operation. Psychosurgery, cutting the brain of a patient to relieve problems such as abnormal aggression, delusions, obsessions, and nervous tensions.

Source: https://commons.wikimedia.org/wiki/File:Turning_the_Mind_Inside_Out_Saturday_Evening_Post_24_May_1941_a_detail_1.jpg

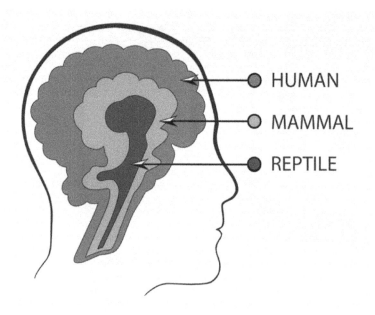

The reptile, mammal and human brain from the most primitive to the most evolved according to evolution. This idea has now been refuted. Drawn by Richard Geer. Used by permission.

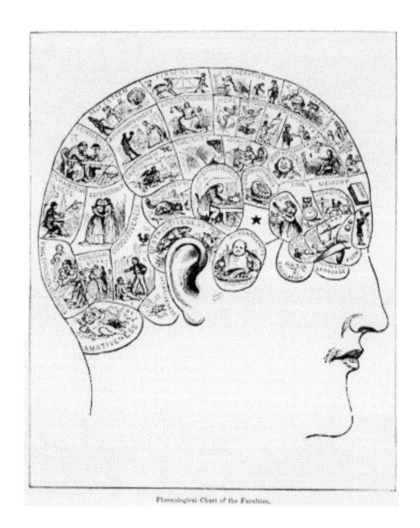

Phrenological Chart of the Faculties.

Phrenology Chart showing the various areas of the skull and what they repersent. Public domain from People's Cyclopedia of Universal Knowledge, 1883. W.H. Depuy (editor). New York, NY: Eaton & Mains.

4

Phrenology: A Myth Behind Darwinism

Introduction

O<small>N MY DESK SITS ONE</small> of the popular, white-porcelain phrenology models of a bald human head covered with words and lines representing different areas of the brain. The phrenology theory essentially reads bumps (called peaks) on the skull surface, which are interpreted as brain areas that are more developed, and indentations (called valleys), which are interpreted as less developed brain areas. Phrenology emphasis focused only on the surface head curvature, not the brain's interior, which is required to study the brain.[1]

By 1838, "phrenological ideas had achieved widespread acceptance throughout the United States."[2] Phrenology lectures attracted thousands of people. The popular lectures covered

---

1. Parker, J.O., F. Alfaro-Almagro, and S. Jbabdi. 2018. An empirical, 21st-century evaluation of phrenology. *Cortex* 106:26–35.
2. McCandless, Peter. 1992. Mesmerism and phrenology in antebellum Charleston: "Enough of the Marvelous." *Journal of Southern History* 58(2):199–230, p. 205.

phrenology advice on matters including the best way to hire new employees or to find a suitable marriage partner (see Figure 5).[3] In the end, phrenology became part of applied psychology accepted by many intellectuals of the 19th and 20th centuries.[4]

Phrenology was mainstream science for decades, attracting millions of followers, until it was finally debunked around the early 1900s.[5] It was empirically discredited only in 2018 by the largest, most carefully designed study ever completed on phrenology. This study used MRI neuroimaging on 5,724 subjects, producing 40,962 vertex measures per subject which were compared with a set of lifestyle measures drawn from the same subjects.[6] No relationship was found between self-reported information and the results of phrenology evaluations done by a trained phrenologist. Yet it had been widely accepted even by very educated persons. Frazire writes:

> Looking back from today, it may be difficult to appreciate the hold the pseudoscience of phenology had on society in Britain, Europe and America in the nineteenth century. It seemed a sparkling new science based on the physical anatomy of the skull, not mystical ideas. Prominent scientific figures such as [evolution co-founder] Alfred Russel Wallace... testified to its values. Phrenology's impact was felt nearly everywhere... it influenced anthropology, criminology, education, medicine, psychology.... it was warm and satisfying, and it seemed to work. Yet it was all

---

3. McCandless, 1992, pp. 209-210.
4. Chambers, Howard. 1968. *Phrenology for the Millions*. Los Angeles, CA: Sherbourne Press, p. 200.
5. Dean, Geoffrey. 2012. Phrenology and the Grand Delusion of Experience. *Skeptical Inquirer* 36(6):31-38, p. 33.
6. Parker et al., 2018.

a delusion. How could such a thing happen?[7]

In short, the phrenology belief has now been firmly rejected by solid scientific evidence.

The Influence of Darwinism

How the world was sold on phrenology occurred for the same reason that Darwinism was accepted, as "a sparkling new science based on the physical anatomy… not mystical ideas" as, evolutionists claimed, was true of religion. The phrenology movement was greatly influenced by Darwinians, specifically Darwin himself, as well as the co-founder of evolution, Alfred Russel Wallace. The enormously popular movement caused harm by diverting attention from empirically based theories of behavior causation, which in turn fostered racism, indirectly helping to open the door to materialism, naturalism, and Darwinism.

A good example of its contribution to racism was the use of evolution-based phrenology to classify the native Rwandans in the early1900s. The leading phrenologist Paul Bout's system was used by the Belgian Colonial Office to help "decide on matters of racial superiority", concluding that the Tutsi were "racially superior to the Hutu, putting" them above the Hutu in all matters and benefits.[8] The result of dividing the Tutsi and Hutu eventually lead to the Rwandan holocaust in 1994 that resulted in the slaughter of an estimated one-million Tutsis and

---

7. Frazier, Kendrick. 2012. Phrenology's Lessons for Today. *Skeptical Inquirer* 36(6):1, p. 1.

8. Donald, Graeme. 2013. *They Got It Wrong: Science: All the Facts That Turned Out to Be Science Fiction*. White Plains, NY: Readers Digest, p. 21.

moderate Hutus.[9]

The History of Phrenology

Developed by 19th-century Viennese medical doctor and anatomist, Franz Joseph Gall in 1796, the idea was very influential in the 19th century, especially from about 1810 until 1900. The term 'phrenology' comes from the Greek φρήν (phrēn), 'mind,' and λόγος (logos), 'knowledge.' It involves measuring skull surface traits in an attempt to predict mental and personality traits. It was based on the materialistic concept that the mind is the brain, and has no existence aside from the physical structure of this organ.[10] Almost from the beginning, the movement was naturalistic and anti-clerical, which attracted Darwin and his father Robert to the philosophy.[11]

It follows that storage of the many "mind" parts must be localized in certain brain areas which have specific functions. Although the function of many general parts of the human brain has now been confirmed by empirical research, mostly from studies of brain damage, phrenology was extrapolated well-beyond the empirical evidence. For example, it is well documented that certain brain structures that are part of the brain stem are separate organs. One example would be the *medulla*, which controls many vital autonomic functions, including heart rate, breathing, and blood pressure. Another example is the *pons*, (a portion of the hindbrain), which helps to coordinate movement on each side of the body.

---

9. Donald, 2013, p. 21.
10. Gregory, Richard. 1987. *The Oxford Companion to the Mind*. New York, NY/Oxford, England: Oxford University Press, p. 618.
11. Staum, Martin S. 2003. *Labeling People: French Scholars on Society, Race and Empire, 1815-1848*. Chapter 3: "The Ambivalence of Phrenology," pp. 49-84. Montreal, Canada: McGill-Queen's University Press, p. 52.

In contrast, phrenologists were concerned with only two structures, *the cerebellum*, which is involved in the coordination of motor movements and basic facets of memory and learning, and *the frontal lobe of the cortex*, located at the front of the brain. This structure is associated with reasoning, motor skills, higher level cognition, and expressive language. Scientists have only recently been able to isolate general cortex areas that control these functions. Phrenologists evaluated only the cortex and cerebellum surface areas as reflected in their effect on the skull, ignoring the brain's interior. This was one reason why phrenology was derisively called bumpology, or craniology.[12] Surface measurements are obviously invalid measures of the brain's internal structure. Furthermore, the thickness of the skin, bones, dura mater (uppermost meninges), and other tissues vary, distorting slightly the measurements of the cortex.

Other phrenologists taught that the brain is actually composed of different separate organs, not just general areas.[13] The organ theory concluded that the bumps represent larger organs, a focus called organology. According to the founder of phrenology, Franz Gall, 27 distinct organs exist in the brain which produce 27 different mental faculties. He later looked for more faculties and the number eventually reached 42.[14] These included persons with a mirthful disposition, (i. e., liking to laugh), who had two prominent bumps on their forehead compared to their more dour contemporaries.[15]

12. Williams, William F. (editor). 2000. "Phrenology" in: *The Encyclopedia of Pseudoscience: From Alien Abductions to Zone Therapy*. New York, NY: Facts on File, pp. 266-268, p. 266.

13. Williams, 2000, p. 266.

14. Mainwaring, Marian. 1980. 'Phys/Phren'-- Why not take each other at face value. *Smithsonian* 11(8):193-212, p. 194.

15. Parker, et al., 2018.

Not all scientists accepted the main ideas that phrenology is based upon, but some who rejected phrenology accepted the related idea, physiognomy, the belief that character can be read in the face and other body parts. Of the numerous articles on physiognomy published in phrenological journals, one article covered character traits as revealed in nose shape and its traits. This idea was later exploited to debase Jews and other ethnic groups.[16]

Most of the behavioral traits the phrenology system measured require a great deal of subjective judgment. Examples include a disposition for delight in colors, circumspection, pride, arrogance, distrust of authority, and the so-called impulse toward propagation (i. e., having large families). A major appeal of phrenology was that it "was seductively simple and logical. . . . it both entertained and educated."[17]

The Importance of Phrenology

Throughout the 19th century, intellectuals discussed the relationship between nature, secularism, and religion. What the "Left found most attractive in phrenology was that it offered the masses an alternative to religion as a means of explaining the world."[18] It is often assumed that the scientific naturalism beliefs of writers such as T. H. Huxley and John Tyndall were the sole result of the 'Darwinian revolution' unleashed in 1859. Darwin's work, though, was born in the context of vigorous debates about naturalism.

At the forefront of these debates were the phrenology ad-

---

16. Parks, Charles Todd. 1902. Character as indicated in the nose. *The Phrenological Journal* 114(3):290-292, September.

17. McLaren, Angus. 1974. Phrenology: Medium and message. *The Journal of Modern History* 46(1):86-97, pp. 91-92, March.

18. McLaren, 1974, p. 88.

vocates who applied their theories to concerns ranging from medicine, treatments of the insane, education, theology, and even economics.[19] Ideas about naturalism and natural law were often first born in early phrenology controversies. One book in particular, *The Constitution of Man in Relation to External Objects* (1828) by **phrenologist** George Combe, "replaced God with natural laws." It had an enormous influence on scientific thinking and the popularity of the 'naturalistic movement'.[20]

The *Constitution*, published from 1828 to 1899, sold far more than Darwin's *Origin of Species*.[21] Combe's book sold 100,000 copies by the end of the century whereas Darwin's *Origin* had sold only 50,000 copies during the same time period. It also, at first, surpassed Darwin's 1859 book both in importance and the intellectual heat generated. Furthermore, its natural law philosophy influenced Darwin's *Origin*.[22] The phrenological community "was rich soil for naturalistic thinking," creating a large population of persons supportive of this worldview. Consequently, it influenced the widespread popular acceptance of this worldview among free-thinkers and secularists.[23]

It "impressed hundreds of thousands of readers with a plausible alternative ... to [the] traditional Christian-based understanding of Man."[24] Combe was also "in complete agreement with . . . this sweeping account of the evolution of life" which

19. Wyhe, John van. 2001. "Phrenology." 52-minute DVD, *BFS Entertainment*. Ontario, Canada: Richmond Hill.
20. Wyhe, John van. 2004. *Phrenology and the Origins of Victorian Scientific Naturalism*. New York, NY: Routledge Publishing, p. 153.
21. Whye, 2001; 2004, p. 128.
22. Whye, 2004, p. 21.
23. Whye, 2004, p. 97.
24. Whye, 2004, p. 127.

influenced Robert Chambers' book *The Vestiges of the Natural History of Creation*. *Vestiges* was the first book to introduce in detail the secular evolutionary theory to the world.[25] And Chambers was almost in complete agreement with phrenology, even ending his *Vestiges* book with an endorsement of phrenology.[26] Chambers was also enormously influenced by Combe's *Constitution* book, embracing the doctrine of natural law.[27] He also cited certain "scientific" studies undertaken by phrenology's founder, Dr. Gall, drawing on "phrenology for further evidence as to the materiality of mind."[28]

Consequently, as early as 1844, phrenology endorsed evolution. The only major area of disagreement was that Combe did not agree with Chambers' "assertion that organic life arose from chemical processes," thus rejecting the naturalistic abiogenesis theory.[29] Reviews of *Vestiges* published in the *Phrenological Journal* were uniformly positive.[30] One review defended the book, and condemned critics, writing, "inconsistently . . . the men of science did not confine their attention to its alleged objections, but urged against its moral and theological objections, calculated to rouse popular prejudices against the unknown au-

25. Tomlinson, Stephen. 2005. *Head Masters: Phrenology, Secular Education and Nineteenth-Century Social Thought*. Tuscaloosa, AL: The University of Alabama Press, p. 304.

26. Tomlinson, 2005, p. 304.

27. Whye, 2004, pp. 175, 178.

28. Millhauser, Milton. 1959. *Just Before Darwin: Robert Chambers and Vestiges*. Middletown, CT: Wesleyan University Press, p. 109.

29. Tomlinson, 2005, p. 304. See also Chambers, Robert. 1844. *The Vestiges of the Natural History of Creation*. London, England: John Churchill.

30. Combe, George. 1846. *Phrenological Journal* 33:159, January. Review of Explanations: A Sequel to *Vestiges of the Natural History of Creation* (1845). London, England: J. Churchill.

thor and his work."[31]

The progressive phrenologists soon also worked Darwinism into their theory. This was not difficult because many similarities existed between the phrenology and Darwinist worldviews. For example, like "Darwinism, phrenology left the laboratory, and thereafter its 'proof' lay in debating forums and public acceptance, not in scientific experiments."[32]

Phrenology and Francis Galton

One example of phrenology's early acceptance is that of Darwin's cousin, Francis Galton. In 1844, Galton's father died when Francis was 22, leaving him a large inheritance. Brooding, depressed, and without goals, Galton consulted a phrenologist to help guide his future. The phrenologist reported that men of his head type were best suited for activities such as colonizing and exploring.[33] Believing that this obviously erroneous advice was true, Galton set off in 1850 to explore a part of the world that was at that time largely unknown to Europeans—the foreboding land of dark Africa. There he saw people that convinced him that his cousin Charles Darwin was right about inferior races. This belief dominated his work in developing his theory of eugenics, eventually resulting in one of the worst catastrophes that has ever been visited on earth.

Phrenology and Materialism

Soon various science disciplines incorporated phrenology into their worldview. Smith College professor, John Davies, from

---

31. Combe, 1846.
32. Davies, John. 1955. *Phrenology: Fad and Science.* New Haven, CT: Yale University Press, p. 162.
33. Kevles, Daniel J. 1985. *In the Name of Eugenics: Genetics and the Uses of Human Heredity.* New York, NY: Alfred A. Knopf, p. 6.

his study of the subject concluded that phrenology "was a precursor of the larger Darwinian movement; years later the same audience who heard Fowler's lectures [on phrenology] and bought Combe's books [on phrenology] would be listening to Robert Ingersoll [atheism lectures] and reading Thomas Huxley's [evolution] books."[34]

In 1858, the leader of The Secular Society wrote that "More converts have been made this last century by *The Constitution of Man* to free thought than any other agency . . . . They hailed phrenology as an atheistic and naturalistic doctrine, a fresh source of ammunition to use in the ongoing battle against revealed religion."[35]

Phrenology also "provided a way station on the road to a secular view of life . . . [and] prepared the way for [Darwin's] *On the Origin of the Species*."[36] As McLaren observed in his study of phenology, the "role played by phrenology in [supporting] early evolutionary theory has not been fully appreciated" by scholars.[37]

As Darwinism became more widely accepted, phrenology received a major boost. In "the 19th century many educated Europeans and Americans accepted the scientific validity not only of face reading (physiognomy) but of head reading (phrenology) as well. The bumps on a person's cranium, they thought, revealed his or her personality."[38]

Support by the Academicians and the Liberal Ministers

Phrenology was proposed by certain leading psychiatrists as a

34. Davies, 1955, p. 172.
35. McLaren, 1974, p. 95.
36. Davies, 1955, p. 172.
37. McLaren, 1974, pp. 92, 94.
38. Mainwaring, 1980, p. 93.

viable model to reform both psychology and criminal corrections. It was in this area that the fad moved from a harmless system of entertainment, which it often was, to causing harm to certain people. Because phrenology was taken seriously in the Victorian era and permeated both literature and novels, it influenced many areas of society. Many prominent public figures, such as the Reverend Henry Ward Beecher (a college classmate and initial partner of one of America's leading phrenologists, Orson Fowler), promoted phrenology actively as a source of psychological insight.

Italian psychiatrist Biagio Miraglia proposed a new classification of mental illness based on brain functions described by Gall. Miraglia relied on Gall's phrenological localization of mental functions in the brain in his therapy practice. He even argued that madness is a consequence of cerebral organ dysfunctions that could be detected by phrenology: "The organs of the brain that may become ill in isolation" or in conjunction with other genes and/or structures, obtain "their activities infected through energy, or depression, or inertia or deficiency. So the madness can take the appearance of these three characteristic forms: i. e., for enhanced activity, or for depressed activity, or for inertia or deficiency of brain activities."[39]

The Darwinian Phrenology Theory

The evolutionary theory that supported anthropological phrenology was simple. We evolved from an ape which had a smaller brain than we have. Called the reptile brain, it was part of the triune brain theory. Specifically, modern apes and humans have a common ancestor, which was an ape-like creature that

---

39. Miraglia, Biagio G. 1847. Reprinted in: A new classification of mental illness based on brain functions. *Dialogues in Philosophy, Mental and Neuro Sciences* 7(2):636–637, 663.

had a smaller brain compared to ours. Humans still retain the primitive brain which is located in the occipital area. Our enormous language, creative, artistic, musical, and mechanical abilities resulted from our more-evolved, thus larger, brain than apes. For evolutionists, the implications of phrenology were obvious: the brain, and therefore the mind, evolved like any other organ.[40] And the more it evolved, the larger it became. The inner part was the most primitive part of the triune brain and the outer, larger parts were more developed. Consequently, phrenology determined the development of the brain parts by measuring their size.

Brain Size and Paleoanthropology

A major concern in both paleoanthropology and evolutionary theory was brain size. For this reason australopithecines are interpreted today as a link between humans and our apelike ancestor largely because they have a brain estimated roughly midway between modern humans and apes. Consequently, they are viewed as our evolutionary ancestors. After the 1860s, phrenologists often related their theory to evolution, especially the evolution of the head and skull. One of the major groups of critics was the clergy, who correctly concluded that phrenology had promoted materialism and fatalism, and dispensed with the need for the human soul.[41]

As noted, even though many phrenologists were not atheists, the underlying conclusion of phrenology was materialism, a view supported by many of its leaders. In short, as also noted above, materialism teaches that mind is purely matter and nothing more. It teaches that humans do not have a soul, and

---

40. Millhauser, 1959, p. 109.
41. Williams, 2000, p. 267.

that death is the final end of life.[42]

Darwin's Exposure to Phrenology

Darwin was exposed to this line of thinking through his undergraduate friend, phrenologist William A. F. Browne.[43] While a
University of Edinburgh Medical School student, Darwin was
an active member of the largely student group called the Plinian Society, which also included a few professors.[44]

While there, he observed the 1826-1827 debates involving
his friend Browne, who is considered the founding father of
British Psychiatry.[45] Desmond and Moore described Browne in
the Plinian Society debate as a "fiery radical" who "gave such
an inflammatory harangue on matter and mind that it sparked
a raging debate . . . with no soul, no after-life, no punishment
or reward, where was the deterrent against immorality?"[46]

Browne, who openly influenced Darwin, "believed the
mind to be completely understandable in terms of material
processes and relished a thorough demolition job on meta-
physical and Christian fantasies."[47] Gruber's careful studies on

42. Gruber, Howard E. 1974. *Darwin on Man: A Psychological Study of Scientific Creativity.* New York, NY: E.P. Dutton, pp. 205-206; Kaufman,
Matthew H. 1998. The Edinburgh phrenological debate of 1823 held
in the Royal Medical Society. *Journal of Neurolinguistics* 11(4):377–
389, October.

43. Walmsley, Tom. 1993. Psychiatry in descent: Darwin and the Brownes.
Psychiatric Bulletin (The Royal College of Psychiatrists) 17(12):748–
751, p. 751.

44. Richards, Robert J. 1987. *Darwin and the Emergence of Evolutionary
Theories of Mind and Behavior.* Chicago, IL: University of Chicago
Press, p. 76.

45. Walmsley, 1993, p. 749.

46. Desmond, Adrian, and James Moore. 1991. *Darwin: The Life of a Tormented Evolutionist.* New York, NY: Warner Books, p. 38.

47. Walmsley, 1993, p. 749.

Darwin's early writing judged the Plinian event to have played a crucial role in both Darwin's thinking and his psychological development.[48]

In 1838, Darwin revisited Edinburgh and his former undergraduate haunts, recording his psychological speculations in his M notebook. At this time, Darwin was preparing to marry his Christian cousin Emma Wedgwood, and was in some emotional turmoil, due, as far as we can tell, to religious conflicts. On September 21, 1838, after his return to England from his voyage on the *HMS Beagle* (1831-1836), he recorded a vivid and disturbing dream in which he was involved in an execution at which the corpse came to life and claimed to have died as a hero. This dream was no doubt related to his conflicts about, in his words, "murdering God."[49]

Another exposure Darwin had with phrenology was with his friend and colleague Hewett Cottrell Watson (1804-1881) who endorsed evolution as early as 1836.[50] In 1836, Watson published a paper in *The Phrenological Journal* titled "What Is the Use of the Double Brain?", referring to the two human cerebral hemispheres. He speculated in this paper on the function of the two human cerebral hemispheres. His idea soon achieved scientific status when, encouraged by the French phrenologist/physician Jean-Baptiste Bouillaud, evolutionist Paul Broca published his research on the brain's speech center, now known as Broca's area.

Watson later turned his energies to the question of evolution, and, after he purchased the rights to the *Phrenologi-*

---

48. Gruber, 1974, pp. 39-41, 205-206.

49. Bergman, 2015 *The Dark Side of Darwin*. Green Forest, AR: New Leaf Press.

50. Wyhe, 2004, p. 147.

cal Journal in 1837, appointed himself editor. In the 1850s, Watson conducted an extensive correspondence with Charles Darwin who gave him a very generous acknowledgement not once, but twice, for his scientific assistance in the second edition of *On The Origin of Species.* His exact words were "...Mr. Watson, to whom I lie under deep obligation for assistance of all kinds,"[51] and to "Mr. H. C. Watson to whom I am much indebted for valuable advice and assistance on this subject."[52]

As an undergraduate, "Charles Darwin privately sympathized [with phrenology], seeing in the process evidence of free will, writing:

> One is tempted to believe phrenologists are right about habitual exercise of the mind altering [the] form of the head, and thus these qualities become hereditary. When a man says I will improve my powers of imagination, & does so,—is not this free will[?]—he improves the facility. . . . an animal improves because its appetites urge it to certain actions which are modified by circumstance.'"[53]

This was an important idea in view of the fact that the major issue Darwin was forced to deal with in justifying his evolution theory was not the *survival*-of-the-fittest, but rather

---

51. Darwin, Charles. 1860. *On the Origin of Species*, 2nd Edition. London, England: John Murray, p. 40.

52. Darwin, 1860, p. 43.

53. Trippett, David. 2015. Exercising musical minds: Phrenology and music pedagogy in London, circa 1830. *19th-Century Music* 39(2):99–124. p. 117. Quote is from page 30 of Darwin's M notebook. The M notebook quote is found here: Charles Darwin, The M Notebook (1838):30. The M notebook was reprinted in Gruber, 1974, p. 271. See http://darwinonline.org.uk/content/frameset?viewtype=side& itemID=CUL-DAR125.-&pageseq=1.

the *arrival*-of-the-fittest. Thus, according to Darwin, phrenology implied that desire and will can alter the body, producing changes that natural selection can act on. In his M notebook, Darwin wrote, "I believe, in Materialism... that emotions, instincts, degrees of talent, which are hereditary, are so because [the] brain of [the] child resembles parent stock.— (& phrenologists state that brain alters [the body])."[54]

Darwin Reneges on His Support of Phrenology

In a letter dated January 3, 1830, Darwin wrote to his cousin and friend, Rev. William Darwin Fox: "I dined with Sir J. Mackintosh & had some talk with him about Phrenology, & he has entirely battered down the very little belief of it that I picked up at Osmaston [the home of the Fox family]." Sir James Mackintosh (1765-1832) was related to Darwin by marriage. He was a philosopher and historian who had studied medicine at Edinburgh. Darwin added that the reason for his doubt about phrenology was that "as long as Education is supposed to have any effect decreasing this power of any organ of the brain, he cannot see how it [phrenology] ever can be proved to be true."[55]

According to these quotes, Darwin still appears to accept the basic idea of phrenology, namely that the cerebellum and cerebrum consist of many different organs in which resides the person, or the "soul" in Christian terms. Burkhart, however, comments that the power of the organs are not innate, but as Darwin noted in his M notebook, education can change these organs, implying that these organs in turn can change the skull's shape. Consequently, the bumps may correspond to an

54. Gruber, 1974, p. 276. Page 57 of Darwin's M notebook.
55. Burkhardt, Frederick. 1985. *The Correspondence of Charles Darwin: 1821-1836*. Cambridge, England: Cambridge University Press, p. 97.

accurate reading when the reading was done, but the reading results may change at a later time if the bump contours change. Evidently, in the Fox family home some discussion in favor of phrenology occurred on the view that education affected the size of the bumps on the head.

Phrenology Ideas Spread Beyond Europe

After the writings by Francis Gall, phrenological teachings soon rapidly spread to much of the Western world. In 1834, Professor Combe lectured in the United States, where phrenology soon become a popular movement. Fowler also began publishing his journal *Phrenological Journal and Science and Health* to spread his ideas. Published from 1839 to 1911, most issues had about 50 pages.[56] (My copies, published in the 1890s, had about 50 pages of small print.) Fowler's journal included a large number of articles written by educated professionals, including many medical doctors and college professors.

The intellectual elite found phrenology especially attractive because it provided a materialistic, evolutionary explanation for mental processes based on observation. For example, within a year of the formation of the French phrenology society, of the 150 members, 82 were physicians, both those in private practice and teaching in academia, and 6 were lawyers.[57] Leek claims that a long list of highly educated persons have supported phrenology.[58] Some intellectuals accepted the organology brand of phrenology while at the same time questioning its cranioscopy orientation.

56. Many issues from The University of Michigan library beginning with 1870 are on line here: https://catalog.hathitrust.org/Record/000677989.
57. Staum, 2003, p. 50.
58. Leek, Sybil. 1970. *Phrenology*. London, England: Collier Books.

The popular success of phrenology in the United States and elsewhere is one reason why supporters could ignore its lack of scientific evidence. Its materialistic underpinnings, though, fostered criticism from creationists and theists. Martin added that phrenology was a "patently wrong idea [that] made a tremendous impact on the nation."[59] Its influence on evolution is illustrated by the fact that the co-founder of the Darwinian theory of evolution, Alfred Russel Wallace, opined that the "greatest failure of the nineteenth century was its turning away from phrenology." As a young man Wallace "became hardened in his naturalistic views by a study of . . . phrenology," and even "in his old age he prized the delineations of his cranium done by Edward Hicks and James Rumball, the later having also read Herbert Spencer's head."[60]

Spencer, a major contributor to evolutionary theory, converted to phrenology as a youth and, although he rejected some of its ideas, remained a believer for much of his life, even writing articles for phrenology journals.[61] For his entire life he accepted the belief that character and intellect were mere materialistic functions of the brain subject to deterministic psychology. This view had a profound effect on his ideas and writings, and consequently on society due to his development, and spread, of social Darwinism, one of the most destructive ideas in history.[62]

---

59. Martin, Michael. 1979. Bumps & Brains. The Curious Science of Phrenology. *Nineteenth Annual Edition: American History*, Volume 1, pp. 38-43, p. 43.

60. Richards, 1987, p. 178.

61. Richards, 1987, pp. 250-251.

62. Bergman, Jerry. 2014. *The Darwin Effect: Its Influence on Nazism, Eugenics, Racism, Communism, Capitalism & Sexism*. Green Forest, AR: New Leaf Press..

Racism Incorporated into Phrenology

The use of the facial angle, a method of measuring the fore-head-to-jaw relationship, which ranges from largely horizontal, such as in fish, to vertical, such as in humans, was incorporated into phrenology.[63] Proponents of the facial angle theory hypothesized that the facial angle was not only the trend from fish to humans, but also could be used to *rank human racial groups* from inferior to superior. The study of face and body features, called physiognomy, accentuated the "tendency in phrenology to establish a rank order of races and nationalities along a scale of perfection" toward the Aryan ideal.[64] Furthermore, physiognomists "habitually used the facial angle to rank races."[65]

For example, an article in *The Phrenological Journal*, by an author using the pseudonym "Cranium," included the illustration commonly found in 19th-century literature ranking life from simple to complex, from snakes to humans. It also ranked humans from inferior to superior.[66] The author included in his presentation photos of actual skulls of a "civilized" Caucasian and a Negro that he called a "savage," adding that Negroes were one of "the lower classes of men" that ever lived.[67]

The facial angle was widely cited as "scientific" evidence by racists, such as Arthur de Gobineau, to justify racism on what they believed were solid scientific grounds. Gobineau was a French aristocrat best known today for helping to legitimize racism by the use of scientific racist theory, and for his Aryan master-race theory adopted by Germans and, eventually, Hit-

63. See Bergman. 2017. *Evolution's Blunders, Frauds and Forgeries*. Chapter 6, pp. 89-100. Atlanta, GA: CMI Publishing.
64. Staum, 2003, p. 54.
65. Staum, 2003, p. 56.
66. Cranium, 1909, p. 206.
67. Cranium, 1909, pp. 208–209.

ler. The facial angle also influenced phrenologists to attempt to determine intelligence levels. An example from phrenology is that the ancients believed that a 90-degree facial line was a sign of a great level

> of knowledge and reflection, and a corresponding contraction of the mouth, jaws, tongue, nose, indicated a noble and generous nature. Hence they have extended the facial angle to 90° in the representation of legislators, sages, poets, and others, on whom they wished to bestow the most august character. In the statues of their heroes and gods they have still further exaggerated the human, and reduced the animal characteristics; extending the forehead over the face, so as to push the facial line beyond the perpendicular, and to make the angle 100°.[68]

Thus, facial angle was believed by scientists to have effectively quantified, not only the "very striking difference between man and all other animals," but also the differences between the various human "races".[69] Science historian John Haller concluded that the "facial angle was the most extensively elaborated and artlessly abused criteria for racial somatology" in the late 1800s.[70]

Phrenology Exploited to Justify Racism

Scientists and others searching for a scientific basis for racism found phrenology very appealing as justification for the belief

---

68. Lawrence, William. 1828. *Lectures on Physiology, Zoology, and the Natural History of Man.* Salem, MA: Foote and Brown, p. 148.

69. Lawrence, William. 1848. *Lectures on Comparative Anatomy, Physiology, Zoology, and the Natural History of Man,* 9th Edition. London, England: Henry G. Bohn, p. 115.

70. Haller, John. 1971. *Outcasts from Evolution.* Urbana, IL: University of Illinois Press, p. 9.

in Western superiority over the evolutionarily inferior races.[71] To find evidence for ranking races from the least to the most evolved, phrenologists compared skulls of different ethnic groups. Gall's disciple, Dr. François J.V. Broussais, proclaimed that the Caucasians were the "most beautiful" race while claiming that groups like the Australian Aboriginal and Māori people could never become civilized because they lacked the cerebral organ required. Other phrenologists even argued against the emancipation of slaves on the basis of their phrenology readings. Conversely, others argued that through education and interbreeding, the less-evolved people could improve.[72]

Evolution also influenced phrenologists on this topic. A review of *Vestiges*, published in a phrenologist's journal quoting the original book, included the following passage:

> Our brain goes through the various stages of a fish's, a reptile's and a mammifer's [obsolete term for mammals] brain; and finally becomes human . . . after completing the animal transformation, it passes through the characters in which it appears in the Negro, Malay, American [Indians], and Mongolian nations, and finally is Caucasian.[73]

The review added that

> the various races of mankind, are simply representations of particular stages in the development of the highest or Caucasian type. The negro exhibits permanently the imperfect brain, projecting lower jaw . . . . The aboriginal American represents the

---

71. Staum, 2003. Chapter 3: "The Ambivalence of Phrenology," pp. 49-84.
72. Staum, 2003, p. 62.
73. *The Phrenological Journal.* 1845. Vol. 18, Review of Vestiges, pp 74-75.

same child nearer birth. The Mongolian is an arrested infant newly born.[74]

This is another example illustrating the fact that evolution influenced phrenology even before Darwin. Furthermore, Darwin's influence after his book was published in 1859 increased significantly. While the racism in phrenology was heavily influenced by evolution, likewise, phrenology significantly influenced evolutionary belief and theory, although often indirectly.

Another argument was that putative human inequality could be used to place people in the most appropriate employment and social station in society. Racial hierarchy was not inevitable in the phrenology worldview, but common, influenced by the fact that "many phrenologists concluded that some 'savages' were innately uncivilizable."[75]

In short, for many, phrenology readings were exploited to reinforce racial prejudice and commonly rated non-Aryans as stupid, ignorant, cruel, hopeless, or having similarly very negative traits.[76] For example, the Hottentots were rated as less-evolved than most other races and supposedly "were under the complete domination of animal instincts," and southeastern Africans were "at the bottom of the human [evolutionary] chain . . . hardly superior to animal instincts."[77] Furthermore, there existed a greater "resemblance between the heads of certain Negroes and of great apes than between Negroes and Europeans."[78] It is obvious that, instead of the bumps doing the talking, the racial bias was used to exploit the terrain of heads

---

74. *The Phrenological Journal.* 1845. Vol. 18, Review of Vestiges, pp 74-75.
75. Staum, 2003, p. 65.
76. Staum, 2003, pp. 58-59.
77. Staum, 2003, pp. 59-61.
78. Staum, 2003, pp. 59-61.

to support preconceived racist opinions.

Gender Stereotypes

Gender stereotyping was also very common in phrenology. Like racial inferiority, gender inferiority assumptions were read into the bump/valley pattern existing on female skulls. For example, women whose occipital (back of their head) was larger and had lower foreheads were believed to have inferior brain organs for success in the arts, sciences, and intellectual tasks in general. Conversely, they had larger mental brain organs in areas related to the care of children and the acceptance of religion.[79] Phrenologists did not deny the existence of talented women, but this minority was too small to provide justification for citizenship, or to allow women's participation in politics.[80]

Conclusions

The 2018 Parker et al. study "sought to test in the most exhaustive way currently possible the fundamental claim of phrenology: that measuring the contour of the head provides a reliable method for inferring mental capacities. We found no evidence for this claim. . . . a more accurate phrenological bust should be left blank since no regions on the head correlate with any of the faculties that we tested."[81] Consequently, the central phrenological notion that measuring the contour of the skull can be used to determine personality traits has now been fully discredited by empirical research using the scalp as a proxy measure as was the procedure of the phrenologist.[82]

One problem among many was "its emphasis on the outer head (i.e.,

---

79. Staum, 2003, pp. 64-65.
80. Staum, 2003, p. 65.
81. Parker et al., 2018, p. 10.
82. Parker et al., 2018.

skull and scalp) as an indirect measure of the brain, and thus of personality and behavior".[83] Likewise, a comparison of the external chest traits usually tell us little about the condition of the internal organs, such as the heart and lungs. The main deleterious effect phrenology caused was its contribution to naturalism, racism, sexism, and other materialistic and atheistic worldviews. This movement was due to Gall's leading, and then advanced by Combe, which "became one of the most influential ideological and cultural developments in Victorian Britain."[84] Ironically, much interest exists today regarding how so many accepted a belief totally without foundation. This topic has been the focus of at least 25 Ph.D.'s and hundreds of books and articles.[85]

83. Parker et al., 2018.
84. Wyhe, 2004, p. 11.
85. Dean, 2012, p. 37.

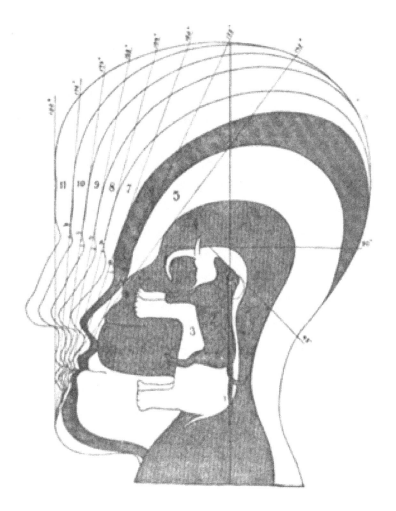

From Cranium (author). 1909. The brain and skull showing evolution from quadrupedal to modern humans From *The Phrenological Journal* 122(7):206, July.

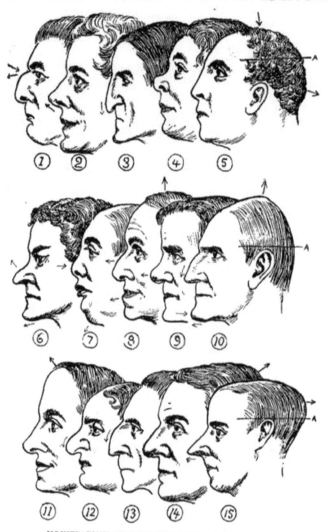

ILLUSTRATIONS OF NOSES BY CHARLES TODD PARKS.

Human Character traits as indicated in the shape of the human nose. From page 291 of Charles Todd Parks 1902 article. *The Phrenological Journal* 114(3):290-292, September.

Young ladies, indelibly fix this shape of head in your memories. Any man who will make a natural, kind and true husband will have a head in outline from a side view like this.

The reason this man is an unreliable husband is because he is very weak in Conjugality and Parental Love and exceedingly strong in Amativeness. Young ladies, beware of such men as husbands.

Advice for women looking for a Husband by a phrenologist. From Vaught, L.A. 1902. *Practical Reader.* Chicago, IL: L.A. Vaught, pp. 28-29.

The sign marking where it was discovered.

5

The Tall Tale of the Cardiff Giant and Evolution

THE CARDIFF GIANT is widely considered the second greatest scientific hoax foisted on the public during the last two centuries. It involved both religion and science, and, although the hoax was exposed not long after it was hatched, the controversy surrounding it has lasted for several decades.[1] Several perpetrators monetarily profited from the Cardiff fraud, but a more important factor was its open anti-Biblical goal, an attempt that largely failed. The influence of Darwinism was also an important factor in motivating the lead offender.

Introduction

The most infamous 20th-century scientific hoax was the Piltdown Man "missing link" fraud. Piltdown Man was used as

---

1. Murphy, Jim. 2012. *The Giant and How He Humbugged America*. New York: Scholastic Press

major evidence for evolution, repeated in scores of textbooks for close to 40 years until it was exposed as a fraud in 1953. Piltdown Man fooled both a large number of high-school textbook writers and many leading scientists. It was listed as a major, if not *the* major, evidence for human evolution at least up to the 1950s.

Some scholars conclude that the Cardiff Giant, a ten-foot-long gypsum stone figure, known as "America's Greatest Hoax" (and, understandably, "America's *Biggest* Hoax"), may be one of the greatest anthropological frauds in American history.[2] New York's "consummate hoax," the Cardiff Giant, was dug out of the ground and entered into American life on October 16, 1869, when it was "discovered" by workers who thought they were digging a well behind the barn of William C. "Stub" Newell in Cardiff, New York.[3] It was, in fact, the buried creation of an enterprising New York businessman named George Hull. The blazing newspaper's headlines about the hoax included such expressions of amazement as: "A Wonderful Discovery!... A New Wonder!... The Petrified Giant!"[4]

The perpetrator George Hull "read several scientific books during this period—an indication of his literacy—but became particularly obsessed with Darwin's theory" of evolution, specifically human evolution.[5] Furthermore, Hall "had studied

2. Williams, William F. 2000. *Encyclopedia of Pseudoscience: From Alien Abductions to Zone Therapy.* New York, NY: Facts on File, p . 45; Wade, Carlson. 1976. *Great Hoaxes and Famous Imposters.* Middle Village, NY: Jonathan David Publishers.

3. Franco, Barbara. 1969. The Cardiff Giant: A hundred year old hoax. *New York History* 50(4):421-440, October, p. 421.

4. Dunn, James Taylor. 1948. The Cardiff Giant hoax. *New York History* 19(3):367-377, July, p. 367.

5. Tribble, Scott. 2010. *A Colossal Hoax: The Giant from Cardiff that Fooled America.* New York, NY: Roman & Littlefield, p. 204.

Charles Darwin's *On the Origin of Species* and followed discussions of his controversial theory about evolution in the newspapers. He'd also attended lectures and read a number of books on fossils and geology."[6]

Darwinism played a part in this hoax specifically because Hall and the "public believed that the fossil record soon would reveal evidence of an early transitional figure that was part man and part monkey."[7] Reading Darwin also influenced Hull to become an atheist, which was a major motivation to carry out the hoax, namely to make Christians look foolish.[8] In short, people were interested in Darwinism and archaeology and "Hull was happy to cash in on this collective desire to know more" about these areas.[9] Furthermore "Hull knew about and admired one of [P. T.] Barnum's most famous frauds from the past, the Feejee Mermaid."[10]

The Question of the Validity of Genesis

While visiting Ackley, Iowa, where his creationist sister lived, Hull met an itinerant Methodist preacher named Rev. Turk who was at the time staying with his sister. While there, Hull engaged in a long discussion about Biblical inerrancy with Rev. Turk regarding the question "Should Genesis be taken literally?" Hull, as an atheist, didn't think it should, but the minister disagreed.[11] In their discussion Rev. Turk mentioned one Bi-

---

6. Murphy, Jim. 2012. *The Giant and How He Humbugged America*. New York: Scholastic Press. pp. 48-49.

7. Tribble, p. 203.

8. Rose, Mark. 2005. When Giants Roamed the Earth. *Archaeology* (A publication of the Archaeological Institute of America) 58(6), November/December, https://archive.archaeology.org/0511/etc/giants.html.

9. Murphy, 2012, p. 49.

10. Murphy, 2012, p. 49.

11. Wade, 1976, p. 209.

ble verse, Genesis 6:4, which spoke about "giants in the earth" called Nephilim, which Turk interpreted as 12-foot-tall giant men.[12]

Hull was unaware that Nephilim is a transliteration of a Hebrew word that could also be translated "tyrant" or "dominators", not physical giants. The Bible clearly teaches that human/angel crossbreeds are not possible because angels are not sexual beings. A more accurate interpretation is that godly Sethite men were physically attracted to ungodly women, and many of their offspring became tyrants on the Earth.

At this time Darwin's *Origin of Species* incited much "interest in the study of natural science. Scientists gathered fossils to prove or disprove Darwinian theories."[13]Hull reasoned that, if Darwin supporters were looking for missing links to prove human evolution, Bible-believing creationists would logically be looking for evidence to prove the Bible true, such as, among other examples, ancient giant men.

It was then that the plan to create a hoax began to take shape in Hull's mind. After his discussions with the minister, Hull thought of making a giant man out of stone, and passing it off as a petrified man: "The more he thought about it, the madder he got. Then and there he resolved to manufacture a giant … to confound religious extremists like Reverend Turk and perhaps make a little money on the side."[14]

Hull assumed that his giant would be widely accepted by creationists and inerrantists preachers, exposing their credulity and gullibility. He also expected that scientists would correctly recognize it as fake, exposing the fundamentalists as the fools

12. Franco, 1969, p. 422.
13. Franco, 1969, p. 428.
14. Dunn, 1948, p. 368.

that Hull thought they were. Both expectations proved wrong.

This example illustrates that lack of accurate Biblical knowledge can mislead Christians, as it evidently did Rev. Turk. Unfortunately, we do not have any record of Turk's beliefs, only Hull's perception of his views. In the end, Hull was going to use the fake giant to poke fun at Biblical literalists, but when he and his backers ended up making a lot of money, their goal did not work out as they had planned. As the money rolled in, "Hull and his partners, still hoping to collect money [after the hoax was exposed]… refused to make any formal confession of guilt or present the final pieces of the puzzle."[15]

How the Hoax Got Started

Hull hired several men to quarry a 10-foot-4.5-inch-long (3.2-meter) block of gypsum in Fort Dodge, Iowa.[16] He explained that the statue was intended to be a monument to Abraham Lincoln or, depending on who asked, George Washington.[17] Hull then shipped the gypsum block to Chicago to the well-known stone cutter Edward Burghardt, who was paid to carve it into the likeness of a man. Hull swore him to secrecy about the fraud. Hull himself served as the model for the sculpture. He even did some paleontological research in an attempt to improve the credibility of his creation. For example, Hull learned that hair did not petrify, so his giant was hairless.[18]

Various stains and acids, including sulfuric, were used to make the naked and anguished-looking giant appear to be old

15. Trebble, 2010, p. 149.
16. Williams, 2000, p. 45.
17. Dunn, 1948, p. 368.
18. Sears, Stephen W. 1975. The Giant in the Earth. *American Heritage* 26(5):94-99, August, p. 95.

and weathered.[19] Its underside was grooved by scoring it with wet sandpaper and small groves were cut into it to imitate the corrosive effects of ground water.[20] The giant's surface was beaten with steel knitting needles embedded in a board to simulate pores. During November of 1868, Hull transported the giant by railroad to the farm belonging to his brother-in-law, William C. Newell, where it was buried. By then, he had spent 2,600 dollars (equivalent to $49,940 in 2023) on the hoax. Needless to say, he was very committed to his plan to expose Genesis believers.

After it was buried, to give the appearance of a long-ago burial, the ground was allowed to settle for nearly a year before Newell hired Gideon Emmons and Henry Nichols to ostensibly dig a well on his property. On October 16, 1869, they "uncovered" the previously buried giant.

Next, to recoup their investment, Newell set up a tent over the dig that contained the giant. He charged 25 cents (equivalent to $4.80 in 2023) for each person to view it and hear a discussion about its discovery and significance. One observer described the mood at the viewing site as the giant was "Lying in its grave, with subdued light from the roof of the tent falling upon it, and with the limbs contorted as if in a death struggle.... An air of great solemnity pervaded the place. Visitors hardly spoke above a whisper."[21]

News about the find was spread by newspapers both in America and as far away as Europe.[22] The exhibit proved so

19. Stein, Gordon. 1993. *Encyclopedia of Hoaxes.* Detroit, MI: Gale Research, p 13.

20. Wade, 1976, p. 211.

21. Magnusson, Magnus. 2007. *Fakers, Forgers & Phoneys: Famous Scams and Scamps.* Edinburgh, Scotland: Mainstream Publishing, p. 185.

22. Wade, 1976, p. 214.

popular that, after only two days he doubled the admission price to $9.60 in 2023 money. From 300 to as many as 2,600 people came by the wagon-load to view the monster.[23] In the first week alone, his income was 1,200 dollars (equal to over 20,000 dollars in 2023).[24] The "roads to Cardiff were jammed with buggies, crude farm wagons, and special stages from Syracuse that carried passengers for a dollar a head" to view the giant.[25]

Business boomed, not only from the Giant display, but also for local shopkeepers.[26] As a result of the good business, the hoaxers had a monetary interest in perpetuating the hoax by openly claiming that it was a valid petrified giant buried eons ago. Although Hull was at this time a very successful entrepreneur, his investment in the Cardiff Giant turned out to be "the best investment of his life."[27] It was a hoax that got away from him.

One reason for the success of the hoax was "the popular if uninformed fascination with natural science... Among the more sophisticated who flocked to see the giant were amateur scientists inspired by Darwin's recent evolutionary theory to dabble in geology and paleontology."[28] Local stories related past accounts of strange fossils and over-sized skeletons which buttressed the Cardiff Giant claims.

The most common mistake about the Cardiff Giant was its age. One of the men reportedly exclaimed, "I declare, some

---

23. Stein, 1993, pp. 13-14.
24. Murphy, J. 2022. p. 32.
25. Sears, 1975, p. 97.
26. Stein, 1993, p. 14.
27. Sears, 1975, pp. 95-96.
28. Sears, 1975, pp. 97-98.

old Indian has been buried here!"[29] Ancient-man fossil expert, Dr. John F. Boynton, the first geologist to examine the "giant," declared it to be a carved statue. He wrote, "The figure was definitely the Napoleon type."[30] Paleontologist James Hall agreed that the statue was of some antiquity and was "the most remarkable object yet brought to light in this country."[31] Professor White opined that the Cardiff Giant was "very generally accepted as a petrified human being of colossal size."[32] All of the controversy produced much publicity, which increased interest in the giant and, as expected, increased ticket sales as well. At first, the "vast majority of folk still felt the giant was a petrified person [including a] University of Rochester professor... It is the opinion of Mr. Owen, and indeed most scientific men who have given it an examination, that it is a petrified human body."[33] The scientific explanations about how the body became petrified included "the cold underground water and 'wet alluvial oil' had speeded up fossilization so much that the body had no chance to rot. Sill others pointed to the thousands of fossilized plants, tree trunks, insects, and fish already unearthed and asked 'Will any one say that under favorable circumstances a fossil man cannot be formed?'"[34] At the least, even some of "the learned men of science were impressed."[35] Professor Hall , a state geologist, observed that the Cardiff Giant was "the most remarkable object ever discovered in this country! No one can

29. Rose, 2005.
30. Sears, 1975, p. 98.
31. Sears, 1975, p. 98.
32. Rose, 2005.
33. Murphy, J. 2012. p. 40.
34. Murphy, J. 2012. p. 40.
35. Boning, Richard. 1972. *The Cardiff Giant*. New York: Dexter & Westbrook. p.25.

solve this mystery. One scientist even looked up the nostrils of the giant to determine if they were those of a human being."[36]

The Fraud Exposed

Eventually, several archaeological scholars pronounced the giant a fake. The geologists noticed certain problems, such as that there was no valid reason to dig a well in the location where the giant was found. Yale paleontologist Othniel C. Marsh examined the statue, concluding that it was made of soluble gypsum, which, had it been buried for centuries in the wet earth where it was found, would not have clear evidence of fresh tool marks on it. He termed it "a most decided humbug."[37] Several scientists correctly recognized the fact that it was not possible for human flesh to ossify into a solid gypsum rock as claimed. Conversely, some people, including some uninformed theologians and preachers, defended its authenticity.[38] As the evidence accumulated, eventually "most scientists believed the Cardiff Giant was man-made."[39]

In the end, George Hull, "seeing that public opinion was [now] turning against his creation and wanting to get his revenge on Reverend Turk, came out with the complete story of the hoax." He admitted it was a hoax to make the Reverend look foolish and to "render all the Bible-bangers ridiculous."[40] Ironically, contrary to what Hull expected, supporters of the Cardiff Giant's authenticity "manifested far less religiosity than

---

36. Boning, 1972. P. 31
37. Stein, 1993, p. 14.
38. Hendley, Nate. 2016. *The Big Con: Great Hoaxes, Frauds, Grifts, and Swindles in American History.* Santa Barbara, CA: ABC-CLIO.
39. Murphy, J. 2012. p. 41.
40. Magnusson, 2007, p. 188; Dunn, 1948, p. 373.

George Hull originally anticipated."[41]   Conversely, one novel "based on fact" about the Cardiff Giant played up the gullibility of the religious folk.[42]

When Hull realized, as the newness of the discovery was waning, that his good fortune would not last forever, he sold his part-interest in the hoax for $23,000 (equivalent to over $465,024 in 2023). A syndicate of five men headed by banker David Hannum purchased it and moved the Cardiff Giant to Syracuse, New York, to increase visitors and profits. From there, its popularity moved it to New York City, then to Boston, Buffalo, Pennsylvania, and numerous other locations.

The large crowds that came to see the fraud motivated famous showman P. T. Barnum to offer the syndicate 50,000 dollars (equal to almost a million dollars today) for the Cardiff Giant. When the new owners refused, Barnum hired a man to model the giant's shape in wax for a plaster replica which was soon drawing more visitors than the real hoax.[43] The Cardiff Giant was so successful a moneymaker that P. T. Barnum's fake of a fake was displayed in New York.[44] P. T. Barnum, who also famously displayed the "Fiji Mermaid" fraud, claimed that his was the real Cardiff Giant, and the other, the original Cardiff Giant, was actually the fake!

Support by Scientists

Soon a "fierce battle erupted in the scientific world. Some sci-

41. Tribble, 2010, p. 89.

42. Jacobs, Harvey. 1997. *American Goliath: Inspired by the True, Incredible Events Surrounding the Mysterious Marvel Known to an Astonished World as the Cardiff Giant.* New York, NY: St. Martin's Press, pp. 40, 120, 168, 219, 236, 278.

43. Kunhardt, Jr., Philip B., Philip B. Kunhardt III, and Peter W. Kunhardt. 1995. *P.T. Barnum: America's Greatest Showman.* New York, NY: Alfred A. Knopf, p. 214.

44. Boning, 1972, P. 36.

entists claimed that both giants were hoaxes; others claimed that only one was a hoax, but could not decide which one; still others said that since there had originally been more than one giant in the world, the possibility remained that both were authentic."[45] Some scientists supported part of Hull's claim. One was Professor James H. Drator, who was "considered the leading paleontologist of the era, and head of the prestigious New York State Museum. Drator boldly proclaimed: 'The statue is remarkable and it is authentic.'"[46]

Another scientist concluded that it was a statue carved by a set of very early missionaries to impress the Indians.[47] However, a major problem for the statue claim was that it lacked a pedestal to stand upon. A group of "eminent regents from Albany State University opined … it is the most remarkable object brought to light in this century."[48] In short, to some "scientists he was a paleolithic discovery of the first magnitude."[49]

The newspapers carried stories both for and against the authenticity of the Cardiff fraud. The frequent publicity reports increased interest in the giant, encouraging even more visitors.[50] As Tribble observed, the "American scientific community was not undeserving of its dubious reputation" and "amateur enthusiasts [some with dubious credentials] stood at the forefront on public matters of science offering ill-informed assessments of fossils, antiquities, and natural processes."[51]

45. Wade, 1976, p. 217.

46. Wade, 1976, p. 215.

47. Williams, 2000, p. 45; Tribble, 2010, p. 211.

48. Magnusson, 2007, p. 187.

49. *Time-Life*. 1991. *Hoaxes and Deceptions*. Alexandria, VA: Time-Life Books, p. 117.

50. Stein, 1993, p. 14.

51. Tribble, 2009, p. 23.

Hull Attempts to Create a Missing Link Between Apes and Humans

Buoyed by his early success, in 1877 George Hull commissioned another, different man made out of plaster, ground bone, blood, and meat, then kiln-fired it for several weeks. It was not claimed to be a missing link but some observers concluded that it was "either a petrified example of the elusive missing link between apes and humans or a statute of great age."[52] In reference to the "Minnesota Iceman hoax", this new example was partly a repeat of the "desire on the part of the researcher to find anything which would substantiate the molecules-to-man myth. This can blind even the most preeminent scientist to reality."[53]

Hull's new creation was exposed as a fraud in 1878 by several unpaid creditors.[54] Numerous other attempts have been made to repeat Hull's original success. All have failed.[55] The New York Historical Association purchased the original giant in 1947 for 30,000 dollars. It now resides to this day at the Farmers' Museum in Cooperstown, New York.

Summary

The goal of proving the lack of credulity for those who accepted Genesis was never realized. The hoax actually showed the gullibility, or at least the curiosity, of the general public. The fraud did not begin with the goal of making money, only recouping the costs of the hoax. However, when it became apparent that

---

52. *Time-Life.* 1991, p. 118.
53. Grigg, Russell. 1998. The Minnesota Iceman Hoax: Another Phony 'Missing Link.' *Creation* 20(1):18-21, p. 20.
54. *Time-Life.* 1991, 118.
55. Nickell, Joe. 2009. Cardiff's Giant Hoax. *Skeptical Inquirer* 33(3):58-60, May/June, pp. 58-60.

several of its supporters were going to get rich from the hoax, the original goal of exposing the assumed naivete of those who accepted Genesis was altered in order to give the Cardiff Giant credibility, or at least to claim that a valid controversy existed about the origin and meaning of the giant man. Even when it was exposed as a fraud, its supporters encouraged the controversy and pushed the 'see it for yourself' position and 'judge its validity for yourself' stance, not to share the truth, but to receive treasure.

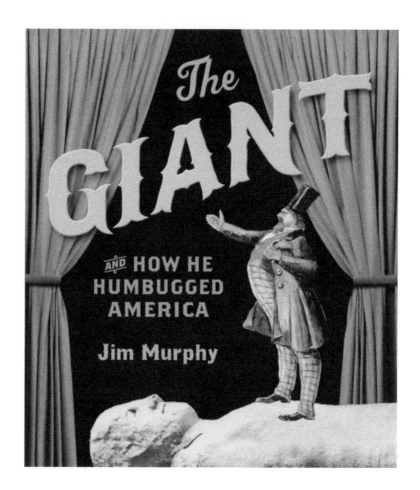

The cover of one of several books about the Cardiff Giant

6

The Tasaday Stone Age-People Hoax

THE TASADAY HOAX STORY helps to explain why so many persons for decades or longer have accepted events that turned out to be hoaxes. Although termed a "tribe", the Tasaday, in the reports that received much of the media coverage, involved at most slightly above two dozen people. As the hoax was exposed, the likely motives behind it were seen to include money, fame, and academic prestige. Relative to Darwinism, the lessons the hoax provides for us today include the problem of ignoring clear evidence. In this case, the group was not a Stone Age people as commonly represented. The example illustrates the tendency to see in a situation what one wants to believe is true. The case also illustrates the complexity of hoaxes and the different reasons why different people are involved in perpetuating them.[1]

History

The Tasaday were introduced to the world as a 'Stone Age' tribe

1. Bolando, A.J. 2017. The Stone Age tribe that never was. https://newslab.philstar.com/31-years-of-amnesia/tasaday.

living in caves in a rain forest where they had lived for over a thousand years. They lived there until their isolation ended when a hunter from a neighboring tribe stumbled onto them while setting hunting traps. This hunter mentioned their existence to Harvard-educated Manuel Elizalde, Jr., who, at the time, was an adviser to Philippine President Ferdinand Marcos on the subject of Filipino minorities. Intrigued, in June 1971, Elizalde chopped his way into the jungle on the southern island province of Mindanao in the Philippines to meet these Stone Age people in an effort to learn how primitive humans once lived in early human evolutionary history.

Elizalde claimed that he learned from tribe members that they used "only the most rudimentary Stone Age tools, scraping a meager living from the rain forest. They had no agriculture, no cloth, no weapons, not even domestic animals," nor art, music, pottery, or metal tools. They wore sparse clothing made from fresh leaves. They lacked spears, or weapons of any type, including bows and arrows used to hunt.[2] Furthermore, they had no formal trade networks or regular contacts with the outside world. They had been "living in almost total social and geographic isolation"[3] for over a thousand years.[4] Their only tools "were made of edge-ground stone, a type of implement dating back more than six thousand years."[5]

Their whole world was their small corner of the forest.

2. Flaherty, T. 1991. "The Stone Age in T-shirts." In: *Hoaxes and Deceptions*. Alexandria, VA: Time-Life Books, pp. 133–139; Brownlee, S. 1990. If only life were so simple. *U.S. News and World Report*, pp. 54–56 February 19, p. 56.

3. Elizalde, M. 1972. "The Tasaday Forest People." *Grolier Encyclopedia: Science supplement*, pp. 300–305, p. 301.

4. Hemley, R. 2003. *Invented Eden: The Elusive, Disputed History of the Tasaday*. New York, NY: Farrar, Straus and Giroux, p. 3.

5. Hemley, 2003, p. 5.

They had no word for, nor had ever seen, an ocean, or even a boat, although the ocean was only a few miles away from their home. Their life was spent "squatted in caves wearing G-strings of leaves ... [dining] on grubs, roots, and wild fruit, especially wild yams scraped from the jungle soil."[6] They were described as living in the very early, long-past "evolutionary phase" of humanity, "distant relatives of Java man and Peking man... the first true man in the evolutionary process, who walked the earth more than half a million years ago."[7] Or so the story went, a fiction that eventually was completely debunked.

The Hysteria Begins

Not long after the find was announced, anthropologists, human evolution researchers, and reporters began flying by helicopter into the area where the tribe lived. They attempted to visit the Tasaday's jungle home to see for themselves how humans lived "a hundred centuries ago," before we humans allegedly evolved beyond the Stone Age.[8] The famous pilot, Charles A. Lindbergh, described his visit to the Tasaday as being like visiting his "ancestors a hundred thousand years ago."[9] Competition among the "journalists and anthropologists for access to the Tasaday became a source of professional friction."[10] The main reason for the excitement was that outsiders believed the Tasadays provided an "unparalleled opportunity in the twentieth century to understand more fully the evolution

6. Flaherty, 1991, p. 133.
7. Nance, J. 1975. *The Gentle Tasaday: A Stone Age People in the Philippine Rain Forest.* New York, NY: Harcourt Brace Jovanovich, Inc, pp. 135, 453.
8. Flaherty, 1991, p. 133.
9. Nance, 1975, Forward by Lindbergh, p. ix.
10. Palmer, A.W. 2000. Primitives among us. *Science Communication* 21(3):223–243, p. 227.

of modern man's culture and behavior before the appearance of agriculture and the domestication of animals."[11]

As a result of this opportunity to learn about primitive people and human evolution, the Tasaday went from being an unknown people to an internationally famous tribe. Pictures of their dirty faces posing nude in their rocky caves soon appeared in leading magazines throughout the world. One anthropologist dubbed them "paleohippies."[12]

Documentaries soon aired on TV, a Tasaday child climbing vines graced a *National Geographic* cover, and NBC News gave Elizalde 50,000 dollars to do a documentary on the Stone Age tribe. The *National Geographic* issue focusing on the tribe was "one of the magazine's best-selling issues in its history."[13] Thick books backed up by hundreds of footnotes were written about them, including a bestseller by John Nance titled *The Gentle Tasaday*. Soon even linguistic studies of the details of their language were begun. The scientists touted that we now had living proof of human evolution from our early primitive-caveman, Stone Age ancestors.

The shy Tasaday's 'peacefulness' also captivated the world. Some who studied them even claimed that the Tasaday lacked words for 'war,' 'enemy,' or even 'conflicts.' They were an uncorrupted version of a rain forest Garden-of-Eden humanity, their presumed gentleness in 1971 greatly contrasted with the images of violence and horror then daily coming out of the Vietnam War.

---

11. Elizalde, 1972, p. 302.
12. Feder, K. 2006. "Hoaxes in anthropology." In: Birx, J. (editor). *Encyclopedia of Anthropology*, Volume 3, Thousand Oaks, CA: Sage Publications, pp. 1174–1175..
13. Hemley, 2003, p. 7.

The press presented the story as a validation of human evolution. Here was a preliterate tribe living without clothes in a cave, unchanged for over a thousand years. The tribe functioned as a time capsule to give scientists a glimpse of life long before civilization appeared on Earth.[14] For evolutionists, it was a picture of the way primitive humans once lived, a compelling snapshot of life at an early stage of human evolution, a much better picture than any set of fossils could ever depict.

Soon the close association of the Tasaday with Manual Elizalde, Jr., began to hint of major problems. When Elizalde was appointed their protector, he tightly controlled access to them. Elizalde was a wealthy man with numerous business interests and lofty political ambitions. Although living a jet-setting life, he promoted himself as a champion of tribal minorities. The tight rein he had on access to the Tasaday angered many who wanted to learn more about the tribe. Elizalde even persuaded Philippines President Ferdinand Marcos to declare the Tasaday's rain forest area a protected reserve. This policy, "not coincidentally, also served to isolate them from those whose only agenda was to study them."[15] Some observers, it turned out, correctly surmised that Elizalde was exploiting the Tasaday to further his own political ambitions.

The Tasaday Story Unravels

Most visitors from the outside that came to observe the Tasaday were carefully supervised and the visits were often brief, usually less than two or three hours, ostensibly to ensure minimal contaminating influence by outsiders. The tribe's supporters claimed that their concern was outsiders corrupting the naïve

14. MacLeish, K.1972. The Tasadays: Stone Age cavemen of Mindanao. *National Geographic* 142(2):218–247, p. 231.

15. Feder, p. 1174.

native peoples. Some anthropologists, such as Daniel Stiles (Ph. D. in anthropology, University of California, Berkeley), found their attempts to do field work with the Tasaday tribe people stymied.[16] Professor Stiles had made all of the arrangements to visit the Tasaday tribe but was "blocked at the last minute," one suspects due to fear that the hoax would be exposed.[17]

In 1986 the Tasaday Stone Age-tribe hoax came crashing to earth. The Marcos government was overthrown, and the Tasaday Stone Age people were again accessible to outsiders. A Swiss journalist with a doctorate in anthropology, Oswald Iten, accompanied by a Filipino reporter, seized the opportunity to find out what had become of the Earth's only living Stone Age people during the previous 15 years. What they found shocked them, and soon became the basis for the conclusion that the entire Tasaday story was an outrageous hoax "equivalent to the fraudulent discovery of Piltdown fossils earlier in the century in Britain."[18]

The team found that the caves the Tasaday had assured the world that they had lived in "always"—"Our father's father and his father were there"—*were empty.*[19] The two dozen Tasaday were now living in clean huts among the Blit Manubo tribe and gone were their dirty faces. They were neatly dressed in stylish slacks, jeans, and t-shirts, wearing jewelry and colorful scarves, living a simple, but not by any means primitive, lifestyle.[20] They grew crops, lived in huts, and slept on wooden beds.[21] Either they had with amazing rapidity both learned and

16. Hemley, 2003, pp. 214–215.
17. Hemley, 2003, p. 215.
18. Palmer, 2000, p. 223.
19. MacLeish, 1972, p 232.
20. Iten, 1986.
21. Flaherty, pp. 133–134.

adapted to modern culture, clothing, jewelry, and habits including cleanliness, or they were part of an elaborate hoax that fooled the world.

The Cavemen Story Turned Out to Be Very Naïve

Most anthropologists agreed that, to sustain themselves as a separate group would have required at least 400 individuals, not around 24. A population at least this large would also serve in helping to avoid the powerful Tasaday taboo against incest. Furthermore, a tropical rain forest offers very little for humans to eat. Even the most primitive jungle diets must be augmented with some cultivated food. The Tasaday could not have survived for very long on the diet they claimed they had survived on for scores of generations.[22]

A careful survey of their claimed cave-home areas also revealed no evidence of long-term habitation. No significant level of garbage, or even evidence of long-term fire usage was present. This evidence would be very obvious if they had lived in these caves for centuries as they claimed. In short, acceptance of the cave story occurred largely because the anthropologists and evolutionists wanted to believe it. Nonetheless, when they began looking into the story in more detail, it very quickly fell apart.

The Motive for the Hoax Unraveled

Upon questioning, two Tasaday tribe members admitted that they were not a Stone Age tribe, and never had been. They claimed that Elizalde had pressured them into posing as one, claiming:

---

22. Feder, 2006, p. 1175.

We didn't live in caves until we met Elizalde. ... Elizalde forced us to live in the caves so that we'd be better cavemen. Before he came, we lived in huts ... and we farmed. We took off our clothes because Elizalde told us to do so and promised if we looked poor that we would get assistance. He gave us money to pose as Tasaday and promised us security from counter-insurgency and tribal fighting.

Judging by their dress that Oswald Iten observed, their acting performances paid off handsomely.Error: Reference source not found Iten's discovery sent shockwaves around the world—a fake Stone Age tribe that had managed to fool even the most experienced journalists and anthropologists. A *Current Anthropology* magazine article that discussed the Tasaday showed how badly anthropologists had been fooled by the hoax . It documented that Tasaday "believers" uncritically assumed that the corpus of "Stone Age tribe" claims were completely legitimate, even though problems should have been noted immediately by critical observers.[23]

After the exposure of the hoax, reporters were soon again making the journey into the Filipino rain forest to visit the Tasaday, only this time for other reasons. A group of German journalists arriving within days of Iten's departure found the Tasaday back at their caves dressed in leaves. But the Germans noticed cloth garments peeking out from beneath the Tasadays' tactfully placed leaves. It turned out that the Tasaday, caught unawares by Iten, had hastily decided to resume the 'Stone Age tribe' act, but weren't sophisticated enough to pull it off without outside help. Consequently, they put on their leaf cover

---

23. Hutterer, Kutter L., et al. 1976. An evolutionary approach to the Southeast Asian cultural sequence. *Current Anthropology* 17(2):221–242.

over their clothes.[24]

The fact that the tribe's "discovery had been staged and scripted by the government of President Ferdinand Marcos cast serious doubt on its authenticity."[25] The claim that the Tasaday were isolated for a thousand years, was not believable in view of the fact that they lived only a few miles away from a nearby village. Why did the Tasaday appear to be resistant to modern diseases? This should have been a problem because their isolation would have left them with little resistance to many diseases, the condition of the South American Indians when the Spanish arrived many years earlier.

Why had Elizalde so tightly controlled outside access to the tribe? And why, if they lacked knowledge of the use of steel, did many of their instruments and utensils appear to have been cut with steel knives? One study done by anthropologist Gerald Berreman of the stone tools the Tasaday claimed to use concluded that they were nonfunctional amateurish-made tools like "seventh graders might be expected to invent in response to a classroom assignment."[26]

Faced with these questions, and armed with confessions from the Tasaday themselves, "The accumulated evidence … left little doubt among many in the academic community that the entire Tasaday episode was a deception perpetrated by political actors, led by Elizalde."[27] They also concluded that the

24. Iten, 1992. "The "Tasaday" and the Press." In: Headland, T.N. (editor). *The Tasaday Controversy: Assessing the Evidence*. Special Publication of the American Anthropological Association Scholarly Series (Washington, D.C.), no. 28, pp. 40-58, p. 48.

25. Palmer, 2000, pp. 224–225.

26. "Hoaxes in Anthropology." In *Hoaxes in Anthropology – Anthropology*. http://anthropology.iresearchnet.com/hoaxes-in-anthropology/.

27. Palmer, 2000, p. 230.

Tasaday hoax, dreamed up by Elizalde, was scripted to make money, now estimated to be more than 35 million dollars.[28] It was now openly called a hoax.[29] This judgement was expressed in documentaries about the 'tribe,' such as *Scandal, the Lost Tribe*, and *The Tribe That Never Was*.

The Tasaday Revenge

However, the Tasaday still had friends, Elizalde in particular, who attempted to repair the tribe's now battered reputation. Despite Marcos's overthrow, Elizalde wielded enough influence in the Philippines to mount a vigorous pro-Tasaday campaign. He led the Tasaday's defense when the Philippine Congress investigated the hoax claims in 1987. The Congress decided that the issue of fraud should be left to the scientists, not politicians.

In 1988, Elizalde flew some Tasaday tribe members to Manila to file a lawsuit against the Philippine professors who were calling the 'Stone Age' claim a hoax. The Tasaday then became the first Stone Age tribe to sue for libel! These efforts paid off when, also in 1988, the new Philippine president, Corazon Aquino, declared that the Tasaday were a "legitimate Stone Age tribe."

Although these political tactics had little effect on scientific opinion, some claims about the tribe were proven true. For example, evidence exists that the tribe did live as semi-isolated nomadic hunter-gatherers until 1971. It was true that a detailed examination of their language by linguist Clay Johnson, who had lived with a neighboring tribe for ten years, concluded that the Tasaday language was "virtually identical to that of

---

28. Feder, 2006, p. 1174.
29. Anonymous. 1986. "Discovery of Cave Man is Called Hoax." *The Toledo Blade*, April 13, Section A.

their neighbors." It nonetheless appears to have been distinct in some minor ways. Linguists came to believe it likely split from the language of the nearby Manobo people around 200 years ago.[30]

Fieldwork, such as by Lawrence Reid of the University of Hawaii, who lived with the Tasaday for extended periods throughout the 1990s, identified their language as a dialect of Cotabato Manobo. Reid also concluded that the Tasaday had not been isolated for a thousand years but likely had splintered off from the Cotabato Manobo community a few years ago, perhaps fleeing into the jungle to escape an outbreak of disease.

Furthermore, the tribe had frequently made contact with neighboring tribes, and through this contact acquired steel tools and learned agricultural skills. Consequently, when the outside world discovered them in 1971, they were definitely not an isolated Stone Age tribe as first claimed. However, they were living in what we would term primitive conditions, as were many tribes in this and other countries, such as some of the tribes in the Amazon in the late 1960s.

How They Hoaxed the World

Supporters of the Tasaday still had to account for the Tasaday's confession that they hoaxed the world. Two Tasaday later claimed that they had made up the confession because they were bribed. Friends of the Tasaday credited this confession to the anti-Marcos sentiment that ran high in the Philippines in 1986. The Tasaday had been a showpiece of his regime, a means by which Marcos projected an idyllic view of the Phil-

30. Reid, L.A. 1992. "The Tasaday Language: A Key to Tasaday Prehistory." In: Headland, T.N. (editor). *The Tasaday Controversy: Assessing the Evidence*. Special Publication of the American Anthropological Association Scholarly Series (Washington, D.C.), no. 28, pp. 180–193.

ippines to the outside world. For this reason they became a choice target for Marcos's detractors. Furthermore, if the Tasaday Stone Age claims were deemed a hoax, the tribe's rights to the reserve that protected their land would vanish, and the loggers could move in.

Making Sense of the Tasaday Hoax

At the least, Elizalde was guilty of having encouraged the Tasaday to attempt to look much *more* primitive for the benefit of the cameras. He asked them to wear leaves and hide their steel tools. Thus, he greatly distorted the truth, as did the Marcos government, which shamelessly promoted the Tasaday as a quaint symbol to showcase an idyllic and exotic view of the Philippines.

However, the Tasaday themselves appear to have willingly played the roles asked of them. They relished the attention and anticipated that Elizalde would provide them with significant financial aid, which he did. The support allowed them to dress in nice clothes, including jeans and t-shirts, when Iten found them.[31] This fact is hard to explain by the 15 years of acculturation they had experienced since 1971. There was also a surreal moment in 1988 when members of the Tasaday agreed to participate in a cultural festival at nearby Lake Sebu, during which they posed in imitation caves, like exhibits in a zoo, for the benefit of onlookers.

Understandably, "Appalled by the apparent humbug that had taken in so many, including most anthropologists, the *American Anthropological Association* asked linguist Thomas Headland to organize a symposium on the Tasaday for their

---

31. Iten, Oswald. 1986. Die Tasaday: Ein Philippinischer Steinzeitschwindel, *Neue Zurcher Zeitung* 12:77–89, April. (The Tasaday: A Philippine Stone Age Fraud).

1989 annual meeting."Error: Reference source not found The contributions, which were published in 1992, found that of most participants, "concluded from the evidence that the Tasaday had been manipulated to play the role of a primeval cave people as part of a cynical hoax."Error: Reference source not found

Stone Age Tribe Myth Completely Sold the Media

The media also repeatedly misrepresented the Tasaday. In 1971 it hyped them as a peace-nik, utopian, Stone Age tribe. It could only view the Tasaday in sensationalistic black-and-white terms, as either throwbacks to the Stone Age, or as a fraud, and never in shades of grey. Almost everyone involved in the Tasaday story distorted the truth for their own purposes. The supposed evolutionary discovery was so "transparent and compelling it ... was not, strictly speaking, dependent on the *truth* [emphasis in original]."[32] In the end, most of the claims about the tribe's primitiveness were documented to be, at best, gross exaggerations, if not major errors of fact.[33]

A major question that arises is, "Why were Westerners, and Americans in particular, so willing—and even eager—to embrace the Tasaday [hoax]? Why were we so fascinated with the notion of noble primitives? They [their claims] never hold up under scientific scrutiny."[34] The answer can be found from reading the many publications about the Tasaday, mostly articles supporting evolution, in this case the evolution from primitive cavemen to modern men. The best illustration of the fact

32. Palmer, 2000, p. 225.
33. Berreman, G.D. 1991. The Incredible "Tasaday": Deconstructing the Myth of a "Stone-Age" People. *Cultural Survival Quarterly* 15:2–45, March.
34. Brownlee, 1990, p. 54.

that the media was completely sold on the 'Stone Age tribe' myth was the example of *National Geographic* Magazine, which published two gullible articles on them, but subsequently gave no hint that their story had been grossly irresponsible.

One of these two accounts described their Stone Age hardware as so primitive that, "For the Tasadays, the height of technological sophistication has been a knife with a bamboo blade or a hammer of chipped stone bound with rattan to a wooden handle."[35] The article also claimed that they used crude digging sticks, stone scrapers, bamboo knives, and had no word in their vocabulary for 'war' as we would expect from self-respecting cavemen. The magazine even added that the Tasaday described some of their visitors as "strangely clad men from the sky, bearing miraculous gifts—beads, mirrors, metal knives, even a flashlight."[36]

The anthropologists, the *National Geographic* added, had long been looking "forward to the rare opportunity of studying firsthand a people who ... have lived in isolation for hundreds of years" or longer. The three-page article had three illustrations of nude 'primitive' men, women, and children doing caveman things with primitive tools.

The *National Geographic* follow-up, a 32-page article that contained 19 pictures of nude men, women, and children, likewise had the Tasaday doing what you would expect Neanderthal cavemen to do. The Tasaday in the picture were very dirty, unkempt with long straggly hair, many sitting naked on rocks in barren rocky caves in a picture that looked staged; and, from what we know now, most of the photos and activities *were*

35. MacLeish, 1971, p. 226.

36. MacLeish, K. 1971. First glimpse of a Stone Age tribe. *National Geographic* 140(6):881–882, p. 881.

staged for the camera. The rugged mountainous area shown in the pictures was described as "a primeval Eden" inhabited by "24 people who lived much as our ancestors did thousands of years ago."[37]

The children looked like they had mud smeared on their faces just for the picture, which is likely what occurred. One young boy was shown "climbing vines ... with the ease of a monkey ... . His major worry was lack of a mate. Only five ... Tasadays are women, and all have husbands."[38] We later learned that one Tasaday man had two wives.[39] I counted nine children in one picture alone. The rest of the tribal persons shown were young adults, and I saw no elderly adults in any of the pictures.

This fact was explained by claiming that their life span was very short, even though the researchers observed little evidence of disease.[40] In the distant past, a smallpox epidemic evidently occurred, but other than this they were very healthy. As noted, slightly more than two dozen people sheltering for thousands of years would have required almost all of them to be involved in incest, a practice forbidden among these people.[41]

Now we know that they found wives among nearby tribes. The person who discovered the Tasadays was, the *National Geographic* claimed, greeted as the "fulfillment of their ancestors' promise"[42] of a savior that would come down from the sky (in

37. MacLeish, 1972, p. 219.
38. MacLeish, 1972, p. 225.
39. Iten, 1992, p. 48.
40. Elizalde, 1972, p. 303.
41. Darrach, B. 1975. Primitive Art: The Gentle Tasaday. *Time* 105(27):47–48, June 30; Anonymous. 1975. Lost Tribe of the Tasaday. *Time* 105(45):58–59, October 18, p. 58.
42. MacLeish, 1972, p. 227.

this case a helicopter they called the "Big Sacred Bird").[43] This outsider would come to love and protect them, and lead them out of darkness. Their savior was recognized as Manuel ('Manda') Elizalde.

A *Time* magazine article indicated that the Tasaday were "the most primitive human beings so far discovered on this guilty planet," adding that, to study these "prehistoric people," several dozen "scientists and journalists and film people" visited the Tasaday.[44] One example of the work of the "film people" is the *National Geographic* video special titled 'The Last Tribes of Mindanao.' The *National Geographic* also "published a cover story with dramatic pictures" about the Tasaday.[45] The hoax was also represented as fact in articles describing them in scientific anthropological detail in major encyclopedias and references books.[46] Feder concluded that the "motivation for the hoax, [was] likely ... to control and to profit from ... a gullible world."

Summary

As concluded by University of Chicago anthropologist Fred Eggan, the claim "that the Tasaday were an isolated Stone Age people is nonsense."[47] Instead, they were people living in poverty close to nature in a Philippine jungle who were swept up in, and manipulated by global events beyond their control. This

---

43. Darrach, 1975, p. 58.
44. Darrach, 1975, pp. 58–59.
45. Anonymous, 1986, p. 32.
46. Elizalde, 1972, pp. 300-305.
47. Begley, S., and D. Seward. 1986. Back from the Stone Age? An anthropological find may be a hoax. *Newsweek*, April 29, p. 55; Taylor, I. 1986. *National Geographic* and the Stone Age swindle? *Creation* 9(1):6–10.

version of events isn't as compelling as the versions that made headlines in 1971 and 1986, but it is a good illustration of how the truth is often far more complicated than it at first appears.

Although proving evolution was not the main motivation of the hoax, evolution was nevertheless a major reason the hoax was uncritically accepted for so long in spite of the irredeemable problems with the original story. It is also a reason why it was so widely repeated as fact in so many sources, including mass-media publications, reference books, and encyclopedias. *The Encyclopedia Americana* described the Tasaday as a primitive tribe of about 25 that survived by gathering wild plants and catching small water creatures by hand.[48] It dismissed the hoax charge by explaining that the drastic changes in their material culture observed after 1988 were due to outside contacts made after they were discovered by the West in 1971.

This rationalization may also explain why almost every U.S. publication that covered the Tasaday hoax, including the *National Geographic* and the *New York Times,* not only did not print a retraction after it had been exposed, but "actively upheld the old story" that claimed the Tasaday were a Stone Age Tribe isolated for generations.[49] The fact is, "The discovery of an isolated primitive tribe living in forest caves on the southern Philippine island of Mindanao in 1971 has become a disputed milestone in the history of cultural anthropology."

It is true that the myth was finally exposed, but, in the end, it was not by Darwinists attempting to critically research the story, but more by those interested in mining the lush, valuable wood where the Tasaday people resided. The Tasaday hoax even

---

48. *The Encyclopedia Americana.* 1995. Volume 26. Danbury, CT: Grolier Incorporated, p. 304.
49. MacLeish, 1971, 1972.

earned a place in *The Encyclopedia of Hoaxes*. The editor, after listing five convincing reasons to classify the Tasaday event as a hoax, wrote in his conclusion that the Tasaday affair was an outright hoax similar to the Piltdown hoax.[50] In the end, the Tasaday people

> admitted to being members of a nearby tribe with normal human vices, who had been recruited for the greatest ever anthropological fraud (more than comparable with Sir Cyril Burt's doctoring of data on inheritance of intelligence within psychology). In recent years the continuing controversy between Tasaday's defenders and detractors has wreaked havoc inside anthropology, with scientific reputations at stake—if not a whole world-view, or even the credibility of science itself.[51]

Part of the problem is that "anthropology fieldwork produces 'fictions' that are vulnerable to criticism like any other work of literature."[52] As concluded by the British Broadcasting Corporation documentary *Tasaday, Trial in the Jungle*, if a group of 27 people were able to have "pulled off the most elaborate hoax in scientific history ... [and] fool every anthropologist who ever saw them, how credible is the science of anthropology?"Error: Reference source not found Actually, most, but not *every* anthropologist was fooled. Although many wanted to believe the Stone Age story, after the 1986 Iten report was published, anthropologists for the first time began to study the Tasaday claims in earnest with a skeptical eye. When they did

50. Stein, G. 1993. *The Encyclopedia of Hoaxes*. Detroit, MI: Gale Research, pp. 5–7.
51. Vine, I. 1989. Myth, Truth, & Method—The Tasaday Tribe. *Ethology and Sociobiology* 10(5):391–392.
52. Palmer, 2000, p. 224.

this, even they were surprised by how inept the hoax was, and how gullible they had been to accept it as valid.[53]

]

---

53. Iten, 1992, p. 48.

Paul Kramer Wikimedia commons

Source: https://en.wikipedia.org/wiki/Paul_Kammerer

7

Proving Evolution by Fraud: The Paul Kammerer Case

O NE OF THE MOST notorious scandals of evolution fraud, that of Viennese biologist Paul Kammerer, was the subject of the now classic book titled *The Case of the Midwife Toad*.[1] The case was once "regularly told to biology students as an object lesson."[2] Furthermore, according to Professor Reville, "every list of famous scientific frauds includes the case of Dr. Paul Kammerer."[3] One of the claims against Kammerer involved his painting so-called "nuptial pads" with India ink on the front feet of the toads he was studying in order to prove his evolutionary theory. A similar case occurred in the 1970s when William Summerlin faked the results of an exper-

---

1. Koestler, Arthur. 1971. *The Case of the Midwife Toad.* New York, NY: Random House.
2. Aronson, Lester. 1975. The Case of the Midwife Toad. *Behavior Genetics* 5(2):115–125, p. 115.
3. Reville, William. 2019. Paul Kammerer may have been an honest scientist. *The Irish Times*, June 28.

iment by drawing black patches on his white test mice with a felt-tip pen.[4]

Even though Kammerer's work, some or much of which was forged to support his Lamarckian theory of evolutionism, was exposed, it was still used for decades to support a specific evolutionary ideology, including those advocated by the Soviet geneticist Trofim D. Lysenko.[5] In spite of the evidence, some well-informed persons, such as Koestler, have attempted to argue that Kammerer was innocent. His support may have been motivated by his agreement with Kammerer's unorthodox evolutionary theory. Kammerer's ideas were also attractive to the Soviet Union. Professor Taschwer writes why this was true:

> Politically left Western scientists were ... fascinated by the Soviet Union during the 1920s. The new government supported for practical reasons as well as ideological reasons, those natural sciences that provided the ruling Marxists with a new ideological alternative to religion. Darwin's theories in particular were highly rated as they were associated with materialism and atheism.[6]

Who was Paul Kammerer?

The fruits of evolution are many and varied, and include the emotional tragedy experienced by many people affected by this worldview, as well as the outright fakery perpetuated in order to prove Darwin's theory. Examples are many, including

---

4. Chang, Kenneth. 2002. "On Scientific Fakery and the Systems to Catch It." *The New York Times: Science Times*, Tuesday, October 15, pp. 1, 4.

5. Kohn, Alexander. 1988. *False Prophets: Fraud and Error in Science and Medicine*. New York, NY: Barnes & Noble Books, p. 47.

6. Taschwer, Klaus. 2016. P. 216.

Piltdown Man, *Hesperopithecus*, Java Man, and Neanderthals.[7]
One other leading, but lesser known example, was Austrian scientist Paul Kammerer. To glean some idea of his achievements,
his obituary in the world's most respected scientific journal,
Nature, called his last book "one of the finest contributions to
the theory of evolution which has appeared since Darwin."[8]
The September 26, 1926, Vienna journal *Neue Freie Presse* es-
teemed him as the "eminent biologist, Dr. Paul Kammerer,
whose books and essays in biology and sociology attracted wide
and justified attention, whose lectures were always attended by
an enthusiastic audience of hundreds of people."[9]

Paul Kammerer (1880-1926) was a scientist working at
the internationally respected *Institute for Experimental Biology*
in Vienna, Austria.[10] Kammerer had a major conflict with his
colleagues when he "refused to accept the Darwinian theory of
evolution based on random mutations—haphazard variations
produced by blind chance."[11] For this heresy, Kammerer "was
exposed only to academic venom" from some of his peers.[12]

Rather than Darwinian evolution, Kammerer "believed
that the main vehicle of progressive evolution was the inheritance of acquired characteristics which Lamarck had postulated
in 1809... [when] useful adaptive changes in the parents were
preserved by heredity and transmitted to their offspring."[13]

7. Bergman, Jerry. 2017. *Evolution's Blunders, Frauds and Forgeries*. Atlanta, GA: CMI Publishing.
8. *Nature*, 30 October 1926, p. 635.
9. Quoted in Koester, 1971, p. 15.
10. Myers, Ellen. 1989. The Story of Paul Kammerer, is Lamarckism Dead?
Creation Social & Humanities Quarterly Journal 11(1):6-13, p. 6.
11. Koestler, 1971, p. 14.
12. Koestler, 1971, p. 15.
13. Koestler, 1971, p. 14.

Kammerer knew that Darwin, unable to find a mechanism for evolution, returned to Lamarck in his later years. This change was reflected in the sixth edition of his *Origin of Species*. For this reason, Kammerer felt that his work was returning "to the ideas of Lamarck, Goethe and Darwin."[14] Kammerer proposed an alternative to then-orthodox Darwinism which elicited the wrath of his colleagues. This history reflects the often unethical squabbling over opinions and beliefs among scientists, many of whom, both then and today, were eminent in their field.

While searching for scientific support for the once popular "acquired characteristics" evolutionary theory, solid evidence exists that Kammerer faked some of his evidence. When he was later exposed, he took his own life. Kammerer's "wacky campaign to prove the heritability of acquired characteristics is as topical today as on September 23, 1926, when he shot himself."[15] After it was documented that he faked a critical experiment, we might assume that his "case was closed. However, if the scientist is the Viennese biologist Paul Kammerer and if the case is the notorious 'Case of the Midwife Toad,' then the docket remains open."[16]

Kammerer possessed a firm belief in evolution, but based on the evidence could not accept the Darwinian explanation, so he proposed a mechanism that he believed *could* explain evolution.[17] He was fully aware of the major scientific problems

---

14. Kammerer, Paul. 1924. *The Inheritance of Acquired Characteristics*. New York, NY, USA: Boni & Liveright. Translated by Paul Maerker-Branden, p. 19.

15. Weissmann, Gerald. 2010. The midwife toad and Alma Mahler: Epigenetics or a matter of deception? *The FASEB Journal* 24:2591-2594, p. 2591.

16. Weismann, 2010, p. 2591.

17. Kammerer, 1924.

that existed with Darwin's theory of evolution by natural selection, including the lack of a viable mechanism to account
for the origin of new genetic variety. Kammerer's goal was to
prove that his specific mechanism, namely the theory that the
environment and internal striving are the major mechanisms
causing evolution. The "internal striving" theory seemed to answer Darwinism's central problem, namely the origin of genetic
information.

Kammerer was confident that proof would someday be
found for his theory if he just kept experimenting, which he
did for decades.[18] Although he had repeatedly failed at this goal,
Kammerer did not give up, widely publishing his research from
1904 until his untimely death in 1926. His 1926 book was
published by a leading publisher, contained 43 illustrations,
many in color, and 35 pages of references, all which appeared
to carefully document his decades of laboratory research.
Consequently, the claim was that he had faked his results, in
order to convince the public until his "acquired-characteris-
tics" evolution theory was "clearly proved" by future experimental evidence. As noted, he was not a minor scientist, but
had published scores of peer-reviewed scientific papers, many
in German, and seven full-length books, most of which are
still in print. Plus, he presented scores of well-attended lecture
demonstrations and pamphlets that attracted very favorable attention from other scientists.

---

18. Gliboff, Sander. 2006. The case of Paul Kammerer: Evolution and experimentation in the early 20th century. *Journal of the History of Biology* 39(3):525-563, January; Gliboff, Sander. 2009. Did Paul Kammerer
discover epigenetic inheritance? No and why not. *Journal of Experimental Zoology--PartB: Molecular Developmental Evolution* 314(8):616–
624.

Kammerer Becomes Disillusioned

When what were judged as faked results were discovered, it caused him to become disillusioned, not only with himself, but also with science and his purpose for living, which was to prove his evolution theory. His suicide was recounted by Koestler.[19] In short, on the early afternoon of September 23, 1926, a road-worker found a dead man dressed in a dark suit on a popular Austrian mountain path.

The body was propped against a vertical rock face. His right hand was still clutching the pistol with which he shot himself in the head. One of his pockets contained a letter addressed to the person who found his body, which clearly tied his suicide to his scientific work, or at least the judgements of his peers about his work:

> Dr. Paul Kammerer requests not to be transported to his home, in order to spare his family the sight. Simplest and cheapest would perhaps be utilization in the dissecting room of one of the university institutes. I would actually prefer to render science at least this small service. Perhaps my worthy academic colleagues will discover in my brain a trace of the qualities they found absent from the manifestations of my mental activities while I was alive.

Kammerer added that he did not care what

> happens to the corpse, buried, burned, or dissected, its bearer belonged to no religious community and wishes to be spared a religious ceremony, which probably would be denied him anyway. This is not meant to express hostility against the individual priest, who is human like everybody else and often a good and

---

19. Koestler, 1971, p. 13.

noble person.[20]

Koestler wrote that Kammerer's death

ended the greatest scientific scandal of the first half of our century. Its hero and victim was one of the most brilliant and unorthodox biologists of his time. He was forty-five years old when the joint pressures of an inhuman Establishment and his own all-too-human temperament drove him to suicide. He had been accused of the worst crime a scientist can commit: of having faked his experimental results.[21]

The details of what happened will now be reviewed.

Blunder or Fraud to Prove Evolution?

Paul Kammerer's life-long ambition was to prove evolution by experimentation that showed exactly how it occurred. He was not an "anti-Darwinist and a neo-Lamarckian as happened time and time again." [22]The many experiments that he performed to prove his idea included forcing sun-loving praying mantises to feed in the dark and amputating the proboscises of sea squirts to determine the effects of the surgery on their future offspring. He once claimed that he could produce amphibians without eyes, like blind fish, depending on how much sunlight they were exposed to when developing.[23]

---

20. Koestler, 1971, p. 13.
21. Koestler, 1971, p. 13.
22. Taschwer, Klaus. 2016. *The Case of Paul Kammerer. The Most Controversial Biologist of his Time.* Montreal, Canada: Bunim & Bannigan. Pp. 85-86.
23. Kean, Sam. 2012. *The Violinist's Thumb: And Other Lost Tales of Love, War, and Genius, as Written by Our Genetic Code.* New York, NY: Little, Brown and Company, p. 327.

The Spotted Salamander Case

His critics were also bothered by claims made by Kammerer's unpaid lab assistant, Fräulein Alma Maria Werfel. She worked with Kammerer on research with his spotted salamanders, the skin patterns of which were alleged to be heritably affected by the color of sand on which they were reared.[24] Kammerer believed that the salamander colors could be changed merely by changing its environment. Werfel's autobiography describes their amphibian research, and its later refutation by E. G. Boulenger of the London Zoo which showed that Kammerer's salamander experiments were invalid.

Fräulein Werfel recognized that Kammerer was sloppy in the lab, keeping terrible records, and she felt he unconsciously ignored results that contradicted his theories. She claimed that these experiments, with which she helped, were rushed into print and not accurately documented. She also corroborated Megusar's description of Kammerer as a mendacious observer, wanting positive results so greatly that he consciously, or unconsciously, misread the results of the salamander mimicry research. Even more damning were several scientific journals which documented Kammerer fudging data.

For example, to cause his test animals to acquire the characteristics of the spotted, oviparous, lowland salamander, and vice versa, the polka dot pattern or pinstripe colors in their integument was achieved by placing viviparous Alpine salamanders into landscapes with polka dot-like patterns or pinstripe color patterns.

One scientist called him "the father of photographic image manipulation."[25] Columbia University Professor Thomas Hunt

---

24. Weissmann, 2010, p. 2592.
25. Kean, 2012, p. 332.

Morgan wrote: "Kammerer has done one more dirty trick in trying to put the fraud over on to one of his assistants. Remember that this is not the first time, either, that he has been caught, and all responsible people will, I think, draw the same conclusion."[26]

The Sea Squirt Fraud

One of Kammerer's most important experiments, which he "maintained … was his most convincing proof of the inheritance of acquired characteristics, involved amputating the two siphon ends that the sea squirt uses to feed by bringing water in and out of its body".[27] This proto-chordate invertebrate is called a *Ciona*. Kammerer claimed that the regenerated siphon tubes were *longer* than the original, and that the elongation alteration was passed on to the next generation. Kammerer wrote that his experiment involved two sequential siphon regenerations, after which a regeneration of a lower section of the body, which contained the gonads, occurred before the animals were crossed for the next generation.

At least three refutations of this claim have been published. In 1923, Cambridge Professor Harold Munro Fox wrote in *Nature* that he repeated the amputation experiments on 59 subjects and again repeated it on 35 subjects, and again on another eight. He found that the regenerations grew to the original length, and not beyond as claimed by Kammerer. Fox concluded that the regenerated siphons do *not* grow beyond the normal length.[28]

26. Morgan, Thomas H. 1926. Letter to G.K. Noble, cited in Aronson, L.R. 1975. The case of the midwife toad. *Behavioral Genetics* 5:115–125, p. 121.
27. Whittaker, 1985, p. 2.
28. Fox, Harold. 1923. Dr. Kammerer's *Ciona* Experiments. *Nature*

In 1930, Russian scientist Julius Wermel published a 26-page study about *Ciona* regeneration and concluded that no elongation occurred, thus no heredity of this trait could occur.[29] The most damning refutation was by J. R. Whittaker, a former director of the Marine Biological Laboratory, who spent two summers following up on Arthur Koestler's challenge that someone repeat the *Ciona* work.[30] Whittaker followed Kammerer's directions to the letter and concluded that *Ciona* siphons did not

> regenerate longer after their surgical removal. But most telling was the gonadal regeneration part of Kammerer's supposed experiment. This involved a completely lethal operation from which [the] animals could not recover . . . I was left with no remaining doubt that the *Ciona* results were also an invention of Paul Kammerer's high-strung imagination.[31]

Other scientists agreed, observing that Kammerer's "statements were not in accordance with the present state of biological knowledge."[32] One fact that raised major questions in Western scientists' minds was that Kammerer never allowed any of his peers to check and verify his scientific work since it

112(2818):653–654, November 23, pp. 653-654.

29. Wermel, J., and Lopaschow, G.W. 1930. Über den Einfluss der Regeneration und Übererna" hrung auf die Siphonenla" nge bei *Ciona intestinalis* L. Ein Beitrag zu Kammerer's Experientmenten. *Arch. Entwicklungsmech. Org* 122:22– 47.

30. Whittaker, J.R. 1975. Siphon regeneration in *Ciona. Nature* 255:224 –225, pp. 224 –225.

31. Whittaker, J.R. 1985. Paul Kammerer and the Suspect Siphons. *MBL Science*, August, pp. 2-3.

32. Cunningham, J.T. 1923. Dr. Kammerer's lecture to the Linnean Society. *Nature* 112:133.

was first published in 1919.[33] As will be discussed below, only in 1926 was his work reviewed by his peers - with disastrous consequences.

Kammerer's Toad Experiments

Kammerer's triumph, as well as his undoing, included a series of experiments on the midwife toad *Alytes obstetricans*. Midwife-toad males mate on land, thus they *lack* the thick pigmented thumb pads called "nuptial pads" that are common on other toads. Males that mate in water have these nuptial pads, which consist of callosities containing horny spines on their forelimbs. These horney spines allow the toad to obtain a better grip onto the slippery wet female while matting.[34] Kammerer claimed that his work causing these pads to develop on midwife toads was proof of the inheritance of acquired characteristics. His critics usually simply denied their existence. It should be a simple matter to document the claim that they did not exist in the past on midwife toads, and now do in the present, due to some condition that Kammerer caused.

Most toads mate in water, then allow their newly fertilized eggs to float away in the watery environment to develop. Amphibians that mate in the water develop nuptial pads during spawning season on the outer surfaces of their forelimbs.[35] The males clasp their slippery mates with their forelimbs and fertilize the eggs as they leave the female's body. Because midwife-toad males fertilize eggs on land that are vulnerable to desiccation, males cover newly-fertilized eggs with sticky insulator material and bundle them to their back legs like a bunch of grapes. They

---

33. Myers, 1988, p. 7.
34. Koestler, 1971, p. 16.
35. Aronson, 1975, p. 117.

then hop along while carrying them until they hatch.[36]

In his experiments, Kammerer created hot desert conditions by increasing the heat in the midwife toad's aquarium home, forcing them to breed in water. He claimed that the midwife toads spent most of their time submerged to prevent them from shriveling up like dried fruit in the heat—and, Kammerer claimed, those eggs that survived became more adapted to water after each generation.

They not only developed "nuptial pads" but also had longer gills and produced the slippery jelly coating to waterproof their eggs, as did their water-mating cousins. Most importantly, Kammerer claimed that when these altered toads were returned to cooler tanks to reproduce, the toads' descendants, who never experienced the desert conditions, inherited the water-breeding preferences and passed them along to their descendants.[37]

Kammerer announced the results of one important study around 1910. For the next decade, he completed other experiments. Evidently, no experiment he completed in this area ever failed, proving in his mind that, given the proper environment, animals could be molded to do, or be, very different, thus producing evolution. His evolution theory postulates that our fish ancestors eventually evolved into humans by many thousands of years adapting to very different environments. He concluded that the proper environment could actually "cause advantageous genes to *spring* into existence."[38]

It needs to be noted that biology was then involved in other

36. Schmuck, Thomas. 2000. Hofrichter, Robert (ed.). *The Midwife Toad and Human Progress. Amphibians: The World of Frogs, Toads, Salamanders and Newts*. New York, NY: Firefly Books, pp. 212–213.

37. Kean, 2012, p. 328.

38. Kean, 2012, p. 329.

major ideological conflicts—Darwinism remained controversial, Lamarckism was close to dead, and Mendel's laws were not yet widely accepted.[39] Kammerer claimed that his theory could actually unite Darwin, Lamarck, and Mendel.[40] His theory also had clear Marxist implications, which held that the only factor keeping the wretched working masses down was their terrible environment.[41] As a committed socialist, Kammerer readily extended his arguments from toads to humans. In his thinking, nurture was nature.

A critical problem is that "not one of his controversial 'discoveries' has ever been [successfully] duplicated."[42] The public and non-scientists were, as a whole, more receptive to Kammerer's ideas and even some evolutionists felt that his ideas were at least plausible. Consequently, his books became best-sellers and he lectured to worldwide audiences in his "big-show talks." Unfortunately, as Kammerer became more prominent, the shakier his science became and Kammerer began to espouse what we today recognize as foolish, if not irresponsible, ideas.

For example, he suggested "curing" homosexuals with testicle transplants and concluded that prohibition in America would result in producing a generation of American Übermenschen, a race "born without any desire for liquor."[43] He also argued that enacting American-style prohibition in Europe would produce a continent of people without a desire for liquor.[44] Part of his problem was his arrogance as a scientist, a

39. Kean, 2012, p. 328.
40. Gerschenowitz, Harry. 1983. Arthur Koestler's Osculation with Lamarckism and Neo-Lamarckism. *International Journal of Heritage Studies* 18:1–8.
41. Kean, 2012, p. 328.
42. Weissmann, 2010, p. 251.
43. Kean, 2012, p. 329.
44. Kammerer, Paul. 1912. Körper, Kultur, und Rasse. *Das Oesterreichische*

problem that to some degree still exists today. He even anointed himself a "second Darwin" as he continued to write and lecture.

The Critics Move In

In his scientific reports, Kammerer withheld many crucial details about his amphibian experiments which were noticed by critics.[45] These omissions added to the doubts of many biologists who became convinced that he was wrong. Mendel's bulldog in Europe, William Bateson, was not shy about attacking Kammerer nor other scientists. During the "eclipse of Darwinism around 1900, he was involved in an especially nasty row with his former mentor, a Darwin defender named Walter Weldon."[46]

Bateson's aggressive determination eventually enabled him to get elected to the board of a scientific society that allocated research funding in biology. As soon as he was elected, Bateson cut all of Weldon's funding. Such was the rancor that, when Weldon died in 1906 of a heart attack, his widow, probably for good reason, blamed Bateson for Weldon's death. In retaliation, Weldon ally, eugenicist Karl Pearson, blocked Bateson's attempts to publish his papers and also attacked Bateson in the journal that Pearson edited, the *Biometrika Journal*.[47] Pearson even refused Bateson the courtesy of responding to his attacks

---

Sanitatswesen 24:441– 452.

45. Letters relating to the controversy. *Nature* 1919, 1923. May 22, 1919: MacBride (L); July 3: Bateson (L); May 12, 1923: Kammerer (A?); May 26: Cunningham (L); June 2: Bateson (L); June 23: MacBride (L); June 30: Bateson (L); July 21: MacBride (L); July 28: Cunningham (L); August 18: Kammerer (L), Perkins (L); September 8: MacBride (L), Sir Arthur Keith (L); September 15: Bateson (L).

46. Kean, 2012, p. 330.

47. Kean, 2012, p. 330.

in print, so "Bateson printed up fake copies of *Biometrika,* complete with facsimile covers, inserted his response inside, and distributed them to libraries and universities without any indication they were fraudulent."[48]

When Bateson demanded an opportunity to examine his (Kammerer's) toads, Kammerer refused, and Kammerer's critics were unimpressed with Kammerer's excuses. The chaos of World War I temporarily halted the debates, but left Kammerer's lab in shambles and his animals dead. Finally, in 1926, Kammerer allowed a herpetologist from the American Museum of Natural History, Gladwin Kingsley Noble, who was an American ally of Bateson's, to examine the only midwife toad he (Kammerer) managed to save. In 1926, Noble journeyed to Vienna to examine Kammerer's last pickled specimen that supposedly had "inherited" nuptial pads.

Noble reported that, in his judgement, someone had injected black ink with a syringe under the toad's skin at the location where the "nuptial pads" would have been to create the illusion of blackened structures. Noble's conclusion, as reported in *Nature,* was that the toad looked entirely "normal," meaning that the nuptial pads were not present. Noble didn't use the word fraud, but he didn't need to.[49] Kammerer claimed to have no knowledge of the injection of India ink into his specimens, and evidence of the identity of the perpetrator was inconclusive.

Kammerer alluded to sabotage by one of his many political enemies. Nonetheless, the howling of scientists increased, and Kammerer despaired.[50]

---

48. Kean, 2012, p. 330.

49. Noble, Gladwin Kingsley. 1926. Kammerer's Alytes. *Nature* 2962(118):209-211.

50. Taschwer, Klaus. 2019. *The Case of Paul Kammerer: The Most Controversial Biologist of His Time.* London, England: Bunim & Bannigan,

The Soviet Union and Kammerer

Because communism sees humans as the product of their environment, in particular their economic conditions, the Russian Communist Party elite embraced Lamarckism as its official creed. In 1925 it offered Kammerer a professorship at the leading University in Russia, the University of Moscow. Just before the damning *Nature* paper came out, he accepted a post in the Soviet Union that was very favorable to his neo-Lamarckian theories. Not long after this, Kammerer realized that he had many enemies in high places, and in response, wrote to Moscow informing them that he could not in good conscience accept the appointment because he felt the negative attention he was receiving would reflect badly on the great Soviet state.

The resignation letter soon took a dark turn when Kammerer wrote, "I hope I shall gather together enough courage and strength, to put an end [to] my wrecked life tomorrow." The very next day, September 23, 1926, he shot himself in the head. It seemed to many to be a sure admission of his guilt.[51] The suicide was probably not caused solely by Noble's exposé of Kammerer, but the paper was no doubt part of the many issues troubling Kammerer.

Regardless of Kammerer's motive, his suicide ended up smearing Lamarckism by association, and supporters in the Soviet Union took up Kammerer's cause. The soon-to-be agricultural czar of the Soviet Union, Trofim Lysenko, director of the Soviet Academy of Sciences Institute of Genetics, considered Kammerer a martyr to socialist biology and began championing parts of Kammerer's theories.[52] Officials decided to shoot

Ltd.

51. Kean, 2012, p. 331
52. Joravsky, David. 1970. *The Lysenko Affair*. Cambridge, MA: Harvard

an agitprop film in an effort to defend his honor. Titled *Salamandra*, the movie tells

> the story of a Kammerer-like hero (Professor Zange) undone by
> the machinations of a reactionary priest (a stand-in for Mendel?). The priest and an accomplice sneak into Zange's lab and
> inject ink into a salamander one night; the next day, Zange is
> humiliated when someone dunks the specimen into a bath in
> front of other scientists and the ink leaks out, clouding the water. After losing his job, Zange ends up begging for food in the
> streets (accompanied, oddly, by a monkey rescued from an evil
> lab). But just as he decides to off himself, a woman rescues him
> and drags him away to the Soviet paradise.[53]

The zealous Lysenko emphasized only Kammerer's neo-Lamarckian ideas that suited Soviet ideology. As a committed
Lamarckian, Lysenko's supporters began liquidating non-Lamarckian geneticists, including a protégé of Bateson, by either
having them killed or starving them in the Gulag. The more
people that disappeared, the more Soviet biologists had to pay
homage to Lysenko's erroneous ideas until he was finally dismissed in February 1965. One British scientist reported that,
at the time, talking to Lysenko about genetics "was like trying
to explain the differential calculus to a man who did not know
his twelve times table. He was … a biological circle-squarer."[54]
In the end, Lysenkoism largely destroyed Soviet agriculture,
and, as a result, millions of people died in the famines that resulted. Tragically, Soviet officials refused to abandon what they
saw as the spirit of Kammerer.

University Press, p. 72.
53. Kean, 2012, p. 332.
54. Kean, 2012, p. 332.

His Few Remaining Defenders

Their association with the Kremlin eventually doomed both Kammerer's reputation and Lamarckism, though some of Kammerer's defenders continued to plead his case, mostly because they agreed with his worldview. Most notably, and ironically, given his denunciation of communism elsewhere, novelist Arthur Koestler wrote, in 1971, *The Case of the Midwife Toad*, to exonerate Kammerer. Koestler dug up a 1924 paper about the discovery of a wild midwife toad with *nuptial pads*. This find doesn't completely clear Kammerer, but it does indicate that midwife toads may have latent genes for nuptial pads. It is possible that Kammerer's experiments caused a mutation, or an epigenetic mechanism had allowed these genes to be expressed.

Alexander Kohn postulated that Koestler was one of the few who attempted to exonerate Kammerer almost a half-century after he died because "Koestler himself entertained a sort of modern evolutionary theory which clashed with the new-Darwinian view."[55] Koestler clearly supported biological transformation, but not the Darwinian mechanism.[56] Nonetheless, Koestler claimed that Kammerer was only following "in the footsteps of Darwin and Wallace" in attempting to discover the secret of the origin of species.[57] Ironically, neither Darwin, Wallace, nor Kammerer were able to achieve that goal.[58] Thus, Kohn argues, Koestler was sympathetic with Kammerer and attempted to view him in the best light possible. Koestler, in his

---

55. Kohn, 1988. p. 47.
56. Gliboff, Sander. 2005. Paul Kammerer and the Art of Biological Transformation. *Endeavour* 29(4):162–167.
57. Koestler, 1971, p. 90.
58. van Alphen, Jacques J.M., and Jan W. Alphen. 2016. Paul Kammerer and the inheritance of acquired characteristics. *Contributions to Zoology* 854:457-470.

will, gave a great deal of money to establish an endowed chair in parapsychology, now located at the University of Edinburgh, hoping that they would discover the secret of the origin of life by a totally different means than evolution.[59]

Kammerer had a few other defenders besides Koestler. Some historians have built a not unreasonable case for his innocence, at least in the midwife toad episode. One claim is that the nuptial pads actually did appear, but Kammerer, or an overzealous assistant, injected ink to "touch up" the evidence. Others believed that his political opponents actually framed Kammerer. The local National Socialist Party, the precursor of the Nazi Party, supposedly wanted to tarnish Kammerer, who was Jewish, because his theories cast doubt on the inborn genetic superiority of Aryans.[60]

Some scientists noted that Kammerer's experiments changed the thickness of the gelatinous coat that surrounds midwife toad eggs. This jelly is rich in methyls, thus changing their thickness might epigenetically switch genes on or off, including genes normally silenced for nuptial pads.[61] Whenever Kammerer mated toads, he insisted that the father's land/water breeding preference "undisputedly" dominated over the female's preference in the next generations. Such parent-of-origin effects play an important role in soft inheritance. These toad trends echo those from the Swedish Överkalix study researching the physiological effects of various environmental

59. Stein, Gordon. 1993. *Encyclopedia of Hoaxes*. Detroit, MI: Gale Group, pp. 247-248, p. 248.

60. Kean, 2012, p. 331.

61. Vargas, Alexander. 2009. Did Paul Kammerer discover epigenetic inheritance? A modern look at the controversial midwife toad experiments. *Journal of Experimental Zoology--Part B: Molecular Developmental and Evolution* 312(7):667–678.

factors on transgenerational epigenetic inheritance.

The Överkalix study, which was conducted utilizing historical records, including harvest levels and food prices, found many sex-specific effects, such as greater body mass index at age nine years in sons, but not daughters, whose fathers began smoking early.[62] A. O. Vargas of Santiago, Chile, reinterpreted the midwife toad case in view of modern epigenetics and paternal imprinting. Based on his analysis of "parent-of-origin" data buried in Kammerer's toad papers, Vargas even argued that Kammerer was the actual discoverer of epigenetic inheritance, a claim aggressively refuted by others.[63] Even if Kammerer did stumble onto epigenetics, he had no understanding of this property and cannot be credited with its discovery.[64] Nonetheless, Kammerer grappled with many issues that geneticists still struggle with today, such as how the environment and genes interact.[65]

Summary

Unfortunately, far too many well-supported examples exist that convict Kammerer even if, as some argue, someone else painted the marks on the midwife toads with ink. Professor Gerald Weissmann concluded from his study of the case that "I'm persuaded that Kammerer's short, frantic career was based on error and—his word in the suicide note— deception. Indeed, error and deception pop up in his science, his personal life, and his public statements" over and over.[66] The case tells us

---

62. Kean, 2012, p. 333.
63. Vargas, 2009; Pennisi, Elizabeth. 2009. The case of the midwife toad: Fraud or epigenetics? *Science* 325(5945):1194–1195, September 4.
64. Gliboff, 2009.
65. Kean, 2012, p. 334.
66. Weissmann, 2010, p. 2592.

much about the myth of scientists as "hard-working men and women dedicated to the pursuit of truth by objective research, no matter where it leads." It also says a lot about the turmoil that Darwin's ideas created in science that are still very much with us today.

An article in a Dutch Journal by Martijn van Calmthout Exposing Kramer

HOW TO READ YOUR RESULTS

BLOOD TYPE	ANTI-A	ANTI-B	ANTI-D	CONTROL
O-POSITIVE	●	●	(reaction)	●
O-NEGATIVE	●	●	●	●
A-POSITIVE	(reaction)	●	(reaction)	●
A-NEGATIVE	(reaction)	●	●	●
B-POSITIVE	●	(reaction)	(reaction)	●
B-NEGATIVE	●	(reaction)	●	●
AB-POSITIVE	(reaction)	(reaction)	(reaction)	●
AB-NEGATIVE	(reaction)	(reaction)	●	●
INVALID	(reaction)	(reaction)	(reaction)	(reaction)

A Wikimedia Commons example of how Blood types are
Determined. No change is indicated by the sold red color.
Precipitation, indicating a reaction, is shown by the many small red
spots inside the circle. This the first set of 4 reveal O+ blood.

From: https://commons.wikimedia.org/wiki/File:1912_Cross_
Matching_Blood_Types.jpg

8

A Blood Test Used to Prove Evolution Refuted

THE RISE AND FALL of the once-major evidential proof of evolution, the blood precipitin test, is one more example of belief triumphing over fact. Although creationists successfully argued against the theory as early as 1925, it was exploited in the textbooks as a major proof of evolution as late as 2014.[1] As documented by various recent articles and books, this is one more example of the many once-common "evidences" for Darwinism that have now been discarded due to advancing scientific knowledge.[2]

Because blood is critical for life, and blood traits vary among different life-forms, the differences that enable making blood comparisons were once used as an important 'proof' of

---

1. Zain, C.C. 2014. *Natural Alchemy: Evolution of Life*. Los Angeles, CA: light.org, pp. 134–135.
2. Guliuzza, Randy 2017. *Twenty Evolutionary Blunders*. Dallas, TX: Institute for Creation Research (ICR); Bergman, J. 2017. *Evolution's Blunders, Frauds and Forgeries*. Atlanta, GA: Creation Book Publishers.

evolutionary relationships.[3] Evolutionists had claimed for decades that blood similarity was strong evidence that certain animals evolved from other animals, or that two animals had a common ancestor. Or that one race was superior to another race.[4] Specifically, leading German scientists concluded that "type B blood was a marker of both racial and eugenic inferiority."[5] The racist ideas that blood was a major marker of racial inferiority were published by major, respected German medical publishing houses.[6]

One common test used to measure blood homology was the precipitin test, also called the serological test. A precipitate is formed when a chemical reaction occurs and a new compound precipitates out of solution. This reaction produces a solid that can easily be seen in the solution either above or below the clear or colored liquid called the *supernatant*.

How the Test Functions

The test uses comparisons of blood serum and other bodily fluids to determine what evolutionists assumed was the evolutionary "closeness" of the life-forms tested. Cambridge University professor George H. F. Nuttall first developed a human blood test that formed the basis for the tests now used in several different disciplines, including criminal investigation.[7]

If an antibody binds to an antigen on a blood cell, a pre-

3. Brown, A. 1947. *Evolution and the Blood-Precipitation Test*. Glendale, CA: Glendale News.
4. Boaz, Rachel. 2012. *In Search of "Aryan Blood"*. Budapest: Central European University Press. pp. 58-59.
5. Boaz, Rachel. 2012. pp. 60-61.
6. Boaz, Rachel. 2012. pp. 102-103.
7. Nuttall, George. 1904. *Blood Immunity and Blood Relationships*. Cambridge, MA: Cambridge University Press.

cipitate forms. If the antibody binds poorly or not at all, no precipitate will form. To determine specifically how close an animal is to humans, the test evaluates the *amount* of precipitate produced in animal blood when adding blood antibodies that were produced to react to human blood.[8]

The theory was based on the belief that the *closer* the evolutionary relationship of the animal tested to humans, the *greater* the level of precipitate was formed.[9] No precipitate forms when human blood antibodies are mixed with reptile blood. A slight precipitate forms when blood antibodies are mixed with bird blood or other animals judged by evolutionists to be evolutionarily closer to humans than reptiles, but still 'low' on the theoretical evolutionary scale.

When antibodies designed to react to human blood are added to the blood of creatures that are purportedly evolutionarily *closest* to humans, such as gorillas and chimpanzees, a significantly *larger* amount of precipitate forms. Furthermore, evolution theory would predict more precipitate with chimpanzee than baboon blood. If this occurs, the test supports the evolutionary theory that places humans evolutionarily closer to chimpanzees than to baboons.[10]

As described in one popular biology textbook, the blood homology test produced one of the most important evidences of evolutionary relationships due to the fact that the more closely related "one animal is to another, the more nearly alike

8. Davidheiser, B. 1969. *Evolution and the Christian Faith*. Nutley, NJ: Presbyterian and Reformed Publishing, pp. 272–279.
9. Kenoyer, L., H. Goddard, and D. Miller. 1953. *General Biology*, 3rd Edition. New York, NY: Harper, p. 516.
10. Moody, P.A. 1970. "Evolution as Seen in Serological Tests." In: *Introduction to Evolution*, 3rd Edition. New York, NY: Harper, p. 106.

will be their blood proteins."[11] The test was even used to help determine the evolutionary closeness of animals that could not be determined by other methods.[12]

How the Test Works

When blood from an animal is injected into a different kind of animal, the white blood cells respond by producing specific proteins called *antibodies*. *Antigens* are proteins located on many cell structures, including blood cells, which are used by the immune system as identification marks to separate self-cells from foreign cells. The test uses antibodies designed to react with human blood which then combine with the human antigens. This causes a clumping or separation from the liquid plasma, called an *agglutination,* to form. This agglutination is usually visible to the naked eye.[13]

If the antibody that combines with human blood is placed into a container containing rabbit blood, the rabbit blood antigens are close enough to human blood that the antigens and antibodies combine. The reaction causes the blood to precipitate out of the blood plasma solution. The assumption was that, the closer the animal's evolutionary relationship was to humans, the greater the agglutination level that would occur.[14] The greater level of precipitate occurs because significantly more antigens and antibodies combine. And the

more alike the blood of the test animals, the closer the [evolu-

---

11. Frazier, R., and H. Smith. 1974. *The Biological Sciences: Investigating Man's Environment.* River Forest, IL: Laidlaw Brothers, p. 442.

12. Kenoyer et al., 1953, p. 516.

13. Alexander, G. 1956. *General Biology.* New York, NY: Crowell, p. 816.

14. Lindsey, A. 1952. *Principles of Organic Evolution.* St. Louis, MO: Mosby, p. 105.

tionary] relationship. By injecting a series of rabbits with serum from different species, it has been possible to obtain a series of antibodies. Each of the antibodies is specific for the blood proteins of one kind of animal. Many thousands of tests have been performed. The results show that cats, dogs, and bears are more closely related to one another than they are to other mammals. Sheep, deer, antelope, goats, and cows are closely related to one another, but not so closely related to bears, dogs, and cats.[15]

Biologists' Support for the Test

Sir Arthur Keith concluded that the test was "a trustworthy and exact method of determining the affinity [evolutionary closeness] of one species of animal to another."[16] Harvard's Ernest Hooton concluded that homology measured by blood tests alone provided sufficient proof to establish human evolution as an established fact, writing that "if there were no evidences of human evolution other than those provided by zoological classification and blood antibody test[s]," these two methods

> alone would be sufficient to convince every impartial thinker that man and the anthropoid apes have evolved from some common ape-like ancestor … from a knowledge of the morphology and physiology of the anthropoid apes and of the lower primates, Huxley's scientific Saturnians would be driven to postulate the existence of man. For man is logically the next evolutionary step beyond the gorilla and the chimpanzee, or perhaps one should say the next *jump*.[17]

---

15. Frazier and Smith, 1974, pp. 442–443.
16. Keith, A. 1928. *Concerning Man's Origin*. New York, NY: C.P. Putnam's Sons, p. 24.
17. Hooton, Earnest A. 1931. "How Blood Tells." In: *Up from the Ape*. New York, NY: Macmillan Co., pp. 46–47.

The chair of the Biology Department at the University of Colorado, Professor Gordon Alexander, in his biology textbook stated that "the most striking line of physiology evidence for organic evolution is that provided by serology based on the antigen-antibody reaction."[18] Arthur Lindsey, Biology Professor at Denison University, wrote in his popular zoology text that "the method is capable of yielding far more accurate evidences of detailed [evolutionary] relationship[s] than Nuttall secured ... and furnish[ing] more precise evidences of the relationships indicated by other taxonomic procedure."[19]

Professor Lindsey concluded that, in "the field of evolution," the precipitin test has become "an even more convincing evidence of the graded relationship of living things" than almost any other measure.[20] The test to document evolution is also found on biology class outlines such as those at University of Texas, Dallas.[21] Yet another example of the use of this test to prove evolution is Presbyterian minister Floyd Hamilton's comment in an article defending evolution in which he called the precipitin blood test "one of the most recent and widely heralded lines of proof for evolution," which was important in his acceptance of Darwinism.[22]

Doubts About the Test's Accuracy

As more tests were done it was discovered that some findings

---

18. Alexander, 1956, pp. 815–816.
19. Lindsey, 1952, pp. 105–106.
20. Lindsey, 1952, p. 107.
21. Dun, D. 2018. All living things evolved from a common ancestor: Evidence for evolution. Lecture Outline 17. utdallas.edu/~cirillo/nats/day17.htm; accessed 7 November.
22. Hamilton, F. 1926. Modern aspects of the theory of evolution. *Princeton Theological Review* 24(3):396–448, p. 437.

fit the evolution model, but many did not.[23] For example, early use of the precipitation test rated Old World monkeys eight parts away from humans, and New World monkeys 22 parts away. As expected, the human vs. human test found 100% similarity; man vs. chimpanzee found 97%, as expected, but man vs. baboon found only a mere 50%. The chimp fits the evolutionary prediction, but the baboon value should be very close to the chimp, thus closer to humans. Man versus dog found 0%, which was a problem because dogs and humans are both mammals.

As more and more comparisons were completed, the number of findings that did not support evolution theory grew. One example was the discovery that sheep and horses were separated by only three parts. Furthermore, when comparing different kinds of apes to humans, the gorilla test produced *less* precipitate than human blood, and chimpanzee blood produced *more* precipitate than human blood! Consequently, this blood test would indicate that humans are a link *between* gorilla and chimpanzee! Pigs and hyenas were found to be closely related to just about every animal that was tested.[24]

In addition, the test results often depended on which specific example of an animal type was used in the test. One test of five different horses found that one horse was related to only sheep and to other horses, while another horse of the same breed was related to man, cat, hog, seal, pig, sheep, and several other different animals. The next horse tested produced another different pattern.[25] As the exceptions piled up, the test

23. Scott, W.B. 1933. "Evidence from Blood Tests." In: Newman, H.H. *Evolution, Genetics and Eugenics*. Chicago, IL: The University of Chicago Press, p. 73.
24. Davidheiser, 1969, p. 277.
25. Davidheiser, 1969, p. 274.

eventually had to be abandoned, relegating yet another 'proof' for evolution to the growing Darwinian scrap heap.

Nuttall himself obtained enough negative results that he believed some common problem, such as the manner of death of the animal or the method of blood withdrawal, was causing incorrect results in a large number of cases.[26] We now know that these factors do not affect the test results. Only the specific antigen of the blood sampled does. Another complication is that, in humans and in many primates, there exist different blood group types. The most common ones in humans are A, B, AB, and O (Figure 17), plus Rh+ and Rh- (Rhesus) factors. So far, a total of 36 human blood group systems and 346 blood antigens are now recognized by the International Society of Blood Transfusion. The chimpanzee blood group uses the, V-A-B-D and R-C-E-F systems, which are counterparts of the human MNS and Rh-Hr blood group systems. Other mammals use yet other systems.[27] Most all of these are not of major importance in blood compatibility typing.[28]

Reasons for Similarity

A survey of biology textbooks published before 1960 revealed that the blood precipitation test frequently was discussed, often in great detail, but biology and evolution texts published after the 1990s rarely mention this specific, now totally discredited, test for evolutionary closeness. Some references still cover this

26. Davidheiser, 1969, p. 273.
27. Socha, W.W. 1980. Blood groups of apes and monkeys: Current status and practical applications. *Laboratory Animal Science* 30(4):698–702.
28. Storry, J.R., et al. 2016. International society of blood transfusion working party on red cell immunogenetics and terminology: Report of the Seoul and London meetings. *ISBT Science Series* 11(2):118–122.

long-discarded test.[29]

The similarity of blood, or any other body organ or part, does not in itself 'prove' evolution. It proves only that a specific design has been reused by the Creator, often because it works perfectly well, or because no need exists to modify it. An understanding of the many past blunders of evolution serves an important lesson today because it forces asking the question, "how many ideas that are currently accepted by evolutionists today are also false?".[30] The test *does support the creation view* that each different animal kind was created separately. The precipitation test is one more proof of that conclusion.

Revised Form of the Test Used Today

A revised form of the test is still used today for medical reasons.[31] This newer, far more complicated test also has some of the same problems. It goes by the term *immunological* testing, which is the topic of another paper.

Other Blood Claims' Adverse Effects

Even though many Nazi scientists eventually dropped most claims about blood's usefulness to determine racial inferiority, this did not stop some Nazi non-scientists from using blood as evidence for racial inferiority.[32] Blood was a "recurring theme in Julius Streicher's, editor of *Der Stürmer*, writing. He opined about his belief of "Jewish blood being 'animal' in origin, or

---

29. Nelson, B. 2017. *After Its Kind: The First and Last Word on Evolution*, 4th Edition. New York, NY: Miriwal Books, p. 28.

30. *In Search of History* (VHS Contributor). 1996 (and 2000). *Hoax of the Ages: Piltdown Man*.

31. Boyden, A. 1963. Precipitin testing and classification. *Systematic Zoology* 12(1):1–7.

32. Boaz, Rachel. 2012. p. 231.

toxic if transfused into an 'Aryan.'"[33] He included in his publications, which had a wide circulation, numerous "Lurid descriptions of 'blood defilement' and photographs of 'blood defilers.'"[34] American law "defined race by the 'one drop rule' which ruled that anyone with so much as 'one drop of colored or Negro blood' would be classified as belonging to those groups."[35] This rule had major repercussions in discrimination in housing and transportation, and even marriage.

Conclusions

One important lesson from this once-promising scientific "evidence" of evolution, as was true of Piltdown Man, is that in view of the overwhelming evidence against the test, "why did it require several decades to disprove its validity?" This case encourages caution in accepting other now-popular 'evidences' of Darwinism. It is also another example of the tendency to uncritically accept evidence that supports a particular worldview, and reject other evidence that does not. In the end, our worldview should *follow the evidence* and not the other way around, as occurred in the case of the blood precipitin test. This is only one example among many that are well-documented as disproving evolution and racism, two worldviews that often share the same "evidence".

---

33. Boaz, Rachel. 2012. p. 233.
34. Boaz, Rachel. 2012. P. 233.
35. Boaz, Rachel. 2012. P. 235.

Figure 1. Dr. James Manby Gully about 1860. The man behind the "Water Cure." From Wikimedia Commons, in the public domain.

Source: https://en.wikipedia.org/wiki/James_Manby_Gully#/media/File:James_Manby_Gully_1860s.jpg.

9

Darwin's Journey Into Pseudoscience: The Water Cure

D ARWIN'S SERIOUS HEALTH PROBLEMS were well-documented both by himself and others, including Columbia University psychiatrist Ralph Colp. Dr. Colp's career focus was researching Darwin's health, eventually producing two books and eight major peer-reviewed articles on this topic. The cause of Darwin's long-term health problems has been the subject of several books and scores of academic publications. Among the many theories include Darwin's acknowledgment that his goal was to "murder God." Darwin attempted to do this by developing an origins theory that negated the most common reason given for belief in God, the beauty, design, and complexity of the physical world.

To achieve this goal Darwin developed his theory of *natural selection*. Nevertheless, Darwin himself was uncertain about natural selection's ability to account for all of creation, a doubt that his modern followers often do not have.[1] In the end, however, this idea changed the world.[2] A good case has been made by several Darwin scholars for the 'murder hypothesis' causing Darwin guilt, accounting for many of Darwin's psychological problems. These psychological issues, in turn, had a major influence on his many physical maladies. The "cold-water cure" supports this conclusion.

Darwin's Health Problems

Darwin's health problems included various combinations of severe psychological (or psychologically influenced) issues. These included severe depression, fits of hysterical crying, shaking, severe anxiety, insomnia, fainting spells, muscle twitches, trembling, nausea, vomiting, depersonalization, visual hallucinations, malaise, vertigo, cramps, bloating, nocturnal flatulence, headaches, nervous exhaustion, dyspnea (labored breathing), tachycardia (increased heart rate), tinnitus, loss of consciousness sensations, and a sense of impending death.[3] That Darwin suffered from several severely disabling maladies is not debated. The only debate is the exact cause of his many physical symptoms.[4] Although Darwin consulted over 20 doctors, a definitive viable diagnosis was never produced.[5]

1.   Ruse, Michael. 2016. "Evolution is the only reasonable explanation for the diversity of life on Earth" In: 5 things we know to be true. *Scientific American* 315(5):46-53, November, p. 49.

2.   Fuller, Randall. 2017. *The Book That Changed America: How Darwin's Theory of Evolution Ignited a Nation.* New York, NY: Viking Press.

3.   Bergman, Jerry. 2017. *The Dark Side of Charles Darwin.* Third Printing. Green Forest, AR: New Leaf Press.

4.   Katz-Sidlow, Rachel J. 1998. In the Darwin Family tradition: Another look at Charles Darwin's ill health. *Journal of the Royal Society of Medicine* 91(9):484-488, September.

5.   Colp, Ralph. 2008. *Darwin's Illness.* Gainesville, FL: University Press of

As a youth, Darwin was actively involved in hunting and numerous outdoor activities. George Pickering, in an extensive study of Darwin's illness, concluded that Darwin became an "invalid recluse" only after around age 30 when he began developing his evolution theory.[6] Darwin scholar Michael Ruse concluded that Darwin "was an invalid from the age of 30 until he died at the comparatively, for the wealthy class, young age of 73."[7]

Detailed research on Darwin's health by Colp and others has ruled out most of the common medical theories. What remains is a theory that attempts to explain his health problems as psychologically caused, specifically anger turned inward. As Colp explained, Darwin was "unable to openly express his anger" and, as is common, "turned the anger against himself"—a common reason for the depression, anxiety, and other symptoms Darwin faced most of his adult life.[8] Colp added: "he always had difficulty in expressing serious anger."[9]

Two of the main reasons for his anger, in this case against God, were (1) the death of his beloved child, Charles and Emma's first daughter, Anne Elizabeth, and (2) his war against God and Christianity.[10] Anne died of tuberculosis at age 10 and Charles never fully recovered from this loss. He was faithfully at Annie's bedside as she suffered terribly for a week before dy-

---

Florida.

6. Pickering, George. 1974. *Creative Malady*. New York, NY: Oxford University Press, p. 34.
7. Ruse, Michael. 2003. Is Evolution a Secular Religion? *Science* 299(5612):1523-1524, p. 1523.
8. Colp, 2008, p.117.
9. Colp, 2008, p. 39.
10. Keynes, Randal. 2001. *Darwin, His Daughter & Human Evolution*. New York, NY: Riverhead Books, p. 210.

ing on April 23, 1851, just three days after Easter Sunday. The main problem with speculating that Annie's death was the initiating cause of Darwin's psychologically related health issues is that his health problems began over a decade *before* Annie died. However, psychologically related health issues do correspond temporally to when he was developing his ideas of natural selection as a substitute agent for God.

It's Like Committing a Murder

Darwin made it clear that the goal of developing his theory of evolution by natural selection was, in effect, to "murder" God by creating another creator to account for the existence of life.[11] Darwin knew that the main reason people believed in God in his day, and in ours as well, was the evidence of creation all around us.[12] Darwin realized that if he could come up with another theory that explained the origin of the physical creation, the main reason people gave for believing in God would no longer exist.

This would result in many people giving up their belief in God, which history confirms is exactly what happened.[13] Specifically, in a letter dated January 11, 1844, to Joseph Hooker, Darwin wrote that in contrast to his original belief, he now believed "species are not immutable (it's like confessing a murder)."[14] *Scientific American* writer Christoph Marty, in a de-

---

11. Bergman, Jerry. 2022. Was Darwin's end goal to 'murder' God? *Journal of Creation* 36(3):60-63, December.
12. Shermer, Michael. 2000. *How We Believe.* New York, NY: W.H. Freeman, p. xiv.
13. Fuller, J.F.C. 1993. *The Second World War, 1939-45: A Strategical And Tactical History.* New York, NY: Da Capo Press.
14. Burkhardt, F., et al. (editors). 1992. *Darwin Correspondence*, Volume 7. *The Correspondence of Charles Darwin*, Volume 3 (1858-1859), p.2. Cambridge, UK: Cambridge University Press.

tailed discussion titled "Darwin on a Godless Creation: 'It's like confessing to a murder'" explained in detail the background of Darwin's statement about murder.

Before his marriage, Charles Darwin had confessed his doubts about Christianity to his first-cousin wife, Emma Wedgwood. He explained that he wanted to rewrite the history of life. His new story of the origin of all life was that "all living things descended from a common ancestor. And that species were not to be attributed to God's endless creativity, but were the product of a blind, mechanical process that altered them over the course of millions of years."[15] The meaning of Darwin's statement has been the subject of several detailed studies, most agreeing with the interpretation presented here.[16] An analysis by Freud's disciple, Ernst Jones, from a study of Darwin, compared

the reactions of the two men who discovered the relation of Natural Selection to Evolution, which meant displacing God from His position as …. Creator specially concerned with mankind, and removing Him to an infinitely remote distance…. Darwin, the one who stood in such awe of his own father, said it was 'like committing murder' – as, indeed, it was unconsciously…. He paid the penalty in a crippling and lifelong neurosis, and in an astonishing display of modesty, hesitancy, and dubiety concerning his work. The other, A. R. Wallace, compensated for the displacement of the supernatural by bringing it back in another

15. Marty, Christoph. 2009. Darwin on a Godless creation: "It's like confessing to a murder." *Scientific American*, February 12. https://www.scientificamerican.com/article/charles-darwin-confessions/.

16. For a careful review, see Colp, 1986; and also Bergman, 2017, pp. 16, 18, 56, 78, 103, 110, 269.

sphere, by his quite naïve adherence to spiritistic beliefs.[17]

Colp summarized Jones' conclusion, which was that by 'murder' Darwin "meant 'parricide,' the murder of God the Father."[18] One of the world's leading Darwin scholars, Michael Ruse, agreed with Jones, writing that

> Darwin knew his theory was much better than Chamber's ... but it was evolutionary and materialistic nonetheless.... When telling Hooker of his evolutionism, Darwin confessed that it was like admitting to a murder. It was murder ... of Christianity, and Darwin was not keen to be cast in this role. Hence the *Essay* [which became the *Origin of Species* published in 1859] went unpublished.[19]

Colp adds that the word *murder* also related to the discussion of the implications of Darwinism, namely to Darwin's

> moral feelings about his theory of evolution: evolution operates not by the morally tolerable Lamarckian mechanism of "slow willing," but by the morally intolerable mechanism of "murder," the massive murder of all unfit, aptly describes and characterizes the War of Nature.[20]

Colp observed further that Darwin realized "his theory would be viewed with opprobrium [harsh criticism] equivalent

17. Jones, Ernest. 1990. *Free Associations: Memories of a Psychoanalyst.* New Brunswick, NJ: Transaction Publisher, pp. 193-194.
18. Colp, Ralph. 1977. *To Be an Invalid: The Illness of Charles Darwin.* Chicago, IL: The University of Chicago Press, p. 30.
19. Ruse, Michael. 1979. *The Darwinian Revolution.* Chicago, IL: The University of Chicago Press, p. 185.
20. Colp, 1977, pp. 29-30.

to that attached to murder and that he would receive a pun-ishment equal in severity to that given to a murderer." Further-more, for "the murder of God, of Christianity… Darwin must have believed that it was honest, manly, and courageous to con-fess what he really believed and to face his punishment."[21] In the end, Darwin received as punishment a life of illness.

This goal of "murdering God" also created a nearly lifelong conflict with Darwin's conscience which began when he devised his non-theistic naturalistic evolution theory. This conclusion is clear when Darwin said he would "give absolutely nothing for the theory of nat[ural] selection if it required miraculous additions at any one stage of descent."[22] Only a non-theistic explanation would be acceptable to him, one that had no need for God at any stage of evolution. In other words, his theory of evolution demanded atheism.

The Cold-Water Cure

In the 1800s, the cold-water cure was a trendy Victorian-spa treatment for disease. Charles Dickens, Alfred Lord Tennyson, Thomas Carlyle, Florence Nightingale, and other well-known Brits all relied on it to treat disease.[23] The treatment involved the use of enormous amounts of very cold water, both for drinking and for bathing. In short, the goal was to keep pa-tients internally hydrated and externally as moist as possible for

21. Colp, Ralph. 1986. "Confessing a murder": Darwin's first revelations about transmutation. *Isis* 77(1):8-32, March, p. 15.
22. Letter to Charles Lyell, dated October 11, 1859; *Darwin Correspon-dence*, Volume 7, p. 345; Darwin, Francis (editor). 1888. *The Life and Letters of Charles Darwin*. London, UK: John Murray, p. 210; and Cobe, John. 2008. *Back to Darwin: A Richer Account of Evolution*. Grand Rapids, MI: Eerdmans Publishing, p. 275.
23. Price, Robin. 1981. Hydropathy in England, 1840-70. *Medical History* 25(3):269-280.

as long as possible.[24]

The cold-water cure evidently was originated by Vincenz Priessnitz, a farmer considered to be the founder of the modern hydrotherapy movement. Priessnitz got the idea from observing an injured deer return several times to a cold spring to bathe its wounds.[25] When Priessnitz suffered from crushed ribs as a result of an accident, the local doctor wrapped his chest, causing even more pain. Among the cures Priessnitz used in an attempt to relieve the pain was the water cure, which was the only therapy that he felt worked.

Priessnitz believed that the body naturally healed itself, but at times it needed outside help.[26] He concluded that the rapid temperature changes that were part of the water-cure treatment allowed skin pores to open, evacuating toxins from the blood. Priessnitz's own positive experience with the treatment motivated him to begin treating others using the same technique. With experience, he modified his treatment protocol, which did not involve drugs or even herbal medicines. Darwin believed that the extreme conditions caused by major water temperature variations improved the balance of the so-called body "humors" which, in turn, facilitated healing.

Priessnitz also required his patients to add strenuous exercise to their daily regimen, and sometimes required his patients to fast. Aside from bland food, the only drink allowed was a minimum of twelve glasses and as many as thirty large glasses of water a day. According to his biographer, Richard Lee Metcalfe, the publicity from several lawsuits against Priessnitz

---

24. Priessnitz, Vincenz. 1842. *The Cold Water Cure: Its Principles, Theory, and Practice*. London, UK: William Strange, pp. 20-30.

25. Kang, Lydia, and Nate Pedersen. 2017. "Hydropathy & the Cold-Water Cure." In: *Quackery*. New York, NY: Workman Publishing, p. 174.

26. Kang and Pedersen, 2017.

for medical malpractice failed to shut down his spa treatment center.[27] Actually, the publicity from the lawsuits encouraged others to attempt his treatment protocol.

In the end, his treatment system made Priessnitz a famous and wealthy man, which helped his program spread to other parts of the world.[28] Priessnitz personally relied totally on his cold-water cure when he became sick or needed medical attention, and refused to see a physician for the rest of his life. He died at the young age of 52.

Darwin Fully Committed to the "Water Cure"

In March of 1849, after every other medical treatment offered by England's leading physicians failed to cure his nearly lifelong incapacitating health problems, Darwin decided to take a chance on the so-called "Water Cure."[29] Darwin first learned about the treatment from friends, then read Dr. Gully's best-selling book *The Water Cure*, before he traveled to Malvern. Ironically, Dr. James Manby Gully was Darwin's former medical school classmate. After considering his options Darwin decided to take his wife, their six children, a governess, and his servants to Malvern to attempt the cold-water treatment based closely on Priessnitz's program.[30]

The "treatment" was administered by Gully, who had not planned to practice medicine. When the family's Jamaican coffee plantation failed because their slaves gained their freedom in 1834, Gully had no choice but to see patients full-time. In

27. Metcalfe, Richard Lee. 1898. *Life of Vincent Priessnitz: Founder of Hydropathy*. Chapter 2: Metcalfe's London Hydro (Richmond Hill, Surrey). London, England: Simpkin, Marshall, Hamilton, Kent & Co.
28. Kang and Pedersen, 2017, p. 175.
29. Colp, 1977, p. 39.
30. Colp, 2008, p. 45.

the 1840s, he opened a resort in Malvern, Western England, based closely on Priessnitz's technique.[31] The specific treatment used on Darwin included frequent, very cold-water baths, drinking copious amounts of water, exercise, and a restricted diet. The details varied, depending on the patient and Gully's experience with the protocol modifications. The recorded details of the treatment Darwin received must rely on Darwin's correspondence and his wife's diaries because, as far as is known, any notes Gully made regarding the treatment used on Darwin have not survived.[32]

Dr. Gully diagnosed Darwin as suffering from a form of indigestion he called "nervous dyspepsia," a common diagnosis for many of the patients Dr. Gully treated. Gully also diagnosed Darwin with "chronic excess and congestion of blood in the nutritive blood vessels . . . of the stomach."[33] This vague diagnosis illustrates how much of the practice of medicine at the time was based on suppositions about physiological mechanisms rather than experimentally derived evidence.

Darwin's treatment in Malvern, a spa town in Worcestershire, England, began as an ordeal for the entire family. After a good night's sleep in a local villa, the Darwin family woke at 5 a.m., the servants wrapped Darwin in wet sheets, then doused

31. Gully, James Manby. 1849. *The Water Cure in Chronic Disease*. New York, NY: Wiley & Putnam; Wilson, James. 1843. *The Water-Cure: Stomach Complaints & Drug Diseases, Their Causes, Consequences and Cure by Water, Air, Exercise and Diet*. London, UK: John Churchill.

32. Ullman, Dana. 2009.The Curious Case of Charles Darwin and Homeopathy. *Evidence-Based Complementary and Alternative Medicine* 7(1):33-39. https://www.ncbi.nlm.nih.gov/pmc/articles/PMC2816387/, See also https://www.huffpost.com/author/dana-ullman and http://ecam.oxfordjournals.org/cgi/reprint/nep168?ijkey=nGCDiG4UTVh6zBx&keytype=ref.

33. Colp, 2008, p. 45.

him with buckets of very cold water. This was followed by a long group hike that included plenty of hydration breaks at various wells and mineral springs along the way. Back at their cottages, breakfast consisted of biscuits and more cold drinking water. The rest of the day consisted of Malvern's main activity, namely bathing in very cold water and drinking enormous amounts of cold water.

Dr. Gully supported a theory that disease is caused by a faulty blood supply to the internal viscera. This condition was treated by hydrotherapy which Gully believed drew blood *away* from the inflamed inner organs and toward the skin, providing relief.[34] Dr. Gully also claimed that he had "successfully treated cases of long-standing dyspepsia with a daily treatment of hydrotherapy . . . [and] the hygienic water treatment seldom, if ever, fails to cure it."[35] Gully also stressed cleanliness, which was not widely practiced in his day. The elimination of infection by improved hygiene may be a confounding reason why some of his patients improved, not the cold-water therapy.

Between cold-water baths, Darwin might have a refreshing cold-water enema, or be strapped into a wet abdominal compress called a "Neptune Girdle." Baths usually lasted until dinner, which often consisted of boiled mutton, fish, and some local cold mineral water. Foods strictly avoided included sugar, butter, spiced tea, and bacon. The long day ended with a very tired Darwin crashing into his very dry bed.[36]

After four months of this hydro-sanitarium, Darwin vomited less at first, then remained vomit-free for months, con-

---

34. Gully, 1849.
35. Colp, 2008, p. 45.
36. Kean, Sam. 2012. *The Violinist's Thumb*. New York, NY: Little, Brown and Company, p. 289.

cluding that "I feel certain that the Water Cure is no quackery."[37] He soon felt so good that he was able to hike seven miles a day without problems. He claimed that he now felt better than at any time since his *Beagle* trip. He previously sometimes had a difficult time walking much more than a city block. In a letter to his cousin, Darwin wrote after he left Malvern that Dr. Gulley "must be making an immense fortune." Darwin also declared that his vomiting and other health problems were "absolutely cured."[38]

When Darwin returned to Down House, he continued the "Water Cure" in a slightly less rigorous form, even constructing a sweat lodge that he used each morning, followed by a polar bear plunge into a 640-gallon cistern he had constructed to hold very cold (40°F) water.[39] Darwin faithfully followed this arduous treatment for months. However, when he returned to his goal of working on his evolution theory, designed to murder God and Christianity, his poor health soon returned, supporting the theory that his goal of murdering God was an important factor in causing his illness.

It may also be that the four-month vacation while living in a very different environment at the spa had a beneficial effect on Darwin, as vacations often do. Bathing in frigid water and the other aspects of the Water Cure could have diverted his mind from concerns about his evolution theory. This is how transcutaneous electrical nerve stimulation (TENS) is theorized to work, namely by diverting one's mental focus to the sharp pain produced by the machine's electricity away from

---

37. Letter to Hooker, dated March 28, 1949; *Correspondence*, Volume 4, p. 227.
38. Letter to William Darwin Fox, dated July 7, 1849; *Correspondence*, Volume 4, p. 246.
39. Kean, 2012, p. 289.

the dull pain produced by the back nerves.[40] The fact that his major health problems plagued him for most of the rest of his life also supports the importance of his work on evolution as a major factor in causing his health problems.

The beneficial results of the treatment, which has no experimental connection to gastrointestinal physiology, indicate that Darwin's close-to-lifelong debilitating health problems were mostly psychological. When his ten-year-old daughter, Anne, became ill, she was also taken to Malvern for the water treatment. Unfortunately, it did not cure her, ending in her death from tuberculosis caused by the bacteria *Mycobacterium tuberculosis*.[41]

The down side of the treatment includes the possibility that the claims for cold-water therapy successfully treating injury and illness discouraged many persons from seeking *proper medical treatment*. Drinking plenty of water, especially in hot climates, frequently exercising, and daily bathing are all well-known practices contributing to better health. Conversely, as a cure-all and to eschew proper medical treatment, as Priessnitz and many of his followers advocated, can be lethal if taken to an extreme.[42] All of Darwin's previous symptoms returned after he became disillusioned with Dr. Gully's treatment, including his stomach problems, dizziness, vomiting, and fainting. Further reasons that Darwin rejected Gully's treatment later included Dr. Gully's acceptance of clairvoyance and other ideas that Darwin disagreed with.

Darwin later tried electrical shock therapy, various herbs,

---

40. Johnson, M., and M. Martinson. 2007. Efficacy of electrical nerve stimulation for chronic musculoskeletal pain: A meta-analysis of randomized controlled trials. *Pain* 130 (1–2):157–165, p. 183.

41. Colp, 2008, pp. 51-52; Keynes, 2001, p. 219.

42. Johnson and Martinson, 2007. .

phrenology, and other treatments, with little improvement. Both Darwin and those who studied his health problems noted that his illness was strongly correlated with certain stressful events in his life which likely aggravated the major source of his stress, his guilt over murdering God.[43]

We know that most of these stressful events were short-lived, unlike the underlying stress caused by guilt. If he avoided the underlying stress caused by guilt, he was able to prevent significantly increasing his stress above its usual level. It can be seen that his open goal of murdering God was a significant catalyst in causing his health problems, no doubt due to his internal conflicts and guilt.

His guilt is illustrated by his mixed feelings towards the Church, exacerbated by the fact that his wife was an active, devout Christian. Darwin was very generous financially with the local church of England where his wife and children attended, although most or all of his children became atheists or agnostics later in life, and several were actively involved in the eugenics movement.[44]

One reason for his support of the church was that Darwin learned about its effectiveness in civilizing the Tierra Del Fuego natives. He initially called the Tierra Del Fuego persons that he encountered during his five-year voyage on the *HMS Beagle* the lowest human race, a link between the apes and man. He added that there was zero possibility this race could be civilized. Dar-

---

43. Barloon, Thomas, and Russel Noyes, Jr. 1997. Charles Darwin and Panic Disorder. *JAMA* (*Journal of the American Medical Association*) 277(2):138-141, p. 138; Desmond, Adrian, and James Moore. 1991. *Darwin: The Life of a Tormented Evolutionist.* New York, NY: Warner Books, Inc., p. 456.

44. Blaney, Tom. 2011. *Eugenics and the Darwins.* London, UK: Matador Publishing.

win later learned that a trusted missionary friend of his, who also was a part of the *Beagle* voyage, had considerable success in converting many of the natives to become civilized Christians. This and other similar experiences influenced him so greatly that, until the end of his life, Darwin regularly supported this specific mission.

Conclusions

Darwin's wife, Emma, was very perceptive, diagnosing her husband's health problems as "always affected by his mind."[45] Professor Hopper opined that Darwin's establishing the idea that evolution, not God, was the creator, changed the world by negating the reason most people believe in God. Destroying the main evidence for God as the creator was, in Darwin's words, like confessing to a murder, namely the murder of God. This, of course, produced enormous internal conflicts in Darwin's mind that resulted in a major toll on his health until he died. Diagnosed today as suffering from the symptoms of congestive heart failure, he died at age 73, a comparatively young age for a British upper-class male.[46]

No evidence exists that his heart caused his lifelong stress, but his health problems likely contributed to his heart failure. Darwin enjoyed very good health until the time he began working on his theory of the origins of life in his 30s, and then was largely an invalid thereafter, except when his mind was diverted while indulging in the cold-water cure.

45. Colp, 2008, p. 51.
46. Hopper, Rowan. 2009. "Charles Darwin: Writing *Origin* 'like confessing a murder'." *New Scientist* 2736(204):29, November 28, p. 29.

Figure 2. Darwin's favorite child, Anne, who died at age ten from tuberculosis. The Water Cured failed to save her life.

From Wikimedia Commons, in the public domain. https://en.wikipedia.org/wiki/Anne_Darwin#/media/File:Annie_Darwin.jpg

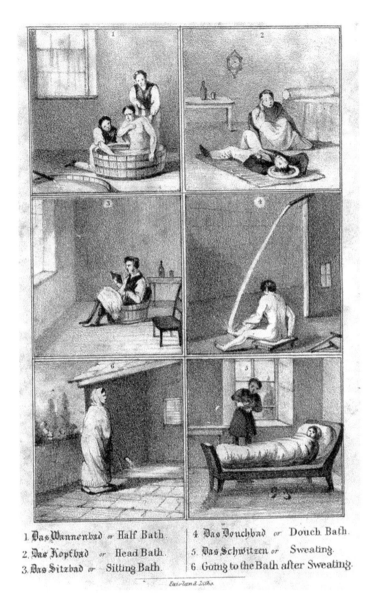

1. Das Wannenbad or Half Bath.
2. Das Kopfbad or Head Bath.
3. Das Sitzbad or Sitting Bath.
4. Das Douchbad or Douch Bath.
5. Das Schwitzen or Sweating.
6. Going to the Bath after Sweating.

East-land Litho.

Figure 3. The Water Cure Treatment described in German and English. Source: https://wellcomecollection.org/works/d67mgt7h/items

From Wikimedia Commons. Source: The Welcome Collection The use permission is here: https://wellcomecollection.org/works/d67mgt7h?page=7&query=%22illustration%22#licenseInformation

Figure 4. Charles Darwin shortly before he died at the age of
73. The picture was taken in 1881; he died on April 19, 1882.
He looked much older than 73. As he was a wealthy upper class
gentleman dying at age 73 as somewhat young. From Wikimedia
Commons, in the public domain.

Source: https://commons.wikimedia.org/wiki/File:Charles_
Darwin_photograph_by_Herbert_Rose_Barraud,_1881_2.jpg.

A Doctor with the Experimental subjects in the Tuskegee Syphilis
Study, From Wikimedia commons,
https://commons.wikimedia.org/wiki/File:Tuskegee_study.jpg

10

Darwinian Medical Experiments on American Blacks

M EDICAL EXPERIMENTATION on Black Americans has occurred from colonial times to the present.[1] Many examples in American history exist of "conscripting Darwin in the service of racism."[2] One of the most infamous examples of Darwinian racism was the Tuskegee Syphilis Study completed in Macon County, Alabama. It began in 1932 and ended only in 1972. The 40-year-long Syphilis Study is one of many examples of the negative fruits of Darwinian racism.[3] The study compared the progression of syphilis in poor, uneducated Black males with a control group of non-syphilitic White subjects. Although an effective treatment for syphilis was avail-

---

1. Washington, Harriet. 2006. *Medical Apartheid: The Dark History of Medical Experimentation on Black Americans from Colonial Times to the Present.* New York, NY: Doubleday.

2. Washington, 2006, p. 76.

3. Bergman, Jerry. 2020. *Darwinian Eugenics and The Holocaust: American Industrial Involvement.* Ontario, Canada: Involgo Press.

able in the 1940s, it was withheld for the purpose of the study.

Syphilis disease progression was well-known in the 1940s, and, as expected, many in the experimental group suffered from progressive paralysis. Many also suffered from deafness, blindness, memory loss, impaired judgment, confusion, delusions, seizures, depression, delirium, mania, and psychosis from brain and central nervous system deterioration caused by syphilis. The study, completed by the U. S. Public Health Service and the Centers for Disease Control (CDC), has, for valid reasons, been compared to the Nazi medical experiments that occurred during World War II.

Using Blacks for the research was based on Darwinian evolutionary beliefs. Darwin was inspired by his cousin, Francis Galton to develop the science of eugenics, of which "Racism was at the center of its founders' thinking. He [Galton] considered Blacks to be at the bottom of the human ladder and argued that they had 'failed to sustain the burden of any respectable form of civilization.'"[4] As Jews and Blacks were useful subjects for medical experimentation in Nazi Germany, likewise Blacks were good for medical research on disease in the United States and consequently were the logical choice for the study.[5]

History of the Study

The ostensible goal of the study was to observe the natural history of untreated syphilis in Black males. All of the African-American men in the study were diagnosed with syphilis and were misled to believe they were receiving free health care courtesy of the federal government.

---

4. Lusane, Clarence. 2003. *Hitler's Black Victims*. New York, NY: Routledge, p 130.
5. Lusane, 2003, p 130.

The investigators first obtained a sample of 600 impover-ished, uneducated African-American sharecroppers from Ma-con County, Alabama. The investigators determined by medi-cal examination those Black males that had syphilis. From this sample a total of 399 men, 25 years of age or older diagnosed with syphilis were selected. In addition, a control group of 201 men who were not infected was selected.[6] Most of the men did not know that they had syphilis because the signs and symp-toms of primary and secondary syphilis are often mild, and thus not noticed or, more often, are ignored.

During the *latent* stage, which lasts from a few weeks to over 30 years, few signs or symptoms of syphilis are normally evident. During this time, the disease parasites bore into the bone marrow, lymph glands, the brain and central nervous sys-tem, and the other vital organs.[7]

The result of *late-term syphilis* includes a deterioration of the brain and central nervous system, causing progressive paralysis, insanity, and often deafness and blindness. Syphilis is one of the most horrible diseases known to humanity, and to ignore even palliative treatment as the study did is grossly inhumane. This fact was well-known by the medical community when the study began in 1932. Yet, when asked about the ethics of doing the experiment, the former director, Dr. John Heller, claimed in 1972 that "There was nothing in the experiment that was unethical or unscientific."[8]

The research goal was to learn about the medical differenc-es between Black and non-Black syphilitic males. The research

6. Jones, James. 1993. *Bad Blood: The Tuskegee Syphilis Experiment.* New York, NY: Free Press, p. 1.
7. Jones, 1993, p. 3.
8. Jones, 1993, p. 8

model used was a Norwegian study, (1891-to-1910), which examined the records of nearly 2,000 untreated syphilitic White male patients at an Oslo, Norway clinic. The follow-up was published in 1929.[9] One major difference between the Norway study and the later Tuskegee study was that fully effective syphilis treatment was available by the 1940s, namely penicillin. The Norwegian study produced a large amount of data on the devastating results of the effects of end-stage syphilis. The American study focused on syphilis progression in an "inferior race," namely Blacks.[10]

The main incentive for participation in the study was the promise of free medical care and burial costs. The subjects were never informed of their diagnosis, but were told only that they had "bad blood." They also were led to believe that the program would last six months, but ended up lasting 40 years. It was finally ended only when the study's methodology and goal was exposed by the media.

As noted, none of the infected men were treated with penicillin even though it was widely available in the 1940s and was by then the standard treatment for this disease.[11] Before penicillin, Salvarsan (dioxy-diamino-arsenobenzol) was widely used to treat the disease. Scores of visits and numerous blood and other medical tests were completed on the experimental subjects. The reason for the frequent testing was because syphilis is

9. Jones, 1993, p. 10.

10. Haller, John. 1971. *Outcasts From Evolution*. Urbana, Illinois: University of Illinois Press, pp. 40-68.

11. Duff-Brown, Beth. 2017. The shameful legacy of Tuskegee syphilis study still impacts African-American men today. *Stanford Health Policy*, January 6. https://healthpolicy.fsi.stanford.edu/news/researchers-and-students-run-pilot-project-oakland-test-whether-tuskegee-syphilis-trial-last.

a systemic disease that requires many tests to properly evaluate.

When a research participant died, an autopsy was completed to better understand the long-term effects of syphilis in Blacks compared to non-Blacks. As expected, the results showed much higher rates of morbidity and mortality among syphilitics compared to controls.[12] Ironically, during slavery the "slaves received the same treatment as their masters… the economic value of slaves made their health a matter of solicitous concern."[13]

In the end, the Tuskegee Study was one of the worst abuses of Darwinian 'science' in America.[14] Darwinian racism was openly a central part of the motivation to complete the study.[15] The scientists involved in the study "discounted socioeconomic explanations of the state of Black health, arguing that better medical care could not alter the evolutionary" inferiority of the Black population.[16] Based on Darwinism, it was widely held for much of the last century that Blacks were evolutionarily inferior because they were less-evolved than Whites. Consequently, improving the diet or social conditions for the Blacks would be a waste of time and money. The Tuskegee Syphilis Study was an attempt to document this racist belief which was widely held by clinicians at the time and was a focus of their medical education.[17]

12. Jones, 1993, p. 2.

13. Jones, 1993, p. 19.

14. Gray, Fred. 2002. *The Tuskegee Syphilis Study: An Insiders' Account of the Shocking Medical Experiment Conducted by Government Doctors Against African American Men.* Montgomery, AL: NewSouth Books.

15. Frederickson, George. 1971. *The Black Image in the White Mind.* New York, NY: Harper and Row, pp. 228-255.

16. Brandt, Allan. 1978. Racism and research: The case of the Tuskegee Syphilis Study. *The Hastings Center Report* 8(6):21-29, p. 293.

17. Lombardo, Paul, and Gregory Door. 2006. Eugenics, medical educa-

Medical Consensus of Black Inferiority

One of the earliest professional organizations to study Blacks in America was the medical profession. In the late 19th- and early 20th-centuries, with some notable exceptions, the medical profession supported Darwinian conclusions which were amplified by many leading biologists, anthropologists, and ethnologists. For this reason their conclusions

> are a necessary adjunct to any analysis of American concepts of race and attitudes of racial inferiority. Racial attitudes, clothed in the authority of medical science, helped to suggest, justify, and dictate biological as well as social categories; indeed, medical science helped to explain and defend the prevailing social structure of early nineteenth-century America.[18]

Evidence of bias was obvious in the physician reports on the health effects of the post-Civil War emancipation of Blacks. They almost universally concluded that "freedom had caused the mental, moral, and physical deterioration of the black population. They substantiated this argument by citing examples in the comparative anatomy of the black and white races."[19] Moreover,

> The social Darwinism of the post-Civil War period enabled traditionalists to reiterate their prejudices with the finality of scientific truth. Little changed in the controversy over female physicians besides the language of the debate. Scientific ratio-

---

tion, and the public health service: Another perspective on the Tuskegee Syphilis Experiment. *Bulletin of the History of Medicine* 80(2):291-316.

18. Haller, 1972, p. 238.
19. Brandt, 1997, p. 392.

nalism predominated by the 1880s, with evolution and eugenics mustered in defense of both sides.[20]

Furthermore, research on the history of "the infamous Syphilis Study" concluded that the college and university academic involvement in the study was very important. Many of the leaders of the U. S. Public Health Service that were involved in the Tuskegee Study

> went to medical school at a time when eugenic understandings of race were central to their education. Eugenics theory was used to explain hereditary differences in intelligence and disease, especially by race, and called for both increased breeding of the more intelligent and state sponsored sterilization of the 'unfit' ... eugenicists believed in a hierarchy of races and that 'bad blood' reflected a racialized 'blood taint—a propensity toward moral and medical degeneracy.'[21]

Reflecting Darwinian ideas, W. T. English concluded that

> A careful inspection reveals the body of the negro a mass of minor defects and imperfections from the crown of the head to the soles of the feet .... Cranial structures, wide nasal apertures, receding chins, projecting jaws, all typed the Negro as the lowest species in the Darwinian hierarchy. Interest in racial differences centered on the sexual nature of blacks. The Negro, doctors ex-

20. Morantz-Sanchez, Regina. 1997. Chapter 13: "The Connecting Link: The Case for the Woman Doctor in 19th-Century America." In: Leavitt, Judith, and Ronald Numbers. 1997. *Sickness and Health in America: Readings in the History of Medicine and Public Health.* Madison, WI: University of Wisconsin Press, p. 218.
21. Reverby, Susan. 2009. *Examining Tuskegee: The Infamous Syphilis Study and Its Legacy.* Chapel Hill, NC: University of North Carolina Press, p. 22.

plained, possessed an excessive sexual desire, which threatened the very foundations of white society.[22]

Professor English estimated the " 'gray matter of the negro brain' to be at least 1,000 years behind that of the White races, [but, in contrast,] his genital organs were overdeveloped."[23] Another doctor, William Lee Howard, even blamed the person's biology for what we now recognize as a socialization problem, namely the distorted view that the

> attacks on the defenseless white women are evidences of racial instincts that are about as amendable to ethical culture as is the inherent odor of the race. ...When education will reduce the size of the negro's penis as well as bring about the sensitiveness of the terminal fibers which exist in the Caucasian, then will it also be able to prevent the African's birthright to sexual madness and excess.[24]

Furthermore, medical studies of the "Negro" were also distorted by the Darwinian "eighteenth century's hierarchical arrangement of the races of man" from the highest, the Caucasians, to the lowest, the Negro or, as some Darwinist proponents argued, the Australian aborigine.[25] As evidence of this, Cartwright concluded that the "size of the Negro brain, ... was

---

22. Brandt, Allan. 1997. Chapter 24: "Racism and Research: The Case of the Tuskegee Syphilis Study." In: Leavitt, Judith, and Ronald Numbers. 1997. *Sickness and Health in America: Readings in the History of Medicine and Public Health.* Madison, WI: University of Wisconsin Press, pp. 392-393.
23. Brandt, 1997, p. 393.
24. Brandt, 1997, p. 392.
25. Haller, John. 1972. The Negro and the Southern physician: A study of medical and racial attitudes, 1880-1860. *Medical History* 16(3):238-253, June 30, p. 238.

about one-ninth less than the white brain, his facial angle was smaller, and the nerves supplying the abdominal and pelvic area were larger than in the white race."[26]

We realize today that these claims were not based on scientific measurements and were grossly incorrect. Nor were they accepted by every doctor at that time. One physician, writing anonymously in the *Charleston Medical Journal and Review*, claimed that the distinctions Cartwright found in the blood, muscle, tendon, lymph, brain, and nerves of Blacks were "the fruit of the imaginative brain of some....aspirant in the race for fame, rather than the actual demonstration of the scalpel.'"[27] Darwin's contribution in motivating the study of inferior races was critical. Harvard professor Allan Brandt writes that a

> review of the prevailing scientific thought regarding race and heredity in the early 20th century is fundamental of an understanding of the Tuskegee Study. By the turn of the century, Darwinism had provided a new rationale for American racism. Essentially primitive peoples, it was argued, could not be assimilated into a complex, white civilization. Scientists speculated that in the struggle for survival the Negro in America was doomed. Particularly prone to disease, vice, and crime, black Americans could not be helped by education or philanthropy. Social Darwinists analyzed census data to predict the virtual extinction of the Negro in the 20th century, for they believed the Negro race in America was in the throes of a degenerative evolutionary process.[28]

Racism by Physicians

Racist views were widely held by many trained physicians. As

26. Haller. 1972, p. 248.
27. Haller. 1972, p. 251.
28. Brant, 1997, p. 392.

Jones observed, Dr. Oliver Wendell Holmes opined that medicine

> is sensitive to outside influences, political, religion… Few examples illustrate this better than the influence racial attitudes have exerted on the perception and response of white physicians to disease in blacks. Nineteenth-century physicians had ample opportunities to inject racial prejudice into daily practice.[29]

Although much disagreement existed in medicine about many subjects, a "rare point of agreement … was that the health of Blacks had to be considered separately from the health of whites."[30] In short "scientists had long claimed that the venereal disease manifested differently in blacks than in whites."[31] The goal of the study was to research exactly how different they were.

Tuskegee Study Well-Known in the Medical Field

The Tuskegee Experiment was well-known among doctors, as illustrated by the fact that the Study's progress was regularly reported in medical journals and openly discussed in conferences at professional meetings. More than a dozen articles appeared in the nation's leading "medical journals describing the study to a combined readership of over a hundred thousand physicians."[32] Relatively few doctors spoke out against the Tuskegee Study, supporting the conclusion that the medical community largely supported the 'inferiority of Blacks' Darwinian belief. Physicians' "letters defending the study appeared in editorial

29. Jones, 1993.
30. Jones, 1993, p. 16.
31. Washington, 2006, p. 157.
32. Jones, 1993, p. 7.

pages across the country."[33] The influence of Darwinism was unabashedly open. For example:

> Tidyman drew a large proportion of his ideas from earlier anthropological writings showing that the black races differed fundamentally from the Caucasian in prognathous, bone system, skull dimension, and also internal bodily organs. Their nervous system… exhibited 'less sensibility and irritability than is generally witnessed among whites', a situation which was imperative in understanding subsequent treatment of the blacks. With the understanding that the black races were substantially different than the Caucasian in mental constitution, Tidyman believed that any investigation of diseases among the blacks would show the necessity for treating them quite differently from the Caucasian.[34]

Some doctors even believed that Negroes were a separate species from Caucasians, an idea called polygenism.[35]

Study Results

In the end, it became very clear that the progress of syphilis was no different in Black men than in White men. The last stage, the tertiary stage, is present from 10 to 30 years after the initial infection. This stage results in severe medical problems affecting the nervous system, brain, blood vessels, heart, and other body organs. If left untreated, the mortality rate is from 8% to 58%, depending on the health and nutritional status of the person. Although a much greater death rate existed in the Tuskegee Study participants, few of the men in the study knew

33. Jones, 1993, p. 10.
34. Haller, 1972, p. 244.
35. Haller, 1972, p. 252.

they even had syphilis. If they had known this, many, or most, of the males would have taken precautions to avoid infecting their partners. It will also never be known how many men infected with syphilis gave their sexual partners the disease, which could have in the end killed many of them. Nor was there any evidence that significant areas of the American population are even aware of the details of the study or its implications.[36]

At Last, Outrage!

Once exposed by the mass media, the outrage was so enormous that "not since the Nuremberg trials of Nazi scientists had the American people been confronted with a medical cause celebre" that, quoting a *Philadelphia Inquirer* editor, had "captured so many headlines and sparked so much discussion." For many persons, it was a shocking revelation of scientific abuse that "happened in this country in our time [which] makes the tragedy more poignant."[37] Alabama Senator John Sparkman denounced the medical experiment as "absolutely appalling" and "a disgrace to the American concept of justice and humanity." One observer asked: "how in the name of God can we look others in the eye and say: 'This is a decent country.'"[38]

The involvement of the U. S. Public Health Service in the experiment was reminiscent of the Nazi's experiments carried out under the auspices of German universities by Josef Mengele and other Nazi doctors, most of whom were at least com-

---

36. McCallum, Jan M. et al., 2006. Awareness and knowledge of the U.S. Public Health Service syphilis study at Tuskegee: implications for biomedical research. *Journal of Health Care for the Poor and Underserved.* 17(4):716-33.
37. Jones, 1993, p. 11.
38. Quoted in Jones, 1993, p. 11.

plicit with this evil.[39] In the mid-twentieth century Weimar Republic,

> more than half of all German physicians became early joiners of the Nazi Party, surpassing the party enrollments of all other professions. From early on, the German Medical Society played the most instrumental role in the Nazi medical program, beginning with the marginalization of Jewish physicians, proceeding to coerced "experimentation," euthanization, and sterilization, and culminating in genocide via the medicalization of mass murder of Jews and others caricatured and demonized by Nazi ideology.[40]

Furthermore,

> Physicians were the most over-represented academic profession in the Third Reich. They participated in the Nazi programs of forced sterilization, systematic euthanasia, human experimentation, and mass genocide…. the German medical community [rapidly] became integrated into the Nazi state.[41]

A common observation in reference to the Tuskegee Study was that "Adolf Hitler allowed similar degradation of human dignity in inhumane medical experiments on humans living

39. Bergman, Jerry. 2012. *Hitler and the Nazi Darwinian Worldview: How the Nazi Eugenic Crusade for a Superior Race Caused the Greatest Holocaust in World History.* Kitchener, Ontario, Canada: Joshua Press.

40. Haque, Omar, et al. 2012. Why did so many German doctors join the Nazi Party early? *International Journal of Law Psychiatry* 35(5-6):473-479, September-December, p. 473.

41. Cohen. E. 1998. The Nazification of German physicians, 1918-1937. *Royal College of Physicians and Surgeons of Canada* 31(7):336-340, October, p. 336.

under the Third Reich."[42] Another commentator had difficulty believing that "such stomach-turning callousness could happen outside the wretched quackeries spawned by Nazi Germany."[43] The movement against reliance on Darwinism was slow, but an entirely new national attitude in medicine eventually began to develop: "No longer was the scene dominated by ... Herbert Spencer's version of social Darwinism which made the patient responsible for his own folly when he chose his physician unwisely."[44] Unfortunately, the major influence of Darwinian evolutionary and eugenic beliefs was rarely mentioned in most of the comments condemning the study.

Attempts to Atone for the Study's Inhumanity

The recent concern about racism in science that has brought to light the injustice of the Tuskegee Study, motivated the "Howard Hughes Medical Institute's six-figure donation ... a step towards addressing racial injustice in the sciences."[45] A *Nature* article proclaimed: "Fighting Racism Demands More Than Just Words: Frustrated and exhausted by systemic bias in the science community, Black researchers call on their colleagues and institutions to take action".[46] Furthermore, despite

---

42. Quoted in Jones, 1993, p. 12.

43. Quoted in Jones, 1993, p. 12.

44. Hudson, Robert. 1997. Chapter 12: "Abraham Flexner in Perspective." In: Leavitt, Judith, and Ronald Numbers. 1997. *Sickness and Health in America: Readings in the History of Medicine and Public Health.* Madison, WI: University of Wisconsin Press, p. 205.

45. Witze, Alexandra. 2020. Wealthy funder pays reparations for use of HeLa cells. *Nature* 58:20-21, October 29, pp. 20-21.

46. Wright, Vashan. 2020. FIGHTING RACISM DEMANDS MORE THAN JUST WORDS. Frustrated and exhausted by systemic bias in the science community, Black researchers call on their colleagues and institutions to take action. *Nature* 583:319-322, July 9.

its lack of scientific rigor or reproducibility, this reliance on race as a biological concept persists in fields from genetics to medicine. The consequences of that reliance have ranged from justifications for school and housing segregation, to support for the Atlantic slave trade of the sixteenth to nineteenth centuries, genocidal policies against indigenous communities around the world, and the Holocaust.[47]

Outrage about the Tuskegee Study resulted in a 1974 out-of-court settlement of ten million dollars which was divided into four categories:

1) Living syphilitic group participants each received $37,500.
2) Heirs of deceased syphilitic group participants each received $15,000.
3) Living control group participants each received $16,000.
4) Heirs of deceased control group participants each received $5,000.[48]

The fact is, racism was for decades endemic in science because Darwinism depends on racial and other variations by which natural selection can select to fuel evolutionary progress. Yet scientists claim to oppose racism.[49] The current problem in science, as documented and cited by Comfort, is akin to the following:

47. Nelson, Robin. 2019. Racism in science: The taint that lingers. *Nature* 570:440-441, June 25, pp. 440-441.
48. U.S. Public Health Service. https://www.cdc.gov/tuskegee/faq.htm.
49. Comfort, Nathaniel. 2014. Genetics: Under the skin. Nathaniel Comfort wonders at the enduring trend of misrepresenting race. *Nature* 513:306-307, September 18.

Theodosius Dobzhansky, a brilliant population geneticist, was intellectually invested in the genetic concept of race, yet morally invested in anti-racism. "Dobzhansky's paradox," in Yudell's phrase, was how to save biological race theory without sounding racist. He never did — nor have we.[50]

The man who did the most to help destroy scientific racism in America was German-born Franz Boas (1858-1942). Now regarded as "the Father of American Anthropology," Boas worked tirelessly to disprove eugenic hereditarianism and Darwinian race science by his research in cultural anthropology, specifically

> Boas coined the word culture in its modern sense, and became perhaps the greatest opponent of the biological concept of race. He and his students studied human societies through an entirely cultural definition of human difference. Boas found, for example, that cranial characteristics that had been claimed to be innately racial were the result of differences in nutrition and overall health. ... Boasian anthropology scientifically proved that *race is not genetic.*[51]

Boas' students included Alfred Kroeber, Ruth Benedict, Margaret Mead, and Zora Neale Hurston. Furthermore, anthropologists frequently argued "that the evolutionary view is ethnocentric, deriving from a human disposition to characterize groups other than one's own as inferior."[52]

In the 1930s, the Nazis in Germany, in response to Boas'

---

50. Comfort, 2014, pp. 306-307
51. Comfort, 2014, p. 307; emphasis added.
52. Tax, Sol. 2021. Franz Boas: "German-American anthropologist." https://www.britannica.com/biography/Franz-Boas.

anti-racist writings, burned his books and rescinded his Ph.D. degree.

Summary

The influence of Darwinian racism in the Tuskegee Syphilis Study is a well-documented and powerful example of the harmful effects of the Darwinian worldview. The problem was that "many scientists who were enamored of Charles Darwin's 1859 theory that posited how apes and men sprang from a common ancestor also believed ... that a *continuous* chain of evolution linked apes and men and that the sub-human 'missing link' was still extant. Scientists swarmed Africa in search of candidate subhumans."[53] In contrast to this view, acceptance of the belief that all people alive today are descendants of one couple, Adam and Eve, negates the view that some people groups are inferior to other people groups. The motive behind the Tuskegee Syphilis Study was fallacious. The time and money could have been far better spent to study effective therapeutic interventions and treatments for syphilis. This approach could have improved the health of all males in all people groups. This is the inevitable conclusion of Acts 17:26 which says that God "made of one blood all nations of men for to dwell on all the face of the earth" (KJV). All human beings belong to one race: *the human race.*[54]

---

53. Washington, 2006, p. 92; emphasis in the original.

54. Ham, Ken, and A. Charles Ware. 2019. *One Race, One Blood: The Biblical Answer to Racism (Revised & Updated)*. Green Forest, AR: Master Books.

A Coelacanth

Source: https://commons.wikimedia.org/wiki/File:201704_
Coelacanth.svg

11

Coelacanth: The Rise and Fall of a Once Important Transitional Fossil

E VOLUTIONISTS TAUGHT for close to a century that coelacanths were an important fossil link between marine fish and terrestrial animals that walked on land.[1] Evolutionists believed that coelacanth fossils possessed several specific traits that indicated they were the precursors of four-limbed vertebrates. For example, instead of a rayed fin, they displayed lobed fins. Lobed fins had a round fleshy base that extended from the fish's body (see Figure 1). They resembled short stubby legs with small fins instead of feet.[2] South African ichthyol-

---

1. Meyer, Axel. 1995. Molecular evidence on the origin of tetrapods and the relationships of the coelacanth *Trends in Ecology & Evolution* 10(3):111-116.
2. Walker, Sally. 2002. *Fossil Fish Found Alive: Discovering the Coelacanth*. Minneapolis, MN: Carolrhoda Books, p. 16.

ogist J.L.B. Smith believed that the coelacanth could walk on the ocean floor with their lobed fins, but detailed observation of them in their natural ocean environment found no evidence of this ability.[3]

In view of their "missing link" status, they were dated by evolutionists as having become extinct about 66 million years ago. The date of extinction varied, but the consensus of ichthyologists was that *they were extinct*.[4] Since ichthyologist Louis Agassiz first described the coelacanth group in 1839, paleontologists have "found dozens of different coelacanth species since then, but always in rocks [evolutionarily dated] older than 70 million years. The lack of coelacanth fossils in younger strata led them to conclude that coelacanths had gone extinct a long time ago."[5]

Finding A Live Example

The 1938 discovery of a *live* coelacanth near Madagascar was a major and important example evidence of "living fossils." Its discovery was momentous because these animals were believed to be extinct since the end of the supposed 'Cretaceous Period,' allegedly 66 million years ago.[6] The finding caused a level of shock so great that "the discovery would astound the entire scientific community. It would be like finding a live dinosaur."[7]

---

3. Walker, 2002, p. 42.
4. Walker, 2002, p. 11.
5. Brouwers, Lucas. 2012. Coelacanths are not living fossils. Like the rest of us, they evolve. *Scientific American*, February 6. https://blogs.scientificamerican.com/thoughtomics/coelacanths-evolve-indian-ocean-is-home-to-distinct-populations/?print=true.
6. Turner, Derek D. 2019. In defense of living fossils. *Biology & Philosophy* 34(2), Article 23. https://link.springer.com/article/10.1007%2Fs10539-019-9678-y.
7. Walker, 2002, p, 12.

Furthermore, as soon as the discovery was confirmed "newspaper headlines all over the world proclaimed the astonishing news."[8]

The discovery of living coelacanths also shocked paleontologists because these fish were an evolutionary line that they believed had disappeared from the fossil record in ancient history. Referring to the evolution of tetrapods, the find was enormously important because the fossil "provides a glimpse of the fish that first walked on land."[9] This find was critical for evolution because the "vertebrate land transition is one of the most important steps in our evolutionary history."[10] As observed soon after their discovery, "the strangest thing about the fish was its fins. They looked more like legs or flippers than fins."[11]

When finally examined by experts in the lab, the 1938 find, although mounted by a local taxidermist, was badly deteriorated.[12] Nonetheless, it was confirmed to be a coelacanth and the results of the examination were published in the leading science journal, appropriately titled *Nature*.[13] Dr. J.L.B. Smith then became obsessed with finding another one, but failed in spite of an extensive search that lasted years. One problem he encountered was the war which tore Europe apart for five long years.[14]

---

8. Smith, Jr., Howard E. 1982. *Living Fossils.* New York, NY: Dodd, Mead & Company, p. 73.

9. Amemiya, C., et al. 2013. The African coelacanth genome provides insights into tetrapod evolution. *Nature* 496:311-316, April 17, p. 311.

10. Amemiya, et al., 2013, p. 311.

11. Clymer, Eleanor. 1963. *Search for a Living Fossil: The Story of the Coelacanth.* New York, NY: Holt, Rinehart and Winston, p. 21.

12. Smith, J.L.B. 1939. A living fish of Mesozoic type. *Nature* 143(3620):455-456, March 18, p. 459.

13. Smith, 1939, p. 459.

14. Clymer, 1963, p. 68.

When WWII ended in 1945, Smith came up with a plan in an attempt to find another live coelacanth. He printed and distributed thousands of leaflets in three languages with pictures of the fish, offering 1,000 British pounds for information leading to locating a new specimen.[15] 1,000 British pounds in 1945 was equal to over 60,000 dollars in today's money.

For seven years Smith was without luck until a friend traveled to where he thought they might be found, near the Comoro Islands. Soon one was caught. The problem now was preservation and transport to Smith's lab hundreds of miles away. If it was not properly preserved within a few days, it would rot like the first one had. One door after another was closed until Smith was able to contact French Prime Minister D.F. Malan. However, Malan did not accept evolution, so some people asked, "Why would he want to help a British scientist retrieve a fish that some people called a missing link?"[16]

It turned out that Malan was a creationist who had read, and admired, Professor Smith's book about African fishes! The Prime Minster arranged for a flight to the Comoro Islands. Smith carried with him two gallons of formalin preservative. When on the island he saw the fish and was in tears, thinking that his 14-year search had finally paid off ! His success soon made headlines around the world. Now the evolution of limbs, it was thought, could be proven.[17]

Between 1938 and 1975 alone, 84 specimens were caught and documented. West Indian Ocean coelacanth have been found off the coasts of the Comoros, Kenya, South Africa,

15. Weinberg, Samantha. 2000. *A Fish Caught in Time: The Search for the Coelacanth*. New York, NY: HarperCollins, p. 50.

16. Walker, 2002, p. 23.

17. Nickum, Mary Jo. 2016. *Coelacanth: The Greatest Fish Story Ever Told*. Swampscott, MA: Aquitaine, Ltd..

Tanzania, Mozambique, Madagascar, and iSimangaliso, located along the coast of South Africa's KwaZulu-Natal Province. In spite of Smith's decades of effort, the research on the actual fish concluded that the coelacanth is not a link to tetrapod evolution. A related animal, the lungfishes, which also still exist today, are now considered to be a link.

Unique Coelacanth Traits

Coelacanths are large, plump, lobe-finned fish that can grow to over three meters (ten feet) long and weigh around 90 kilograms (200 pounds).[18] They are estimated to live for as long as 60 years. Its unique traits, that are found in no other animals, make it difficult to speculate from what it could have evolved, or what creature might have evolved from it. For example, most fish have smooth scales; however the coelacanth scales are smooth on the lower half and rough on the upper half.[19] Coelacanths are a "unique combination of bony fishes and of sharks."[20] They have a hollow, bendable notochord, a spiral valve in their intestine, a rectal gland that secretes salts, and are live-bearers like sharks.

Live-bearers hatch their eggs inside of the mother's body where they develop. The offspring are born alive when they are well-developed, which is an advantage because they are better able to defend themselves against predators. Immature young at birth are often defenseless against predators. Conversely, coelacanth's have bones, scales and lateral lines like bony fishes. The scales' steel-blue color is also unique.[21] Their other unique

---

18. Walker, 2002, p. 11.
19. Walker, 2002, p, 15.
20. Bruton, Mike. 2018. *The Amazing Coelacanth.* Cape Town, South Africa: Penguin Random House South Africa, p. 7.
21. Clymer, 1963, p. 16.

features include their ability to lift their upper jaw even though they lack an upper jawbone. Another unique trait is a heart arranged in a straight line and the lowest hemoglobin count of any known fish.[22] Consequently, determining the evolution of coelacanths has baffled Darwinists.

The discoverer of the coelacanth, Louis Agassiz, "like many other scientists of that time, did not believe in Charles Darwin's theory of evolution. Instead, he believed that species were" created by God.[23] For this reason he was not baffled by the coelacanth's evolution, but, as evolution became popular, speculation began about its role as a missing link. Agassiz did postulate that the coelacanth was closely related to placoderm (plated skin) fish, an idea that turned out to be incorrect.

They have eight fins – 2 dorsal, 2 pectoral, 2 pelvic, 1 anal, and 1 caudal. Four are lobed fins resembling stubby legs that stick out from the body.[24] The only other fish with lobed fins is the lungfish. The lobed fins are one reason evolutionists speculated that the coelacanth was on its way to evolving legs. It was even difficult to determine why their lobed-fin design existed, except perhaps to "walk" on the ocean floor! The pectoral fins are supported by bone, which is another reason why the claim was made that they are limb precursors. The posterior fin has an "extra tail called an epicaudal fin found on no other modern fish."[25]

The eyes are very large, while the mouth, even though comparatively small, can open very wide. Actually, they are also the

22. Bruton, 2018, p. 7.

23. Bruton, 2018, p. 27

24. Hublin, Jean-Jacques. 1984. *Hamlyn Encyclopedia of Prehistoric Animals*. London, UK: Hamlyn.

25. Walker, 2002, p. 16.

only living vertebrate with a jointed skull that swings up to greatly increase the mouth gape. To achieve this, the *Latimeria* (modern coelacanth) skull is completely split in half by the "intracranial joint." It allows the animal to rapidly open its mouth with enough force to create suction, pulling its prey in towards its mouth.[26]

Although they are vertebrates, instead of a backbone, coelacanths have a hollow cartilage notochord filled with yellow oil. In fact, the name "coelacanth" means "hollow spine." Their brain is only 1.5 percent of the entire braincase volume, and much of it is dedicated to vision.[27] They have an intestinal, spiral-shaped valve like sharks to allow food to be digested more slowly, and thus more completely.

Their large eyes contain an abnormal number of rods and a tapetum like a cat that reflects light back to the retina. This design provides excellent vision for surviving in their dark undersea world.[28] Its swim bladder, instead of being filled with gas as it is in most other fish, is filled with fat, allowing it to naturally hover effortlessly at a consistent depth underwater.[29] Oil and fat even fill the small spaces in its body, which in most fish are filled with air. They are clearly well-designed for their deep-water environment and not as a land-living terrestrial animal. Its acute hearing is achieved by a basilar papilla, used by all land-dwelling mammals, but no other fish.[30] The coelacanth is the only exception.

---

26. Walker, 2002, p. 34.
27. Thomson, Keith S. 1991. *Living Fossil: The Story of the Coelacanth.* New York, NY: W.W. Norton & Co, pp. 172-173.
28. Thomson, 1991, p. 173.
29. Walker, 2002, p. 32.
30. Fritzsch, B. 1987. Inner ear of the coelacanth fish *Latimeria* has tetrapod affinities. *Nature* 327(6118):153–154, May 14.

Although called a "primitive" fish, it has an "advanced electro-sensitive organ which allows them to find prey in the dark ."[31] The "advanced" mechanism which detects weak electric current is in the rostral organ on their snouts.[32] In short, the coelacanth is very well-designed for its environment contradicting any claims of its being primitive, and is so unique that postulating an evolutionary history for it is not viable.

Attempts to Capture a Live Coelacanth

Comoran island fishermen alone caught 150 between 1952 and 1987. They attempted to save a few of them, even placing them in aquarium-like tanks, but all died within a few hours. So far most attempts to keep them in captivity have failed.[33] They were clearly designed to fill a very specific niche and cannot survive outside of this environment. This is due to their specialized gill and metabolism design which was crafted to thrive in their deep-water environment. These facts all argue against them being the precursor of terrestrial land animals. Many of the same problems exist for all other proposed evolutionary links from fish to land animal, including Tiktaalik, a controversial "missing link" that was claimed to exist in-between water fish and land tetrapods.[34]

The Controversy

Paleontologists hypothesize that the missing link between fish and animals that walked on all four feet was a lobe-finned fish

---

31. Bruton, 2018, p. 26.
32. Bruton, 2018, p. 15
33. Bruton, 2018, pp. 54-55.
34. Walker, Tas. 2010. Is the famous fish-fossil finished? Tiktaalik, the transitional star, faces an evolutionary dead-end. *Creation* 32(3):38-39; Curtis, John. 2020. What's so great about Tiktaalik? *Journal of Creation* 34(1):110-114.

that lived during the Devonian Period, allegedly between 360 and 420 'million years ago.' The two chief candidates were the lungfish and the coelacanth, and "scientists argued for decades over which of these fishes might have given rise to the missing link" between fish and tetrapods.[35] When the live coelacanth was discovered in 1938 some "seized on the dramatic idea that the coelacanth was the missing link" - an idea still held by some today even though "no one had any real evidence to prove this theory". [36] Those who recognized that the coelacanth could not be a link between fish and tetrapods believed that the intermediate was some other, very different, type of lobe-finned fish.

Evolutionary Evidence

No evidence exists of coelacanth evolution. Although dozens of coelacanth fossils have been located, as far as can be determined, those examples found in the fossil record are all *anatomically identical* to living examples.[37] Although believed to have become extinct around 70 million years ago, they were assumed to have lived for millions of years before dinosaurs first roamed the Earth.[38] Thus, judging by detailed external morphology, except for being much smaller in size than the fossil coelacanth genera of *Mawsonia* and *Megalocoelacanthus*, according to the evolutionary time scale, coelacanths have not changed in over 410 million years![39]

Summary

The most significant observation between the extinct and the

---

35. Walker, 2002, p. 13.
36. Walker, 2002, p. 14.
37. Walker, 2002, p. 11.
38. Walker, 2002, p. 5.
39. Walker, 2002, pp. 8-9

extant coelacanths which evolutionists claim are separated by 70 million years is the following admission: "it is difficult to separate the new living fish from some of the old genera which are represented by fossils."[40]   Researching the coelacanth has been long and expensive, but in the end has supported the conclusions of creationists that *the first coelacanth was a fully-formed coelacanth.*[41] Furthermore, decades of research

> have shown that *Latimeria chalumnae* (the African, Indonesian or East Indian Ocean coelacanth) [along with] the (*Latimeria menadoensis*) near the island of Manado Tua, have not radically evolved from the way coelacanths appeared millions of years ago. Its main body structure still closely resembles that of ancient coelacanths. So studying *Latimeria chalumnae* is almost like being able to examine an ancient fossil as if it were alive.[42]

An enormous amount of research has been expended on the coelacanth in an attempt to document its position as a "missing link" between fish and terrestrial land animals. This review has summarized only a tiny fraction of the research that has involved decades, scores of articles, and dozens of scientists from five nations. The reason the lungfish is now favored as an important link between fish and terrestrial animals is because they share many more traits with land dwellers than coelacanths.[43] Actually, the coelacanths appear to be more closely related to a type of frog. Thus, "clearly the missing link question has not yet been resolved."[44]

---

40. Woodward, Arthur Smith. 1940. The surviving crossopterygian fish, *Latimeria. Nature* 146(3689):53-54, July, p. 53.
41. Weinberg, 2000.
42. Walker, 2002, p. 37.
43. Walker, 2002, p. 37.
44. Walker, 2002, p. 37.

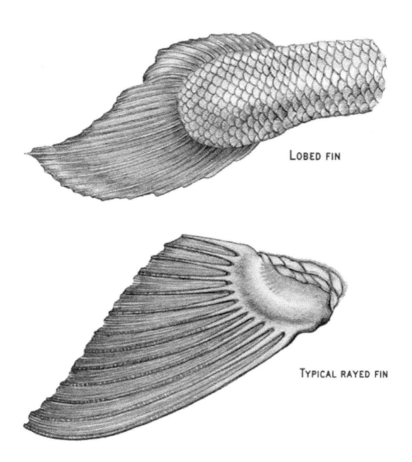

LOBED FIN

TYPICAL RAYED FIN

A lobed fin used by the Coelacanths in contrast to a rayed fin. The lobed fin resembles a leg more than a rayed fin, thus was used by evolutionists to indicate Coelacanths were evolving into tetrapods. From J.L.B. Smith, 1956. *Old Four Legs: The Story of the Coelacanth*. New York, NY: Longmans, Green and Co., p. 60.

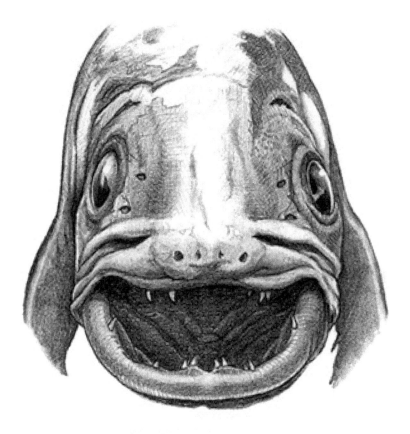

**SIX SMALL OPENINGS IN HEAD;
TWO NOSTRILS IN CENTER OF SNOUT**

The six small openings in the head by the eyes and in the nostrils which still baffle the experts. From J.L.B. Smith, 1956. *Old Four Legs: The Story of the Coelacanth*. New York, NY: Longmans, Green and Co., p. 60.

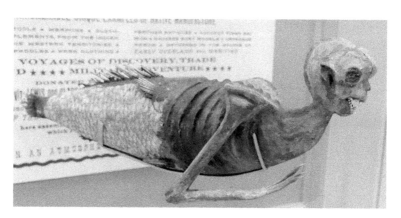

One of many examples of the Fiji Mermaid. From Wikimedia Commons

12

The Fiji Mermaid
Evolution Hoax

THE FIJI (ALSO SPELLED FEEJEE AND FEJEE) mermaid was a putative evolutionary link between fish and terrestrial animals popularized by the circus great P. T. Barnum and others in the 1800s.[1] It is a good example of how non-scientists have reinforced Darwinism in the public's mind by a forgery. A superb money-maker, the Fiji claim was one of many events that "made Barnum the most famous trickster of the nineteenth century."[2] Barnum's almost three-foot-long Fiji mermaid had a contorted face resembling a monkey with sagging breasts and a salmon fish-like body.

One of the first Fiji mermaid exhibits was by Samuel Barrett Eades, who bought it from a Japanese fisherman and exhibited it in London where it was "London's greatest scientific sensation."[3] The mermaid's supporters claimed that the Fiji

1. Saxon, A.H. 1995. *P.T. Barnum: The Legend and the Man*. New York, NY: Columbia University Press, p. 97.
2. Cook, James W. 2001. *The Arts of Deception: Playing with Fraud in the Age of Barnum*. Cambridge, MA: Harvard University Press, p. 120.
3. Bondeson Jan. 1999. *The Feejee Mermaid and other Essays in Natural*

mermaid was caught in Japanese waters, then dried and skillfully prepared by a taxidermist.[4] Several naturalists evaluated the mermaid, and "the majority of them supported Dr. Rees Price" who concluded that it was a real animal.[5]

The Mermaid Obtained by Barnum

The Fiji mermaid's location was unknown from 1825 to 1842. It evidently resurfaced in 1842 and then came into Barnum's possession via Boston Museum curator Moses Kimball. Kimball claimed that he had purchased it from the son of a local sailor who stated that he bought it from another sailor for 6,000 dollars.[6] That sailor claimed that he bought it from yet another sailor whose father bought it in Calcutta in 1817 from a man who said he bought it from a Japanese sailor.[7] This last claimed owner ended the questionable trail of its source.

On June 18, Barnum and Kimball entered into a written agreement to exploit this "curiosity [that was] supposed to be a mermaid." The agreement allowed Kimball to remain the creature's owner and Barnum could lease it for $12.50 a week.[8] Barnum claimed that "the reporters and editors who examined this animal were honestly persuaded that it was what it purported to be—a veritable mermaid."[9]

and *Unnatural History*. Ithaca, NY: Cornell University Press, p. 41.

4. Bondeson, 1999, p. 38.
5. Bondeson, 1999, p. 41.
6. Cook, 2001, p. 81.
7. Barnum, Phineas T. 1927. *Struggles and Triumphs: Or, The Life of P.T. Barnum, Written by Himself.* George S. Bryan (editor). New York, NY: Alfred A. Knopf, p. 200.
8. Kunhardt, Jr., Philip B., Philip B. Kunhardt III, and Peter W. Kunhardt. 1995. *P.T. Barnum: America's Greatest Showman.* New York, NY: Alfred A. Knopf, p. 41.
9. Barnum, 1927, p. 203.

Presumably, to convince readers of the exhibit's authenticity, Barnum wrote a review of the history of the mermaid, concluding that the mermaid could not have been assembled by a taxidermist because the monkey and fish parts blended together so well that an assembly point could not be detected.

Furthermore, the fish spine "proceeded in a straight and apparently unbroken line to the base of the skull—the hair of the animal was found growing several inches down on the shoulders of the fish, and the application of a microscope absolutely revealed what seemed to be minute fish scales lying in myriads amidst the hair."[10] In addition, the

> teeth and formation of the fingers and hands differed materially from those of any monkey or orangutan ever discovered, while the location of the fins was different from those of any species of the fish tribe known to naturalists. The animal was an ugly, dried-up, black-looking, and diminutive specimen, about three feet long. Its mouth was open, its tail turned over, and its arms thrown up, giving it the appearance of having died in great agony.[11]

Barnum's widely advertised "Fiji Mermaid" was greatly aided by the story that it was caught in the faraway exotic land of the Fiji Islands by a "Dr. J. Griffin," who actually was one of Barnum's close associates, Levi Lyman. On the exhibit's first day, thousands of people attended, including some "prominent naturalists."[12] Sellout crowds followed at other exhibits where the mermaid was displayed.

---

10. Barnum, 1927, p. 203.
11. Barnum, 1927, p. 203.
12. Kundardt, 1995, p. 41; Sims, 1997, p. 275.

Success Breeds Imitations

The exhibit was so successful that fake copies soon followed, including one by famed showman Robert Ripley of *Ripley's Believe It or Not!* fame.[13] Some claim that the original exhibit Barnum displayed around the United States was lost in 1865 when Barnum's famous Boston museum burned to the ground. Conversely, scientist and author Jan Bondeson concludes that it was destroyed in the early 1880s in another fire.[14]

The Fiji Mermaid as a Missing Link

Belief in some form of evolution pre-dated Darwin. Even before Charles Darwin announced to the public his evolutionary theory, there existed a evolutionary theory called the "Great Chain of Being". Dr. "Griffin," (aka Levi Lyman), contended in support of this theory that "the mermaid was the missing link between humans and fishes," and that "the flying fish connected the birds and fishes."[15] Lyman "pulled people's legs by the thousands, and ... delivered his harangues about mermaids, sea dogs, and the Great Chain of Being."[16] For finding one of the first Fiji mermaids, an explorer named Dr. Eades expected to be honored "as one of the greatest explorers who had found the missing link between man and fish."[17]

As early as 1846, Barnum was looking for "the Grand Con-

---

13. Bondeson, Jan. 1999. *A Cabinet of Medical Curiosities: A Compendium of the Odd, the Bizarre, and the Unexpected.* New York, NY: W.W. Norton & Co., p. 55.

14. Bondeson, 1999, p. 56.

15. Bondeson, 1999, pp. 51-52.

16. Bondeson, 1999, p. 53.

17. Laslo, Greg. 2013. *The Mythical Mermaid: The Missing Link Between Man and Fish?* http://www.dtmag.com/Stories/Weird%20Stuff/08-07-feature.htm, p. 5.

necting Link between two great families, the Human and Brute Creation," meaning animals, to display in his museum. He did not need to wait for the publication of Charles Darwin's *Origin of Species* in 1859 because the public interest in the evolutionary origins of man had been aroused by the 1844 publication of Robert Chamber's *Vestiges of Creation*.[18]

The Fiji Mermaid originally had no Darwinian association or agenda. "Unlike the Piltdown Man hoax, the Feejee Mermaid didn't come bundled with any persuasive evolutionary claims. But it did mimic the type of scientific specimens that were often mobilized on behalf of evolutionary arguments."[19] Therefore, it eventually became part of a long line of hoaxes exploited to 'prove' evolution.

Other evolutionary intermediates that connected various other animals were proliferating at this time, providing several potential "missing links" that the owners touted as supporting evolution.[20] For example, the proprietor of the London Museum collected many Natural History specimens including

> THE ORNITHORHINCHUS, from New Holland, being the connecting link between the Seal and the Duck. THE FLYING FISH, two distinct species, one from the Gulf Stream, and the other from the West Indies. This animal evidently connects the Bird with the Fish. THE PADDLE-TAIL SNAKE from South America. THE SIREN, or MUD IGUANA, an intermediate

---

18. Betts, John Richards. 1959. P.T. Barnum and the popularization of natural history. *Journal of the History of Ideas* 20(3):353-368, pp. 353-354.

19. Sappol, Michael. 2010. The Feejee mermaid. http://vcande.blogspot.com/2010/04/49-what-were-relationships-between.html, p. 2.

20. Gilliams, E. Leslie. 1922. Side-Show Freaks as Seen by Science. *Illustrated World* 38(3):213-215, October, p. 306.

animal between the Reptile and the Fish. THE PROTEUS SANGUIHUS, a subterraneous animal from a grotto in Australia—with other animals forming connecting links in the great chain of Animated Nature. [21]

These putative "intermediates" were fertile ground to both "prove" and establish specific routes of evolution for various animals prior to Darwin's 1859 *Origin of the Species.*

Why the Excitement?

Hornberger explains that part of the excitement for later Fiji exhibits was due to the fact that this period of history

> was just on the crux of Darwin and his controversial theories of evolution. For that reason, naturalists jumped on the chance to examine the sapien-fish. And while doubt mixed heartily with the findings of these new scientists, the public was still prepared and excited to pay their coin for a chance to gawk at what they wanted to believe was a miracle of nature [and proof of evolution].[22]

Although a main goal of the hoax was to make money by passing it off as a missing link, some persons, both professionals and others, did not accept the mermaid claim.[23] The evolutionary "missing link" claim seemed more plausible during the early debate about evolution theory, and may have allowed the hoax to continue for a few more years.

---

21. Barnum, 1927, p. 207.
22. Hornberger, Francine. 2005. *Carney Folk: The World's Weirdest Sideshow Acts.* New York, NY: Citadel Press, pp. 141-142.
23. Sims, Michael. 1997. *Darwin's Orchestra.* New York, NY: Henry Holt, pp. 275-276.

The Hoax Exposed

Though many people believed Barnum's claim of its authenticity, Barnum admitted in his tell-all autobiography that, although the Fiji mermaid was manufactured, it was an important artifact because it was the work "of some ingenious Japanese, Chinaman, or other eastern genius."[24] One expert anatomist, William Clift, examined the specimen carefully, and concluded that it was a forgery. The negative publicity that resulted from Clift's claims motivated clergyman naturalist Rev. John Bachman to form a committee of scientists, which unanimously declared the Fiji mermaid a fake. This was one of the factors that brought about the end of the last American Fiji tours.[25]

It is now well documented that the Fiji mermaid was a fraud. It consisted of the torso and head of a baby orangutan or monkey very skillfully sewn to the back half of a large salmon fish and stuffed with artificial filler covered in paper-mâché.[26] The two were joined together so well that detecting where they were joined was difficult, thus the fake fooled many people, including some experts, for decades.[27] Bondeson noted that, in view of the lack of

> knowledge in natural history in the early 1800s, it is no surprise that a mermaid like this one could be accepted by medical men and zoologists. If scholars like Dr. Philip and Dr. Rees Price were unable to see through the imposition, it is easy to imagine the mermaid's effect on simple, uneducated individuals: thousands

---

24. Barnum, 1927, p. 203.
25. Bachman, 1999, p. 54.
26. Hornberger, 2005, pp. 142-143.
27. Cook, 2001, p. 81.

of people must have left the exhibition convinced that it was real.[28]

As noted, the motivation for the hoax was primarily money, but exploiting the Darwinism fad and the mermaid myths were important factors in selling the Fiji fraud to the public—and even to a few scientists.[29] Over a dozen of these mermaids have been identified by Bondeson. One of the copies is now in the attic storage room of Harvard University's Peabody Museum of Archaeology and Ethnology. Claims that Fiji mermaid copies still exist surfaced as late as 1994, the year that one was auctioned in Iowa City, Iowa.

As far as could be determined, all of the copies had their origin in Japan or the East Indies, and all were a combination of ape and fish assembled by skilled craftsmen.[30] Evidently, constructing fake mermaids, dragons, and other monstrosities for money or religious ceremonies was a long tradition in Japan.[31] And, as Laslo wrote, the whole mermaid myth "just won't go away, no matter how many times they're debunked as myths and hoaxes" by competent authorities.[32]

The same could be said for the comprehensive molecules-to-man-evolution myth. The history of the Fiji Mermaid illustrates the readiness of both highly educated persons and people in general to accept any theory no matter how outlandish in lieu of the creation account that God created life as revealed in Genesis.

---

28. Bondeson, 1999, p. 63.
29. Saxon, 1995, p. 95.
30. Bondeson, 1999, p. 61.
31. Nickell, Joe. 2005. *Secrets of the Sideshows.* Lexington, KY: University Press of Kentucky.
32. Laslo, 2013, p. 2.

Rolling the Tongue was one of the most common traits that biology teachers used to demonstrate basic genetic principles that can easily be tested. It turns out not to be a one gene one trait as once taught.

Source: https://commons.wikimedia.org/wiki/Category:Rolling_the_tongue#/media/File:Rolled_tongue_flikr.jpg

13

The One Gene-One Trait Myth Exposed

HIGH SCHOOL AND COLLEGE biology students are taught that many basic human traits are due to a simple one-gene control. This is reflected in common statements, such as "twenty thousand years later, another mutation allowed the hair on our heads to (unlike monkey hair or body hair) grow indefinitely long—a haircut gene," a claim that American author Sam Kean made scores of times in his best-selling book on genetics.[1] Many traits long-assumed to be a result of one mutation, or one gene, have turned out to be produced by numerous genes. This trend results in ever-increasing levels of complexity which renders evolution even less plausible than it was before.

The ten most common examples of the "one gene-one trait" myth found in textbooks have been evaluated, and each example has been documented to be controlled by *numerous* genes. University of Delaware Genetics professor John McDonald has

---

1. Kean, Sam. 2012. *The Violinist's Thumb: And Other Lost Tales of Love, War, and Genius, as Written by Our Genetic Code.* New York, NY: Little, Brown and Company, p. 221.

documented 20 examples, (including arm folding, asparagus urine production, beet-urea production, cheek dimples, hair whorls, and toe length), commonly used to teach the one gene-one trait concept in high school and college biology textbooks.[2]

Shape of the Nose

In studying what factors cause a human nose to have distinct traits, researchers analyzed about 6,000 photographs. From this analysis, scientists have so far identified 14 different facial traits. Two genes were linked to nostril shape (GLI3 and PAX1), one (RUNX2) affected the bridge, and the DCHS2 gene was found to influence how far the nose extends outward and the tip angle.[3] No doubt hundreds more gene links exist that determine the human nose traits. McDonald concluded: "It is an embarrassment to the field of biology education that textbooks and lab manuals continue to perpetuate these myths" of one gene-one trait, even today.[4]

The significance of the one-gene myth for evolution can be easily explained by William Paley's classic watch example. A wind-up watch has hundreds of parts, all of which function as part of a unit. If any one part in the movement mechanism is removed, the watch will not properly function, or most likely, will not function at all. The only exception may be the four to six screws that hold the movement mechanism together where, if one is removed, it may still function. However, the loss of snugness in the area where the screw was removed, even if mi-

---

2. McDonald, John. 2011. *Myths of Human Genetics*. Baltimore, MD: Sparky House Publishing.
3. Adhikari, Kaustubh, et al. 2017. A genome-wide association scan implicates DCHS2, RUNX2, GLI3, PAX1 and EDAR in human facial variation. *Nature Communications* 7:11616.
4. McDonald, 2011, p.1.

nor, may cause a slight sloppiness that could eventually cause uneven wear and less accurate time, leading to significant inaccuracies and eventual failure.

Likewise, if most genetic functions are controlled by several genes, a mutation, even if it improves some aspect of the organism, will likely have an adverse effect on some other part of the living system because, like the watch, all of the parts function together as a unit with many, or at least several, other genes and even gene systems.

Furthermore, the concept of what defines a single gene has now been blurred by unexpected complexity, such as the fact that differential splicing of introns can produce many different proteins from one single gene transcript. The classic view of the genome, that genes are distinct segments of DNA transcribed into one RNA and in one direction, has now been overthrown. It is now recognized that multiple and overlapping genes often occupy a single section of DNA that produces several functional mRNAs. An estimated 94 percent of human genes generate more than one product by alternative splicing, producing proteins with dramatically different functions despite being formed from the same gene.

This fact is solace to those disappointed by the small number of genes in the human genome: humans have roughly the same number of genes as *Caenorhabditis elegans*, a mere transparent worm. A homologue of the human gene, Dscam (Downs Syndrome Cell Adhesion Molecule) as expressed in *Drosophila melanogaster* produces 95 alternative spliced exons and 38,000 possible isoforms.[5] In comparison, the entire *Dro-*

---

5. Neves, G., J. Zucker, M. Daly, and A. Chess. 2004. Stochastic yet biased expression of multiple Dscam splice variants by individual cells. *Nature Genetics* 36(3):240–246, February.

sophila melanogaster genome contains only 15,016 genes. This fact allows us a glimpse of the complex interconnectivity of the genome.

The Ten Most Common Examples of the One Gene-One Trait Fallacy

A literature search was completed on the ten most common examples of the one gene-one protein claim selected according to my experience teaching college genetics. The genetics workbook we used was the Pearson Custom Library which, besides the examples discussed below, included the shape of the face, the hair curl, eyebrow size and shape, eyelash length, tongue folding, and others to produce a total of 27 examples.[6] I found evidence that all of the examples selected were controlled by *numerous* genes, not by one single gene, as is often claimed in our genetics and biology textbooks.

Examples of the Refutation of the One-Gene Control System

1. Eye Color. A common example is the genetic control of eye color, actually the color of the iris diaphragm which controls the amount of light allowed to enter the eye. Its function is protection.[7] For example, light-blue eyes cause many problems because the lack of brown pigment on the iris diaphragm does not fully protect the retina against the adverse effects of excessive bright light.[8] Iris color is determined primarily by the

---

6. *Pearson Custom Library*. 2015. Boston, MA: Pearson Learning Solutions, pp. 129-139.

7. Brues, A. M. 1975. Rethinking human pigmentation. *American Journal of Physical Anthropology* 43:387-391.

8. Sturm, R.A., and M. Larsson. 2009. Genetics of human iris colour and patterns. *Pigment Cells and Melanoma Research* 22:544-562.

ratio of eumelanin, which produces a dark-brown color, and pheomelanin, which produces a reddish color. Also important is how melanin is distributed on the iris.[9]

The common iris color categories are blue, green, hazel, and brown. A more detailed analysis has produced at least nine hue and saturation values, which are: (i) light blue; (ii) darker blue; (iii) blue with brown peripupillary ring; (iv) green; (v) green with brown iris ring; (vi) peripheral green central brown; (vii) brown with some peripheral green; (viii) brown; and (ix) dark brown.[10] This more complete categorization obviously requires far more genetic input than the traditional two genes, which is what genetic research has found. Furthermore, eye color can also change, especially during early childhood.[11] The two main genes involved in color variation are the HERC2 and OCA2 genes which are located next to each other on chromosome 15. Furthermore, at least ten other genes and the complicated interactions between them are involved in determining iris color.[12]

2. Earlobe Attachment. A common genetics classroom exercise is to examine each other's earlobe type and determine

9. Lai, L.Y.C., and R.J. Walsh. 1966. Observations on ear lobe types. *Acta Genetica* 16:250-257.
10. Mackey, D.A., C.H. Wilkinson, L.S. Kearns, and A.W. Hewitt. 2011. Classification of iris colour: Review and refinement of a classification schema. *Clinical and Experimental Ophthalmology* 39:462-471.
11. Matheny, A.P., and A.B. Dolan. 1975. Changes in eye colour during early childhood: Sex and genetic differences. *Annuals in Human Biology* 2(2):191-196, April.
12. Sturm and Larsson, 2009; Liu, F., et al. 2010. Digital quantification of human eye color highlights genetic association of three new loci. *PLOS Genetics* 6:e1000934; Pospiech, E., et al. 2011. Gene-gene interactions contribute to eye colour variation in humans. *Journal of Human Genetics* 56:447-455.

how many had attached versus unattached or "free" earlobes. Attached earlobes blend in with the side of the head, and unattached earlobes have hanging lobes that can dangle. Usually, many more students have unattached than attached earlobes.

The Mendelian claim is that this trait is due to a dominant and recessive dichotomy. In this case, the claim is that the free earlobe trait is dominant, the attached is recessive.[13] The attached-free variant is used as an example of a classic single-gene recessive trait, an explanation that implies genetic control is relatively simple.[14] In fact, earlobes do not fall into two categories, attached and free, rather there exists a continuum of variations in attachment points, from up near the ear cartilage to well below the ear.[15]

This observation has caused biologists to question the oversimplified paradigm even before the advent of modern genomics. As early as 1937, one anatomist suggested that earlobe attachment may be a *multi-gene* trait.[16] One recent earlobe genetics study analyzed DNA sequences and earlobe measurements from 74,660 people, including those of European, Latin American, or Chinese ancestry. By associating DNA sequences across the genome with ear development patterns, the researchers identified 49 genomic regions related to earlobe-attachment design. They also sequenced the products of genes activated during ear development, confirming that the *many different*

---

13. Lai and Walsh, 1966.
14. See the Arizona State University website 'Ask A Biologist' for the Mendelian claim which is incorrect as documented in this paper. https://askabiologist.asu.edu/mendelian-traits-humans.
15. Dutta, P., and P. Ganguly. 1965. Further observations on ear lobe attachment. *Acta Genetica et Statistica Medica* 15:77-86.
16. Wiener, A.S. 1937. Complications in ear genetics. *Journal of Heredity* 28(12):425-426.

genes that were discovered in their DNA trait study were *lo-cated among many different regions* in the genome. The authors of the paper concluded, "These genes provide insight into the complex biology of ear development."[17]

As expected, the genetics behind these variations are very complicated. In short, it is a "myth … that earlobes can be divided into two clear categories, free and attached, and that a single gene controls the trait, with the allele for free earlobes being dominant."[18] Modern research techniques have now con-firmed that "even the concept of what clearly defines a single gene is blurred by unimaginable and unexpected complexity."[19] The largest genome-wide study of earlobe genetics found *at least 49 genes* play a role in the simple attached or free-hanging earlobes difference.[20] This finding has disproven the once-sim-ple 'dominant vs. recessive' determination for ear-lobe design. By the way, this was a surprising level of research in view of the fact that this area is not a research priority because, as far as is known, earlobe variations are unrelated to disease causation.[21]

3. Hair Color. Another common example of the one-gene myth is the belief that red hair is determined by a single reces-sive red allele. Most studies divide hair color into four discrete colors, namely blond, red, brown, and black. As is true of eye color, hair color is also determined by the amount of eumel-

17. Shaffer, J.R., et al. 2017. Multiethnic GWAS reveals polygenic archi-tecture of earlobe attachment. *The American Journal of Human Genetics* 101(6):913-924.

18. McDonald, 2011, p. 14.

19. Tomkins, 2018. Human Traits Not So Simple After All. *Acts & Facts* 47(2):15.

20. Shaffer, 2017.

21. Dutta, P. 1963. A note on the ear lobe. *Human Heredity* 13(3):290-294 [formerly *Acta Genetica et Statistica Medica*, 15(3):290].

anin (dark-brown color) and pheomelanin (a reddish color). The amount of eumelanin in hair ranges from very little, producing light-blonde hair, to relatively large amounts, producing jet black hair. In addition, people with large amounts of pheomelanin have red hair, which ranges from pale red ("strawberry blond") to bright red and reddish-brown.[22]

Because light-level variations and color-hue differences can affect the viewers' perception of hair color, Professor Reed used a reflectance spectrophotometer to measure the light levels reflected by hair at different wavelengths in persons labeled redheads.[23] He found no evidence of a clear separation of hair into two categories. Instead, intermediate colors were noted that could not easily be classified as, for example, red or non-red. The three most common amino acid polymorphisms associated with red hair are: R151C, R160W, and D294H, indicating that many more genes are involved in other hair shades.[24]

4. Skin color. Other human genetics studies have debunked the belief that skin color is controlled by only a few major genes.[25] Several studies have utilized human subjects from the continent with the largest spectrum of skin color diversity in the world, namely Africa. One study found that six major

22. McDonald, 2011, p. 37.

23. Reed, T.E. 1952. Red hair colour as a genetical character. *Annals of Eugenics* 17:115-139.

24. Box, N., J. Wyeth, L. OÓGorman, N. Martin, and R. Sturm. 1997. Characterization of melanaocyte stimulating hormone receptor variant alleles in twins with red hair. *Human Molecular Genetics* 6:1891Ð1897.

25. Crawford, N.G., et al. 2017. Loci associated with skin pigmentation identified in African populations. *Science* 358(6365):867-868; Martin, A.R., et al. 2017. An unexpectedly complex architecture for skin pigmentation in Africans. *Cell* 171(6):1340-1353; Tomkins, J.P. 2017. Skin color research confirms Biblical narrative. *Creation Science Update*. ICR.org.

genes contributed only 30 percent of the total skin color variability,[26] and *numerous other genes* were responsible for the other 70 percent contribution. In another study, researchers found that a total of 15 different genes make major contributions to skin color.[27]

5. Hitchhiker's Thumb. "Hitchhiker's thumb" is the ability to bend the thumb significantly backwards with a large angle between the two thumb bone segments. The common claim was that there exists two kinds of thumbs, straight, where one cannot bend it backwards (dominant) and hitchhiker's thumb (recessive), a trait controlled by a single gene with two alleles. This idea was proposed by Glass and Kistler[28] in 1953, and the claim, which could easily be evaluated in a large classroom of students, has been widely repeated since then.

At least two studies have falsified this myth. Harris and Joseph [29] used X-rays of 294 individuals to accurately measure the bone angle between the first and second bones of the thumb. Their analysis found a continuous distribution, and most individuals had intermediate values, not a dichotomy as described in the myth. A similar study using a protractor held against the outside of the thumb to measure the thumb angle obtained a normal bell curve.[30] Although hitchhiker's thumb is often used to demonstrate Mendelian genetics, the extant data falsify the claim: thumbs don't fall into two discrete categories, and the

26. Shaffer, 2017.
27. Martin, 2017.
28. Glass, B., and J.C. Kistler. 1953. Distal hyperextensibility of the thumb. *Acta Genetica* 4:192-206.
29. Harris, H., and J. Joseph. 1949. Variation in extension of the metacarpo-phalangeal and interphalangeal joints of the thumb. *Journal of Bone and Joint Surgery* 31:547-559.
30. Glass and Kistler, 1953.

trait is not controlled by a single gene.

6. PTC tasting. Small amounts of the compounds phenylth-iocarbamide (PTC) or propylthiouracil (PTU) impregnated into paper strips are then tasted by students to determine if the taste is very bitter or, for non-tasters, the only taste is the paper. I have used the test with hundreds of students when teaching a wide variety of science classes. The idea came from Du Pont chemist A.L. Fox, when working with phenylthiocar-bamide. When a colleague complained about the bitter taste of the chemical dust Fox insisted that it was tasteless.[31] To recolve the problem Fox asked his colleagues to taste the PTC. He dis-covered that for some people it had a strong bitter taste, while others found it tasteless.[32]

Guo and Reed reviewed the subject of PTC tasting, citing 392 references, and concluded that how the test is administered makes a big difference in the results.[33] Early studies put PTC crystals directly on the tongue, others used solutions of PTC, or paper soaked in PTC, which is then dried and afterwards tasted. [34] When this factor is controlled, some people would be classified as tasters with one technique, but non-tasters with a different technique.[35] Genetic analysis found a linkage to DNA

31. Fox, A.L. 1932. The relationship between chemical constitution and taste. *Proceedings of the National Academy of Sciences of the USA* 18:115-120.

32. Boyd, W.C. 1950. *Genetics and the Races of Man: An Introduction to Modern Physical Anthropology.* Boston, MA: Little, Brown and Company.

33. Guo, S.W., and D.R. Reed, 2001. The genetics of phenylthiocarbami-de perception. *Annals of Human Biology* 28(2):111-142.

34. Guo, S.W., F.M. Shen, Y.D. Wang, and C.J. Zheng. 1998. Threshold distributions of phenylthiocarbamide (PTC) in the Chinese popula-tion. *Annals of the New York Academy of Sciences* 855:810-812.

35. Hartmann, G. 1939. Application of individual taste difference towards

polymorphisms in 26 large families and much of the variation in PTC tasting was associated with chromosome 7 and a variation with chromosome 16, indicating that *several* genes are involved.[36]

The claim that there exists only two kinds of people, tasters and non-tasters, and that the trait is controlled by a single gene, with the allele for tasting dominant over the allele for non-tasting, is a common but incorrect myth. The fact is, after "almost 70 years, the origins of that variability, apparently due in large part to genetic factors, remains a conundrum."[37]

7. Tongue Rolling. Some people can easily roll their tongue into a small tube, others can't. This is one of the most common traits that biology teachers use to demonstrate basic genetic principles that can easily be tested. The trait is attributed to the pioneer of *Drosophila* genetics, Alfred Sturtevant, whose description of tongue rolling was as a simple two-allele trait with the allele for rolling dominant and that for non-rolling recessive.[38]

It has now been determined that the tongue-rolling skill is often learned. The fact that some people learn to roll their tongues after first being unable to do so is evidence that this

phenyl-thio-carbamide in genetic investigations. *Annals of Eugenics* 9:123-135; Lawless, H. 1980. A comparison of different methods used to assess sensitivity to the taste of phenylthiocarbamide (PTC). *Chemical Senses* 5:247-256.

36. Drayna, D., et al. 2003. Genetic analysis of a complex trait in the Utah Genetic Reference Project: A major locus for PTC taste ability on chromosome 7q and a secondary locus on chromosome 16p. *Human Genetics* 112:567-572.

37. Guo and Reed, 2001, p. 111.

38. Sturtevant, A.H. 1940. A new inherited character in man. *Proceedings of the National Academy of Sciences USA* 26:100-102.

trait is not the result of a simple genetic character. Further evidence that the trait is not genetic is the finding that identical twins are discordant in tongue rolling.[39] The proportion of people who learn to roll their tongue ranges from 65 to 81 percent, and a slightly higher proportion of tongue-rollers exists in females.[40]

The skill also exists on a continuum. Some people can only roll their tongue's edges slightly and cannot consistently be classified as rollers or non-rollers.[41] Even though numerous studies have shown that the skill is not genetic but largely learned, tongue rolling remains a popular test for Mendelian genetics.[42] In short, the tongue-rolling myth has been debunked.

8. Widow's Peak. Some people possess a prominent V-shaped point at the center front of their hairline, called a "widow's peak", in contrast to a hairline that goes straight across. The textbooks have taught for generations that the allele for a widow's peak is dominant over the allele for a straight hairline. A major problem with this claim is that there are ambiguities about who has a widow's peak. Hairlines exist on a continuum, requiring imprecise judgements to make this determination. One study of male medical students concluded that only 32 out of 1,039, (or three percent), had a "slight but noticeable"

---

39. Matlock, P. 1952. Identical twins discordant in tongue-rolling. *Journal of Heredity* 43:24.
40. Lee, J.W. 1955. Tongue-folding and tongue-rolling in an American Negro population sample. *Journal of Heredity* 46:289-291.
41. Reedy, John, et al. 1971. Tongue Rolling Among Twins. *Journal of Heredity* 62(2):125–127, March.
42. Brownie, Marie. 2015. Tongue-rolling myth totally 'debunked'. https://www.usatoday.com/story/news/nation/2015/08/17/tongue-rolling-myth-totally-debunked/31841559/.

widow's peak.[43] Another study of 360 women concluded that 81 percent had a widow's peak.[44]

Then there is the problem of age. The hairline of many men and some women recedes over time, often more slowly in the middle. It may be very difficult to distinguish between a receding hairline and a true widow's peak in adult men. The problem with the myth that the widow's peak is controlled by one gene with two alleles, is that researchers have been unable to locate these genes. McDonald states that he does not know how or where the myth began, nor any experimental evidence that supports it in spite of a careful search of the scientific literature.[45]

9. Hand Clasping. Most people have a strong preference in clasping their hands, either with the left thumb on top or the right thumb on top. It is also experienced as very unnatural to clasp the hands in the opposite way than one usually does. Roughly half of the people studied were right thumb on top and the other half were left thumb on top.[46] From the first study done on this topic onwards to today, no clear evidence has been found supporting the hand-clasping preference fitting the dominant-recessive myth.[47]

A review of nearly 100 publications that have surveyed hand-clasping frequencies in populations around the world

43. Smith and Cohen, 1973.
44. Nusbaum, B.P., and S. Fuentefria. 2009. Naturally occurring female hairline patterns. *Dermatologic Surgery* 35:907-913.
45. McDonald, 2011, p. 67.
46. Reiss, M. 1999. The genetics of hand-clasping: A review and a familial study. *Annals of Human Biology* 26:39-48. Smith, D.W., and M.M. Cohen. 1973. Widow's peak scalp-hair anomaly and its relation to ocular hypertelorism. *Lancet* 2(7838):1127-1128.
47. Lutz, F.E. 1908. The inheritance of the manner of clasping the hands. *American Naturalist* 42(495):195-196.

found that most populations had between 40 and 75 percent preferring "left on top", while "no preference" for either was at about 1 percent.[48] One theory was that left-handed persons, when folding their hands, strongly tended to put their left thumb on top, and right-handed persons their right on top.[49] Another theory is that preferences are probably chosen by each individual as a young child and reinforced over many years until the opposite thumb feels unnatural. No evidence has indicated that the trait is genetic.

10. Cleft Chin. Some people have a prominent dimple or crease in the chin's front called a "cleft chin". The claim is that this trait is controlled by a single gene with two alleles, called the dominant cleft chin (C) and recessive smooth chin (S) trait. The little available genetic data does not support this claim.[50] Again, the major problem is that many chins are intermediate between cleft and smooth, and chins come in a variety of shapes, including round, dimpled, and with vertical and Y-shaped furrows.[51] Furthermore, a significant increase in cleft chin occurs with age; about 5 percent of boys 6- to 10-years old have cleft chins, while 10 percent of men over age 35 have a cleft chin. This change with age is also evidence against the simple genetic model. Weight gain and loss also influences the

48. Reiss, 1999.
49. McManus, D., and M.P. Bryden. 1992. The genetics of handedness, cerebral dominance, and lateralization. *Handbook of Neuropsychology*, Volume 6. New York, NY: Elsevier Science Publications.
50. Lebow, M.R., and P.B. Sawin. 1941. Inheritance of human facial features: A pedigree study involving length of face, prominent ears and chin cleft. *Journal of Heredity* 32:127-132.
51. Günther, H. 1939. Anomalien und Anomaliekomplexe in der Gegend des ersten Schlundbogens. *Zeitschrift für menschliche Vererbungs- und Konstitutionslehre* 23:43-52.

cleft chin trait.

Summary

The oversimplified evolutionary paradigm that evolutionists use to justify their worldview is not supported by human genome studies that consistently show much greater levels of complexity in producing these traits than once assumed.[52] Actually, *very few traits are the result of simple gene pairs.* As more genetic information becomes available, the number of different genes that determine most physical features increases. Seemingly simple traits turn out to be very complex due to the genetic network interconnectivity of functioning in complex dynamic systems throughout the genome.

One 2017 study identified 6,500 genes that produce human sexual dimorphism—and are, therefore, expressed differently in men and women—is not unexpected in light of the findings of this review of the "one gene-one trait" theory . Many of the traits which define sexual dimorphism that were long assumed to follow this one gene-one trait rule, do not follow it.[53] Consequently, the 20 major traits that make up human sexual dimorphism may actually be determined by *several hundred genes*, not just 20. Another influence is genetic pleiotropy, the situation where one gene influences two or more, often many more, seemingly unrelated phenotypic traits.[54]

52. Tomkins, J. P. 2014. Gene Complexity Eludes a Simple Definition. *Acts & Facts* 43(6):9.

53. Gershoni, Moran, and Shmuel Pietrokovski. 2017. The landscape of sex-differential transcriptome and its consequent selection in human adults. *BMC Biology* 15:7, p. 2.

54. Bergman, Jerry. 2010. The Pleiotropy Problem for Evolution. *Creation Research Society Quarterly* 46(4):284-289, Spring.

Widows Peak in a Male. It refers to the hair protruding in the middle of the man's forehead that biology teachers used to demonstrate basic genetic principles that can easily be tested. It turns out not to be a one gene one trait as once taught.

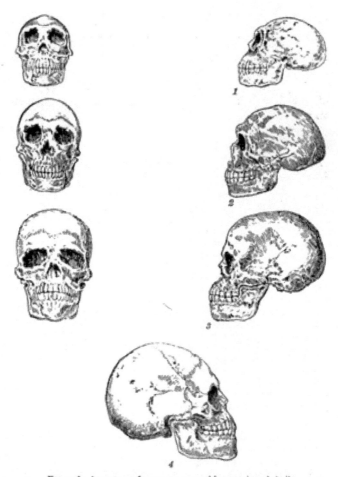

FIG. 256. Ancestors of man represented by remains of skulls

1, Pithecanthropus erectus, the "erect ape-man" of Java; *2*, the Neanderthal man; *3*, the negroid man of Laussel; *4*, Nebraska glacial man. These four types represent successive advances in the evolution of the human races, although we must not think of them as a straight series of our ancestors. Compare the size of the brain at different stages of development: Pithecanthropus, 850 cc.; Piltdown, 1300 cc.; Neanderthal, 1600 cc.; modern man, 1500–1800 cc.

Illustration 1. From the popular high school textbook by Benjamin Gruenberg. 1924. Elementary Biology. Boston, MA: Ginn, p. 493. Note it included Java man, Neanderthal man, Piltdown man, Negro man, and Nebraska man, all of which have now been refuted.

14

The Neanderthal Blunder

ADDED TO THE INFAMOUS Piltdown Man, which turned out to be a human skull poorly assembled with the jaw of a modern chimpanzee, and the equally famous Nebraska Man, which was constructed from what turned out to be the tooth of a type of pig called a peccary, is the Neanderthal Man blunder. He turned out to be, not a primitive human or an evolutionary link as was almost universally believed for over 150 years, but another people group, like the Chinese. In some ways, the Neanderthal blunder was worse than the other two because it fostered racism that then dominated the last century. The Piltdown and Nebraska Man blunders lasted from 1912 to 1953, or over 40 years, and continued to be listed in the textbooks for a few years after 1953. In contrast, the acceptance of Neanderthal Man was close to universal for over a century and a half.

In short, our *view* of Neanderthals has been evolving for the last century and a half. New discoveries show that Neanderthal was not a "hunched-over Caveman" as was believed for decades, but walked upright and "had spines straighter than those of modern man."[1] The newest research has documented that they were strong and sturdy men. We have come a long way from viewing them as a "missing link" to *one of us*, the phrase the *National Geographic* used to describe Neanderthal as part of the one human family.[2]

Some History of Neanderthal Man

Neanderthal fossils were first discovered in 1829 inside of caves in what is now Belgium. This widely touted 'Ape-Man' was named Neanderthal, after the Düssel River's Neander Valley, a Rhine River tributary-stream valley near Düsseldorf, Germany. The name was coined after a skull cap, ribs, part of the pelvis, and some limb bones were found in a small cave in the Neander Tal, forming the name 'Neanderthal', *tal* meaning valley. Soon many other discoveries of similar types of bone fragments were made, mostly in France and Germany.

The many skeletons uncovered showed that Neanderthals had shorter legs and stockier bodies then the average European. Consequently, since many of the bones were found in caves, the picture of an ancient, primitive, evolutionarily inferior cave man developed. We now realize that their short, stout-body adaptation helped them to preserve body heat in the cold climates where they lived.

Judging from some early skeletons, the leading anatomist/pathologist of the time, creationist Professor Rudolf Virchow (1821-1902), correctly concluded that Neanderthals were modern *Homo sapiens*, but some skeletons showed evidence of

1. 3-D model of Neanderthal rib cage myth of 'hunched-over caveman'. https://www.timesofisrael.com/3-d-model-of-neanderthal-rib-cage-busts-myth-of-hunched-over-cavemen/.
2. Hall, Stephen. 2008. The other humans: Neanderthals revealed. *National Geographic* 2014(4):34-59, October.

deformity, likely due to childhood rickets and arthritis later in life. His assessment was widely mocked for decades even though he was one of Europe's leading pathologists.

As Darwinism began to dominate science in the late 1800s, the almost universal picture of Neanderthal Man, judging by mannequins and illustrations produced for museums and text-books, was of a primitive, hairy, stooped-over, sloped-skulled, ape-like brute. An 1888 illustration of Neanderthal produced by Professor Schaaffhausen is actually more accurate than many, but still shows him looking very apelike.

Neanderthal Man was also for many decades commonly pictured in the textbooks as an important evolutionary link in human evolution from some hypothetical ape-like creature (see Illustration 1). Hundreds of other examples exist. The display in the prestigious American Museum of Natural History's *Hall of the Age of Man* showed Neanderthal to be evolutionarily be-tween Cro-Magnon and Piltdown, notwithstanding that the later fossil has since been proven to be a forgery.[3]

A leading high school textbook described Neanderthal Man as part of the chain of "successive advances in the evolution of the human races."[4] Professor Gruenberg put the brain capacity of Pithecanthropus at 850cc, Piltdown at 1300cc, Neanderthal at 1600cc and modern man from 1500 to 1800cc, showing that the brain capacity progressed as humans evolved.[5]

Typical of the image of Neanderthal Man is found in a popular young readers' book titled *The Story of Man*, subtitled

3. Bergman, Jerry. 2017. *Evolution's Blunders, Frauds and Forgeries*. Chapter 11, pp. 161-188. Atlanta, GA: CMI Publishing.
4. Gruenberg, Benjamin. 1924. *Elementary Biology*. Boston, MA: Ginn and Company, p. 493.
5. Gruenberg, 1924, p 493.

From Cave Men to Spacemen.[6] After discussing Piltdown Man, which the author of *The Story of Man* assumed was a true missing link, he moved on to Neanderthal Man.[7] Its brain was larger than the apes, which author Harold Peake has stated proved "that the brain led the way in human evolution" in the early history of man.[8] Peake concluded, from a large set of discoveries and scientific concessions, that the Neanderthal skull was not due to a diseased condition, but rather was a type of man which he described as having a large braincase:

> but the brain was of a lowly type.... The chin is underdeveloped. The teeth are very strong and have many primitive features. The legs are relatively short compared with those of modern man and the type did not walk quite erect... the proportions of the arms and legs are more human than ape-like, though not quite of modern type."[9]

He also, Peake adds, had prominent ape-like brow ridges. Clearly this type of man, Peake claims, is evolving toward modern man, but is not yet modern man. As late as 2014 Perez wrote, "the large, stooped-over brute we came to know as Neanderthal Man turned out to be parts of a large, severely arthritic human skeleton."[10]

---

6.   Lacre, Michel. 1960. *The Story of Man: From Cave Men to Spacemen.* New York, NY: Grosset & Dunlap.

7.   Lacre, 1960, p. 5.

8.   Peake, Herald, and Herbert John Fleure. 1927. *Apes & Man.* New Haven, CT: Yale University Press, p. 106.

9.   Peake and Fleure, 1927, pp. 117-118.

10. Perez, Al. 2014. *The Journey We Must All Take.* Bloomington, IN: iUniverse, p. 108.

Neanderthal Man Image Evolves

As more and more discoveries and research have been completed, the image of the Neanderthal has gradually changed. He became less and less brutish and, as more skeletons were discovered, evidence was found that Neanderthals walked upright like modern men. Eventually enough bones were discovered to assemble an entire skeleton. The skeleton was then clothed with muscle by forensic anthologists who, by the 1980s, had perfected the profession. Lastly, skin, eye balls, fingernails, and hair were added to enable an accurate recreation of his entire physical body. Due to new discoveries, some authors now have been attempting to correct the false "stooped cave man" idea. One scientist wrote, "Unfortunately, the *Neanderthals* have been plagued with an undesirable image as a *stooped-over* hulking *brute with a massive skull*, beetle brows, and a malevolent disposition."[11]

Welcome to the Human Family, *Finally*

Science has now moved the picture of Neanderthals from a primitive, brutish, less-evolved evolutionary ancestor to the typical family next door. Research on where they lived, (often in caves), and also at their burial locations, further supported the modernization of Neanderthals.[12] A report in *Science* admitted "Once seen as brute cavemen, Neanderthals have gained stature as examples of sophisticated technology and behavior have turned up in their former territory across Europe."[13] For

11. Sukys, Paul. 1999. *Lifting the Scientific Veil: Science Appreciation for the Nonscientist.* New York, NY: Rowman & Littlefield, p. 326.
12. Shackley, Myra. 1980. *Neanderthal Man.* Hamdon, CT: Archon Books; Trinkaus, Eric, and Pat Shipman. 1980. *The Neanderthals: Changing Image of Mankind.* New York, NY: Alfred A. Knopf.
13. Tim Appenzeller. 2018. Europe's firsts artists were Neanderthals. *Sci-*

example, in their cave homes, evidence was found documenting that they used jewelry, fire,[14] played musical instruments,
produced cave paintings, buried their dead, and were even capable of speech (evidence included possessing the hyoid bone
in the throat). Hunting took most of their time, but some were
artists, painting or carving pictures of the animals they saw in
the forests. The question "was he an evolutionary ancestor of
modern humans or a modern human?" has finally been conclu-
sively answered.[15] *He was a modern human.*

> The "size and shape of the Neanderthal thorax has been a subject
> of scientific debate for more than 150 years." [16]The latest discov-
> ery, written by an international team of scientists, documented
> that he breathed deeply from a bell, not barrel-shaped chest as
> once thought, and that his rib cage was very much like those of
> modern mankind.[17] Thus, he would have had, not a stooped pos-
> ture as was often shown for decades, but a fully modern upright
> posture and breathed deeply from his diaphragm. These conclu-
> sions came from a recently completed 3-D virtual reconstruction
> of the rib cage from the Kebara 2 skeleton, a headless but almost
> complete Neanderthal skeleton unearthed in a northern Israeli
> cave.[18] This research by scientists teaching at universities in Isra-

---

ence 359(6378):852.

14. Zhang, Sarah. 2018. The mystery of how Neanderthals got fire. https://
www.theatlantic.com/science/archive/2018/07/neanderthals-fire-mys-
tery/565514/.

15. Asier Gómez-Olivencia et al., 2018. 3D virtual reconstruction of the
Kebara 2 Neandertal thorax. *Nature Communications*, 9(4387):2.

16. Asier Gómez-Olivencia et al., 2018, p. 1.

17. Borschel-Dan, Amanda. 2018. 3-D model of Neanderthal rib cage
busts myth of 'hunched-over cavemen'. https://www.timesofisrael.
com/3-d-model-of-neanderthal-rib-cage-busts-myth-of-hunched-
over-cavemen/.

18. Asier Gómez-Olivencia et al., 2018, p. 2.

el, Spain, and the United States, put the last nail in the coffin of "the myth of the arm-dragging, hunched-over caveman."[19]

Some small differences between modern and Neanderthal rib cages were found, including the fact that Neanderthal had a slightly larger costal cartilage skeleton, with longer mid-thoracic ribs compared to modern humans, which probably resulted in a slightly more voluminous thorax. This shape of the rib cage suggests a larger diaphragm and, thus, greater lung capacity than modern humans. Their larger thoracic volume could be due to the requirement for more oxygen intake as a result of their larger body mass and hypothesized hunter-gatherer lifestyle in the very cold climate where they lived in Europe.[20] Another difference is that most modern humans have a lumbar curve which, in Neanderthals, was less pronounced. Furthermore, the "Neanderthal spine is located more [deeply] inside the thorax, which provides more stability. The thorax was wider in its lower part. Their spines were straighter than those of modern man, making them a strong and sturdy people".

In short, Neanderthals, judging by the specimens discovered, had an upright posture with greater lung capacity and a straighter spine than present-day humans. The Neanderthal rib cage was slightly broader at its base, with horizontal ribs, versus modern man's angled ribs. As the cover of a *National Geographic* article showed, Neanderthals are now fully recognized as one of us.[21]

They Were Homebodies Just Like We Are

All the fragments of claimed pre-modern human ancestors,

19. Borschel-Dan, Amanda, 2018.
20. Asier Gómez-Olivencia et al., 2018, p. 2.
21. Stephen, 2008.

such as the most famous, Lucy, were found, not in caves or even near caves, or rock shelters, but on the plains. Lucy was found on the hilly plains of Hadar in the Afar region of Ethiopia, a country in Africa.[22] This was not the case with Neanderthals. Many, or even most Neanderthal bones were found in caves. Furthermore, "evidence is growing that . . .Neanderthals may have been the original homebodies. A picture is emerging of their domestic life that would have been unthinkable just a few years ago. Far from being brutish, they may have enjoyed nothing more than spending time indoors around a cozy fire."[23] This difference is more evidence that Lucy and other australopiths were apes and Neanderthals were human. One reason they lived in cave homes could be the fact that necessity "may well have spawned this particular invention because the Europe that Neanderthals inhabited . . . was far colder and more arid than it is today ...with temperatures falling to -20°C at times, and not rising above 12°C even in summer."[24] This little ice age frigid cold would cause a major survival problem.

Life around camp fires is common today, and would have affected social interactions which likely included gossip, complaints, practical discussions of life problems and a variety of concerns, telling stories, and discussions of daily activities about the things that matter to humans, especially the events that emotionally bind people. A fire social-gathering around food also "provides opportunities for non-verbal communica-

---

22. W.L. Jungers. 1988. Lucy's length: Stature reconstruction in *Australopithecus afarensis* (A.L.288-1) with implications for other small-bodied hominids. *American Journal of Physical Anthropology* 76(2):227–231.

23. Spinney, Laura. 2019. Cozy up with the Neanderthals, the first humans to make a house a home. *New Scientist* 241(3216):28-31, February 9-15. p. 28.

24. Spinney, 2019, p. 28.

tion in the form of eye contact and who sits where, and for other social bonding activities such as singing and dancing."[25]

Another study concluded that Neanderthals were "people who liked nothing better than spending time indoors around the fire . . . and having friends over for dinner."[26] A home, even in a cave, is important because, as University College of London archaeologist Matt Pope argues, home "marked a critical threshold in the long march towards civilization. . . . a conceptual leap that shaped the way our ancestors thought and interacted."[27]

A study published in the leading American science magazine concluded after a careful analysis of cave paintings that

> Neanderthals are our closest extinct relatives, but for a long time, they had a reputation for being pretty backward. Early modern humans, for example, made cave paintings. But even though Neanderthals used pigments and decorated themselves with eagle claws and shells, there was no clear proof that they painted [pictures in] caves.[28]

The newest evidence supports the opposite conclusion, namely that many cave paintings were done by Neanderthals. We now have clear evidence that Neanderthals decorated their abode with artwork.[29] This is important because "few researchers imagined them engaging in one of the most haunting prac-

25. Spinney, 2019, p. 31.

26. Spinney, 2019, p. 28.

27. Quoted in Spinney, 2019, p. 28.

28. Becker, Rachel. 2018. Ancient cave paintings turn out to be by Neanderthals, not modern humans. https://www.theverge.com/2018/2/22/17041426/neanderthals-cave-painting-spain-uranium-dating.

29. Appenzeller, 2018, p. 852.

tices in human prehistory: creating paintings—vehicles for symbolic expression—in the darkness of caves."[30]

Jean-Jacques Hublin, professor of Evolutionary Anthropology at the Max Planck Institute in Leipzig, Germany, added: "People saw cave painting as a major gap between Neandertals and modern humans. This discovery [of Neanderthal cave painting] reduces the distance."[31] The unanimity of this conclusion was: "For once, the fractious scientists who study the Neandertals agree about something: that a study has dropped a bombshell on their field, by presenting the most persuasive case yet that our vanished cousins had the cognitive capacity to create art."[32] The conclusion of the art experts was, "Neandertal artistic creativity [was] equivalent to the art and symbolism practiced by modern humans."[33]

Consequently, from this evidence, University of Leiden archaeology professor Marie Soressi admitted, "The discovery adds to a growing body of evidence *upending* the idea that Neanderthals were less evolved than early modern humans. . . . These cave paintings are the very last piece of evidence we were [previously] lacking."[34] Max Planck Institute for Evolutionary Anthropology geochronologist Dirk Hoffmann admits that the major

> reason we didn't know Neanderthals were cave painters until now is because it's hard to figure out when cave art was created. The most common dating method can only be used on organic material, like bones, so it usually doesn't work for cave paintings.

30. Appenzeller, 2018, p. 852.
31. Appenzeller, 2018, p. 852.
32. Appenzeller, 2018, p. 852.
33. Appenzeller, 2018, p. 853.
34. Becker, 2018; emphasis added.

Another [dating] technique uses the rate of uranium's radioactive decay as a clock. But it required lots of material to come up with a date, and cave paintings are too rare to risk damaging. Rock art "is unique, it's precious — there's a lot of pressure on you not to make a mistake."[35]

Deep within one cave in southern Spain, researchers have found the ancient markings of the Neanderthals they believe once inhabited the caves there. The art is beneath layers of calcium carbonate. Cave explorers, called "spelunkers", located designs, hazy circles in red ocher, in one of three sites in Spain. Separated by hundreds of miles, the caves house handiwork— vivid artwork patterns (spheres, ladders, or hand stencils). Using drills and surgical scalpels, they ground and scraped the minerals that dripping groundwater had deposited on top of the artwork for centuries. At each spot, "to avoid damaging the paintings," a few milligrams of veneer were carefully removed without touching the final coat of calcite overlaying the ocher.

One dispute centers on whether or not the abstract patterns qualify as symbolic expression. Dirk Hoffmann, a lead author of the cave-art study, noted that one of the main arguments for the conclusion of Neanderthal humanity is evidence of the

emergence of symbolic material culture [which] represents a fundamental threshold in the evolution of humankind… the debate over whether the cave art qualifies as symbolic expression "touches deeply on a concern that goes far beyond academic rivalries. It confronts the issue of how special we, as modern humans," are. Zilhão has been the Neanderthals' loudest and most persistent advocate. At 62, he's more or less the de facto leader of

35. Becker, 2018.

the movement to rehabilitate a vanished people.[36]

These results have changed scientists' understanding of the so-called prehistoric artistic creations. The findings are yet more evidence that the world's first artists were Neanderthals, people once believed to be "stocky, stooped figures, preternaturally low-browed, who became extinct as sapiens inherited the earth."[37] University of Barcelona research professor and archaeologist João Zilhão opined, "the paintings have turned out to be the oldest known art in Europe, and, with current knowledge, the oldest in the world."[38] Hoffmann concluded that the cave paintings date to the exact time the Neanderthals were believed to have lived.

We also know that they learned to work with animal hides, "turning them into leather and stitching them together with long strips of hide, so they could have made simple tents. By lighting a fire inside a tent, they could have raised the temperature from -20°C to 20°C and, through such engineering of their environment, endured a cold winter night."[39] As a result of this technology, Professor Matt Pope concluded, "For hundreds of miles around, there isn't going to be any bubble of warm, survivable air other than the one the Neanderthals have managed to capture and seal."[40]

Living in a frigid, cold environment was one issue the Neanderthals faced, but not the only one. If family groups that hunted together and shared meat lived at their butchery sites,

---

36. Lidz, Franz. 2019. What Do We Really Know About Neanderthals? *The Smithsonian Magazine* 50(2):24-35, May, p. 29.

37. Lidz, 2019, p. 26.

38. Lidz, 2019, p. 26.

39. Spinney, 2019, p. 30.

40. Quoted in Spinney, 2019, p. 30.

the smell could have attracted scavengers such as wolves and lions. Thus, a "cave or rock shelter could have contained the smell while allowing its occupants to control access and stay safe."[41] Evidence of this was the large number of fire pits "found at many Neanderthal living sites, some containing burnt bones. Armed with light and a means of warding off dangerous animals, Neanderthals could bring sleeping and food-sharing activities together in a single space – home."[42] For example, at a site in southern Jordan, Neanderthals

> piled up stones and wood to create windbreaks inside the shelter. Later, they began building windbreaks in the open, using wood and even mammoth bones. At La Folie, a 60,000-year-old site near Poitiers in France, post holes preserved in sediment point to some kind of circular wooden structure, perhaps covered with skins or brush [that was built to protect Neanderthal families].[43]

Professor Matt Pope and other Neanderthal researchers have concluded that Neanderthals possessed the technical skills to construct warm dwellings and had even "mastered the art of combining different materials, binding stone points to wooden shafts with animal sinew or plant fiber to make spears, for example, and sealing the joints with resin or birch bark pitch."[44]   Birch bark pitch has been called the world's first superglue.[45] They also unearthed "shells from a fourth

41. Spinney, 2019, p. 28.
42. Spinney, 2019, p. 30.
43. Spinney, 2019, p. 30.
44. Spinney, 2019, p. 30.
45. New Study Reveals How the Neanderthals Made Super Glue. 200,000 Years Ago: The World's Oldest Synthetic Material. Open Culture. 2017. https://www.openculture.com/2017/09/new-study-reveals-how-the-neanderthals-made-super-glue-200000-years-ago-the-worlds-oldest-

EVOLUTION'S DANGEROUS IDEAS

Spanish cave, pigment-stained and pierced as if for use as body ornaments."[46] Catalan Institute of Human Paleoecology, Professor María Gema Chacón and her colleagues, have uncovered one 300-square-meter cave floor where Neanderthals lived. One level contained over 40 hearths, at which "You can still smell the roasted deer."[47] This was only part of a new body of research that

> has emerged that's transformed our image of Neanderthals. Through advances in archaeology, dating, genetics, biological anthropology and many related disciplines we now know that Neanderthals not only had bigger brains than sapiens, but also walked upright and had a greater lung capacity. These ice age Eurasians were skilled toolmakers and big-game hunters who lived in large social groups, built shelters, traded jewelry, wore clothing, ate plants and cooked them, and made sticky pitch to secure their spear points by heating birch bark. Evidence is mounting that Neanderthals had a complex language and even, given the care with which they buried their dead, some form of spirituality. And as the cave art in Spain demonstrates, these early settlers had the chutzpah to enter an unwelcoming underground environment, using fire to light the way.[48]

Neanderthals were also fairly sophisticated cooks who consumed a wide variety of foods.[49] Findings at digs and dental calculus on their skulls provide evidence that they boiled bones

---

known-synthetic-material.html.
46. Appenzeller, 2018, p. 852.
47. Spinney, 2019, p. 30.
48. Lidz, 2019, p. 28.
49. Henry, Amanda G. 2011. Microfossils in calculus demonstrate consumption of plants and cooked foods in Neanderthal diets (Shanidar III, Iraq; Spy I and II, Belgium). *PNAS* 108(2):486-491, January.

to extract nutrients, used wild herbs such as yarrow to flavor their meat, and even at times adopted a vegetarian diet. Neanderthals show evidence of medicinal plants entrapped in dental calculus. Specifically the scientists used

> morphological analysis of plant microfossils, to identify material entrapped in dental calculus from five Neanderthal individuals from the north Spanish site of El Sidrón. Our results provide the first molecular evidence for inhalation of wood-fire smoke and bitumen or oil shale and ingestion of a range of cooked plant foods.[50]

From this and other research, it appears that the Neanderthals were very much like us, which we would expect if they were also the children of Adam and Eve. One article, which includes reprints of cartoons maligning our Neanderthal relatives, opined: "Revolutionary discoveries in archaeology show that the species long maligned as knuckle-dragging brutes deserve a new place in the human story."[51]

False Evolutionary Ideas Slowly Overcome by Science

The story that began in the summer of 1856, "when quarrymen in Germany's Neander Valley dug up part of a fossilized skull with a receding forehead", has now confirmed that the missing-link story is false, just as the Piltdown and Nebraska Man claims were false. The Neanderthal "evolutionary-link" myth began soon after Darwin published his book that overturned the creation worldview. From the beginning, *Homo neander-*

---

50. Hardy, Karen, et al. 2012. Neanderthal medics? Evidence for food, cooking, and medicinal plants entrapped in dental calculus. *Natur wissenschaften* 99(8):671-626, August.

51. Lidz, 2019.

thalensis "got a bad rap as lamebrained brutes who huddled in cold caves while gnawing at slabs of slain mammoth. Nature's "down-and-outs" were judged to be too dimwitted for moral or theistic conceptions, probably devoid of language and behaviorally inferior to their modern human contemporaries."[52]

These ideas were produced as a result of many preconceived ideas about human evolution. If scientists would have gone where the scientific facts led them from the very beginning of the bones discovery, a very different picture would have emerged decades ago. Unfortunately, old ideas based on evolutionary presumptions have for decades resulted in "squabbles over the intelligence and taxonomic status of these archaic humans" that

> have gotten so bitter and so intense that some researchers refer to them as the Neanderthal Wars. Over the years battle lines have been drawn over everything from the shape of Neanderthals' noses and the depth of their trachea to the extent to which they interbred with modern humans. In the past, the combatants have been at each other's throats over authorship of the cave art, which had been hampered by lack of precise dating—often sapiens couldn't be ruled out as the real artists.[53]

The Dating Problem

A major problem, which still exists today, is dating the Neanderthal bones and fragments. Researchers have been arguing "about the position of this group of early people in the human family tree ever since," speculating that "they apparently thrived in Europe and Western Asia from about 400,000 to 40,000

---

52. Lidz, 2019, p. 28.
53. Lidz, 2019, p. 29.

B. C."[54] If Neanderthals lived from 400,000 to 40,000 years ago as claimed, the Neanderthal variants must have managed to survive intact that long. DNA deteriorates very rapidly due to several causes, including background radiation from cosmic rays and the radiation that seeps up from the ground as radon gas, a byproduct of uranium-238 decay. Radon in turn decays by the emission of alpha particles to polonium, bismuth, and lead in successive steps, most also radioactive.[55] Mutations are constantly damaging genes which, fortunately, in living humans are repaired successfully 99.99 percent of the time. About 100 or so new mutations per generation are a result of the 0.01 percent that are not repaired. In dead bodies, DNA damage by radiation and other sources is not repaired, thus damage to the DNA accumulates rapidly.

The half-life of DNA, the point at which fully half the DNA-molecule backbone-bonds are broken, is 521 years. Professor **Morten E. Allentoft,** Director of the Ancient DNA Laboratory, after extensive study, concluded that, after 521 years, DNA would be useless for comparisons or sequencing, thus little would be left to do DNA analysis after 40,000 years.[56] Specifically, his lab found that by analyzing

> mitochondrial DNA (mtDNA) from 158 radiocarbon-dated bones of the extinct New Zealand moa, we confirm empirically a long-hypothesized exponential decay relationship. The average DNA half-life within this geographically constrained fossil

54. Lidz, 2019, p. 28.
55. Report of the United Nations Scientific Committee on the Effects of Atomic Radiation. UNSCEAR Publication dated September 4, 2021.
56. Allentoft, Morten E. 2012. The half-life of DNA in bone: Measuring decay kinetics in 158 dated fossils. *Proceedings of the Royal Society Biology* 279(1748):4724–4733.

assemblage was estimated to be 521 years for a 242 bp mtDNA sequence, corresponding to a per nucleotide fragmentation rate (k) of 5.50 [X] 10^{-6} per year.[57]

Furthermore, the estimated 400,000 to 40,000-year range is based partly on rocks and the surrounding environment. Hydrolysis, oxidation, and non-enzymatic methylation of DNA occur at significant rates both in vivo and in vitro. The spontaneous decay of DNA sets limits for the recovery of DNA fragments from fossils.[58] The early 1990s claims of DNA recovered from fossils claimed to be a million years old are now widely regarded as modern contaminants, a major problem as anyone who has done sequencing of DNA is fully aware.[59] This problem has been recognized for over 25 years by Lindahl, who observed that DNA, as the carrier of genetic information, is not chemically stable.

The only way to reduce this problem is to work in a level-5 clean room, as anyone who has sequenced the mitochondrial and nuclear genomes of the Neanderthal would know.[60] The fact is, "the kinetics of long-term post-mortem DNA decay is still poorly understood."[61] Teaching forensics has exposed this author to debates about the quality of DNA of a woman known to have died in 1947. The claim is that the DNA was far too fragmented to make any valid conclusions. None-the-less, this field is developing and becoming more sophisticated, so

---

57. Allentoft, 2012, p. 4724.
58. Lindahl, Tomas. 1993. Instability and decay of the primary structure of DNA. *Nature* 252(6422):709-715, April 22.
59. Allentoft, 2012, p. 4724.
60. Pääbo, Svante. 2014. *Neanderthal Man*. New York, NY: Basic Books.
61. Allentoft, 2012, p. 4724.

these concerns may not exist in the future.[62]

The topic of Neanderthals has a special meaning for me. Knowing that several colleagues of mine at the college where I taught for 31 years had Neanderthal DNA, I had mine analyzed by *23 and Me* and found that I am 51.6 percent Finnish-Swedish, which I already knew. I also found that I have 360 Neanderthal variants, which is more than 96 percent of others in the enormous five million-person database *23 and Me* used as a comparison.

In my case, Neanderthal ancestry accounts for about four percent of my overall DNA analyzed. The only larger percent, besides Finnish-Swedish, was British and German. One does not think of Neanderthal as related to blond, blue-eyed Scandinavians, but from what we know about Neanderthals, they were well-adapted to the cold, so when the post-Flood Ice Age swept over Europe, the Neanderthals no doubt moved up north into Scandinavian lands where my distant relatives lived.

---

62. Herrmann, Bernd, and Susanne Hummel (editors). 1994. *Ancient DNA: Recovery and Analysis of Genetic Material from Paleontological, Archaeological, Museum, Medical, and Forensic Specimens.* New York, NY: Springer Publishing.

Neanderthal From Wikipedia Commons

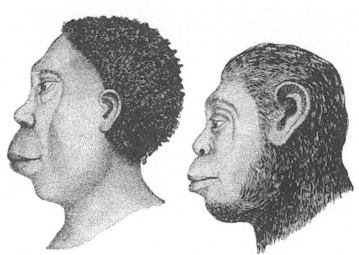

FIG. 46.—Female Hottentot.   FIG. 47.—Female Gorilla.

An illustration of the Racism by a University of Michigan Professor of Paleontology. Note both of these pictures are greatly distorted.

From Alexander Winchell 1880 *Preadamites*. Chicago Griggs and Company. p. 253

15

Evolution Influences the Eugenics and Abortion Movements

THOMAS MALTHUS PROPOSED that human population growth would continue unchecked until it is eventually culled by the less fortunate members dying from famine and disease. Malthus believed that population growth would preclude long-term progress towards a better society because the Earth's ability to produce food would be unable to keep up with the normal population growth.[1] Checks on population, including poverty, misery, vice, crime, and starvation, would begin when the population level exceeded the land's ability to produce food. In developing their idea of evolution, both Darwin and Wallace exploited this idea, concluding that the effect of Malthus' prediction was to cull the least-fit, resulting in the survival of the most-fit, thus promoting evolution. Ironically, Malthus, the man who influenced Darwin, was proven spectacularly wrong!

---

1. Malthus, Thomas. 1895. *An Essay on the Principle of Population.* New York, NY: Macmillan, p. 49.

Malthus is rated as one of the 100 most-influential people of all time, partly due to his influence on several modern social movements.[2] It "was from Malthus that Darwin derived the principle of Natural Selection, the central mechanism in his theory of evolution."[3] Malthus also inspired the population control movement, which was a major influence on both the birth-control and abortion movements.[4] Thomas Malthus is most widely known today for his book titled *An Essay on the Principle of Population*. Although first published in 1798, it is still in print, which indicates both its popularity and significance even today.

His Background

Thomas was the sixth of eight children of Daniel and Henrietta Malthus.[5] Daniel Malthus, a friend of David Hume and Jean-Jacques Rousseau, was from a "good family."[6] In 1798, Thomas Malthus was appointed an Anglican curate at Okewood near Albury in Surrey.[7] On April 12, 1804, Malthus married his cousin, Harriet, a marriage that produced three children. Also, in 1804, Thomas became Professor of History and Political Economy in Hertfordshire, Haileybury.[8] His students affec-

2. Bonar, James, 1885. *Malthus and His Work*. London, England: Macmillan, p. 1.
3. Wade, Nicholas. 2014. *A Troublesome Inheritance: Genes, Race and Human History*. New York, NY: Penguin, p. 155.
4. Lopez, Mario. 2012. Hijacking immigration? *The Human Life Review* 38(4):49-73, Fall.
5. Lieberman, Janet. 1973. Malthus: His life and work. *The American Biology Teacher* 35(3):130-131, p. 130.
6. Peterson, William. 1999. *Malthus: Founder of Modern Demography*, 2nd Edition. Transaction, p. 21.
7. Venn, J., and J.A. Venn (editors). 1922. "Malthus, Thomas Robert." *Alumni Cantabrigienses*, 10 volumes.
8. Peterson, 1978, p. 30.

tionately referred to him as "Pop" or "Population" Malthus due to his focus on population theory.

An Essay on the Principle of Population

Between 1798 and 1826, Malthus published six editions of his famous treatise, updating each new edition to address the many criticisms that arose against his theory. Malthus observed that a segment of every human population most always ended up in poverty. If left unchecked, the human population tends to grow in a geometrical ratio (2,4,8,16), but food production increases occur only in an arithmetical ratio (2,4,6,8,10 …). This means that the power of population growth is greater than the power of the Earth to produce the necessary subsistence for human growth.[9] Consequently, populations expand in times and regions of plenty until the population size, relative to the resources available, subjects the "lower classes to poverty, which causes disease and premature death."[10]

As the population increases, the means of subsistence that previously adequately supported the people must now be divided among a larger population. Consequently, the population will rapidly outstrip food production, resulting in serious widespread famine and thousands of deaths.[11] Furthermore, the poor would then also be forced to live in much worse conditions, and many of them reduced to abject poverty.[12]

Malthus also observed that societies throughout history have experienced epidemics, famines, and wars, all events

---

9. Grigg, Russell. 2010. Don't blame Malthus! Darwin and Wallace both credited an English clergyman for inspiring their evolutionary theories. *Creation* 32(3):45–47, July 2, p. 45.

10. Malthus, 1859, p. 10.

11. Lieberman, 1973, p. 131.

12. Malthus, 1859, pp. 10-11.

which masked the fundamental problem of populations over-stretching limited resources.[13] His writings strongly argued against the popular 18th-century European view which concluded that humans have an almost limitless ability to improve society.[14] Malthus' ideas rapidly became hugely influential in economic, political, social, and even scientific thought.

Proposed Solutions

Malthus argued that two types of checks can hold a population to within its resource limits. The first were *negative checks*, which include famine, disease, and war. The second was *preventive checks* including birth control, abortion, and celibacy. The application of population control, as later proposed by Francis Galton, called "eugenics", was necessary to produce improvements in the average size and strength of humanity by forcing the less-fit to a life of celibacy.[15]

As a Christian clergyman, Malthus put more emphasis on positive eugenics, such as marriage postponement until the couple could support a family. This, he felt, "coupled with sexual abstinence …was the best means … of easing the poverty of the lower classes."[16] Malthus also addressed the question of how an omnipotent and caring God could allow so much suffering to exist all around us. He concluded that humans were solely to blame for human suffering, writing,

---

13. Malthus Thomas R. 1798. *An Essay on the Principle of Population*, in Oxford World's Classics reprint.
Chapter VII, p. 61.
14. Lieberman, 1973, p. 131.
15. Malthus,1798. Chapter IX, p. 72.
16. Gilbert, Geoffrey. 1798. Introduction to Malthus. An essay on the principle of population. Oxford World's Classics reprint, p. xviii.

it is the intention of the Creator that the earth should be replenished… with a healthy, virtuous and happy population, not an unhealthy, vicious and miserable one. And if, in endeavoring to obey the command to increase and multiply, we people it only with beings of this latter description and suffer accordingly, we have no right to impeach the justice of the command, but our irrational mode of executing it.[17]

Malthus also wrote that, if society relied solely on human misery to limit population growth, hunger, disease, and war would inevitably increase.[18] Conversely, "preventive checks," such as limiting birthrates by birth control and abortion, (which were later added to the list of population controls), could ensure a higher standard of living for all, while concurrently increasing economic stability.[19]

In Malthus' day, many observers regarded high fertility as an economic advantage because it increased the number of workers. Malthus, however, convinced most economists that, even though high fertility might increase the gross economic output, it tended to reduce the per capita output. In 1823, Malthus contributed an article on population in the *Encyclopædia Britannica* supporting his view.

Darwin Exploits Malthus

When trying to solve the origin of species problem, Darwin "read all sorts of books" including, in 1838, Thomas Malthus' *Essay on the Principal of Population.* In this book Malthus cov-

---

17. Malthus, 1826. *An Essay on the Principle of Population, Sixth Edition,* App.I.6.
18. Malthus, 1826, p. 2.
19. Lopez, Kathryn Jean. 2010. Defining Eugenics Down. *The Human Life Review* 36(1):11-17, Winter.

ered the checks on population growth which included disease, famine, and death. Charles Darwin openly acknowledged the central role that Malthus played in the development of his own ideas about biological evolution. Darwin even referred to Malthus as "that great philosopher."[20]

Darwin added that when he read Malthus' book on population, "it at once struck me that under these circumstances favorable variations would tend to be preserved, and unfavorable ones ... destroyed. The result of this would be the formation of new species."[21] Thus Malthus' writings were the source of Darwin's single most important contribution to evolution theory, which was the doctrine of survival-of-the-fittest by natural selection.

Darwin even felt that Malthus had explained the origin of all species, but recognized that the application of Malthus' remedy, namely *preventive checks,* would actually work against evolution.[22] Darwin ignored Malthus' humanitarian response to the problem and, instead, concluded that the ruthless, brutal survival-of-the-fittest force caused evolution. Thus, instead of the solutions that Malthus advocated, Darwin taught that for evolution to occur, biologically inferior animals must be selected out by "red in tooth and claw" natural selection, leaving the superior animals to take over the Earth.

Darwin's theory is actually Malthus' theory slightly modified.[23] Specifically, Darwin altered Malthus' thesis from the

---

20. Letter to J. Hooker, dated June 5, 1860. In *The Correspondence of Charles Darwin.* Edited by Frederick Burhardt, Volume 8. New York, NY: Cambridge University Press, p. 238; Spencer, 1864, p. 444.
21. Darwin, Charles. 1958. The Autobiography of Charles Darwin. Edited by his granddaughter Nora Barlow. New York, NY: Norton, p. 120.
22. Darwin, Charles. 1859. *The Origin of Species.* London, England: Murray, p. 63.
23. Johnson, Paul. 2012. *Darwin: Portrait of a Genius.* New York, NY: Vi-

poor and less fortunate dying due to overpopulation, to the biologically inferior dying off as a result of being unable to compete against the more-fit life-forms.[24] Darwin called his process *Natural Selection* to differentiate it from the artificial selection process that humans use to modify animals for human goals. Darwin also believed that the solution Malthus stressed would not work because "the doctrine of Malthus, applied with manifold force to the animal and vegetable kingdoms, [would fail because] … there can be no artificial increase of food, and no prudential restraint from marriage."[25]

Thus, Darwin realized that the end result of Malthus' *negative checks* would be the formation of new plant and animal species; thus was born his 'species theory' which "would grow and develop over the next few years. He quickly connected the analogy between the role of nature in shaping her species and the role of humans in shaping breeds," a process we call animal breeding.[26] The problem was, the Darwin-Wallace theory only explained the *loss* of a species. The *new* genetic information required to produce *new* species was a problem that neither Darwin, nor anyone else since then, has been able to solve.[27]

Evolution's co-founder, Alfred Russel Wallace, also acknowledged that the importance of Malthus' writings was critical for his (Wallace's) own evolutionary theory, noting that without it he probably would "not have hit upon the theory of

king Press, p. 41.
24. Lieberman, 1973, p. 131.
25. Darwin, 1859, p, 63.
26. Carroll, Sean, 2009. *Remarkable Creatures: Epic Adventures in the Search for the Origin of Species.* Boston, MA: Houghton Mifflin Harcourt, pp. 41-42.
27. Gregg, 2010, p. 47.

Natural Selection."[28] Wallace explained:

> the most important book I read was Malthus' *Principles of Popu-*
> *lation...* It was the first great work I had yet read treating of any
> of the problems of philosophical biology, and its main principles
> remained with me as a permanent possession, and twenty years
> later gave me the long-sought clue to the effective agent in the
> evolution of organic species.[29]

Malthus Proven Wrong

Even during Malthus' lifetime, the many major problems with
his theory soon became obvious. As mentioned above, geometric population growth in the 20th century did not result in a
Malthusian catastrophe as he expected due in part to greater
labor specialization, and because capital investment in mechanical equipment,(such as tractors and combines), resulted
in major improvements in agricultural production. Other improvements included the use of fertilizers and petrochemical
pesticides to control crop pests, and the introduction of high-
yield farm crop varieties. Humans have also learned how to
exploit past solar income—fossil fuel—to greatly increase agricultural production by generating electricity to pump water
for irrigation. One of the most critical agricultural innovations
was Justus von Liebig's 1840s discovery that nitrogen was a
central factor in plant growth. Liebig learned how to synthesize
the bio-available form of nitrogen called nitrate, and began the
fertilizer revolution.[30]

---

28. Wallace, Alfred Russel. 1908. *My life: A Record of Events and Opinions.*
    London, England: Chapman & Hall, p. 130.
29. Wallace, 1908, pp. 123-124.
30. Ransom, Cliff. 2015. *100 Inventions that Changed the World.* New
    York, NY: Time Home Entertainment, p. 59.

Later, in the early 1900s, chemist Fritz Haber developed a process to synthesize fertilizer by using high temperatures to combine hydrogen derived from methane with atmospheric nitrogen.[31] The energy-intensive Haber-Bosch process is now used throughout the world to fixate atmospheric nitrogen, producing low-cost artificial fertilizers. All of these developments have now largely negated Malthus' major thesis.

As a result, the seemingly common-sense Malthusian premise has been falsified. Zubrin, in a chapter titled "The Data That Proves Malthus Wrong," reviews world population growth data plotted against GDP per capita growth, documenting how crop production has historically outstripped population growth. The data also show that

> with the right political and social conditions, men's inventiveness, creativity, collaboration and innovation actually accelerate the production of food and other resources as population increases, rather than deplete them… Food production in the past few decades has grown exponentially and… new technologies have replaced the need for scarce or outdated resources.[32]

An increased supply of labor produced a situation where both the hawk and man eat chickens. The more hawks, the fewer the chickens, but more men usually means *more* chickens.[33] Scientists who have regarded Malthus as a failed prophet include the late editor of *Nature*, John Maddox.[34]

---

31. Ransom, 2015, p. 59.
32. Zubrin, Robert. 2012. *Merchants of Despair: Radical Environmentalists, Criminal Pseudo-Scientists, and the Fatal Cult of Antihumanism.* New York, NY: New Atlantis Books/Encounter Books, p. 16.
33. Zubrin, 2012, p. 5.
34. Maddox, John. 1972. *The Doomsday Syndrome: An assault on pessimism.* New York, NY: McGraw-Hill.

For the reasons noted above, the food situation has actually improved significantly since Malthus.[35] Despite the world population doubling between 1960 and 2000, calories produced per day, per capita, has globally increased by 23 percent during this same period. Furthermore, as any restaurant worker knows, about half of all food grown today is wasted due to various reasons, including high crop yields destroyed by waste and government price control programs. If the waste was reduced, the Earth could easily support a much larger population than exists today. One estimate is that the carrying capacity of the Earth is 50 billion persons.

Another factor is that, in many areas, including Europe, Japan, Canada, and the United States, the birth rate is now significantly below replacement level, which is about 2.1 children per family. Some nations now actually use financial incentives to encourage larger families in order to help maintain their population level. Because these programs have had very limited success, immigration now appears to be the only way that many countries can maintain their current population level.

The Harmful Results of Malthus' and Darwin's Theories

Malthus' idea also became the intellectual basis of natural selection, not only for Charles Darwin and Alfred Russel Wallace, but also for Herbert Spencer, who coined the term the 'survival-of-the-fittest' and birthed modern ecological-evolutionary social theory.[36] Historians today call Malthus "the most dismal

---

35. Lomborg, Bjørn. 2001. *The Skeptical Environmentalist: Measuring the Real State of the World.* New York, NY: Cambridge University Press, p. 62.

36. Browne, 1995, pp. 385-390; Raby, P. 2001. *Alfred Russel Wallace: A Life.* Princeton, NJ: Princeton University Press, pp. 13, 21; Spencer, Herbert. 1864. *Principles of Biology*, Volume 1, p. 444. London, England: Williams and Norgate.

scientist" because his doctrine "served to rationalize the starving of millions" of people for what was believed the good of humanity as a whole.[37]

Darwin's theory argued, as did Malthus', that most animals produce more young than the environment can support. Consequently, they must struggle with each other in order to survive. This "struggle for existence" results in those life-forms best adapted to their environment surviving, while others perish. If certain characteristics allow the animal to be able to survive to reproduce, these characteristics would be passed on to its descendants and, by this means, a new species would gradually be formed.[38]

Believing that basic human nature could not be changed, Malthus wrote "the actual population [is] kept equal to the means of subsistence by misery and vice."[39] Individual decisions regarding sex, children, and work determine the population's expansion, an idea that inspired the abortion movement as well as government regulation of the population, such as in communist countries.[40]

Among the many scientists who disagreed with Malthus was evolutionist Ronald Fisher who was skeptical of using Malthusianism as a basis for natural selection.[41] Fisher did not deny Malthus' basic premises, but emphasized the importance of the role of controlling fecundity in solving the problem.[42] Further-

---

37. Zubrin, 2012, p. 5.
38. Davis, Ira C., and Richard W. Sharpe. 1940. *Science: A Story of Progress and Discovery.* New York, NY: Henry Holt, pp. 431-432.
39. Malthus, 1859, p. 49.
40. Lopez, 2010.
41. Fisher, Ronald. 1930. *The Genetical Theory of Natural Selection.* Oxford, England: Clarendon Press. Second Revised Edition, 1958.
42. Quoted in Sober, 1993, p. 400.

more, Professor Beth Houston wrote that:

> But Darwin, like Malthus, was wrong in assuming that populations always outpace resources. Researchers have found that populations are held in check not by starvation, disease, or predation but by intrinsic forces; there is no overarching "struggle for existence," no natural selection that preserves the strong and destroys the weak. This doesn't mean that there is no struggle, only that some cosmic fundamental struggle is not the core motivation for life; life is not created and sustained by a struggle for food. Even in times of catastrophe, such as extreme drought, species survive by adapting or moving on, and geneticists now know that the ability to do either is already preprogrammed in the species.[43]

George Washington University anthropologist Eric Ross depicted Malthus' work as a major rationalization not only for the eugenics and abortion movements, but also for the social inequities produced by both the Industrial Revolution and the anti-immigration movement.[44] Malthus' theory implied that, if the population continued to grow unhindered, doom for humans would result, providing justification for widespread use of abortion, such as in China and Russia.[45]

Far from being the result of overpopulation, historians claim that events such as the 1846 Irish famine and the massive starvation in India in the late 1800s were more the result of attempts to apply Malthus' doctrine to control people rather

---

43. Houston, Beth. 2012. *Natural God: Deism in the Age of Intelligent Design.* Bradenton, FL: New Deism Press, p. 133.

44. Trewavas, Antony. 2002. Malthus foiled again and again. *Nature* 418:668–670, August 8, pp. 668–670; Lomberg, 2001, p. 61.

45. Zubrin, 2012, p. 9.

than the results of the potato disease and drought that are normally claimed to cause these human tragedies.[46]

Malthus also had a critical influence on Supreme Court Judge Oliver Wendell Holmes, who in the *Buck v. Bell* Supreme Court case allowed eugenic sterilization of those persons that the eugenic supporters determined were inferior people. In 1914 Holmes purchased a copy

of a new edition of Thomas Malthus's *An Essay on the Principle of Population.* Holmes was thoroughly won over by the book's bleak vision of the future, in which human population outstripped the food supply. In a letter to his friend Frederick Pollock, Holmes wrote, "Malthus pleased me immensely—and left me sad." ...Holmes said "that politicians and labor leaders still live on." Holmes would later declare himself a "devout Malthusian." Malthus appealed to Holmes's cynical, misanthropic side. He later explained to a friend, "I look at men through Malthus's glasses—as like flies—here swept away by a pestilence—there multiplying unduly and paying for it."[47]

In 1915, Holmes made his most direct plea

for eugenics, in an essay in the *Illinois Law Review* titled "Ideals and Doubts." The way to achieve the "wholesale social regeneration" that forward-looking people wanted, he argued, was not through "tinkering with the institution of property"—as the communists were urging—but "only by taking in hand life and

---

46. Póirtéir, Cathal (editor). 1995. *The Great Irish Famine.* Cork, Ireland: Mercier Press, pp. 88, 104.

47. Baker, Liva. 1991. *The Justice from Beacon Hill: The Life and Times of Oliver Wendell Holmes.* New York, NY: HarperCollins, p. 601; Cohen, 2016, p. 241.

EVOLUTION'S DANGEROUS IDEAS

trying to build a race."[48]

He concluded that building a superior race involved apply-
ing Darwin to society. The fact is that "Malthus' predictions
of a struggle for survival by cataclysm could not have been
less accurate."[49] We now know that, "instead of blind struggle,
there was ingenuity; instead of selfish grab, there was co-oper-
ation; with an increase in population, there actually followed
an increase in food" due to better farming techniques and new
hybrids.[50]

His Influence Today

Although his theory has continued to fail for several reasons,
Malthusian ideas continue to influence scholars today. Stanford University professor Paul Ehrlich, who was inspired by
Malthus, penned several books in the late 1960s predicting
that hundreds of millions of persons would die from the over-
population crisis that he and other leading biologists expected
to occur in the 1970s unless birth control and abortion were
widely utilized by the population.[51]

Ehrlich envisioned that the horrific future that awaited humanity included the starvation of millions, or even billions,
of people. All of his predictions have now failed and his work
"has been proven spectacularly wrong."[52] *The New York Times*
summarized his failure as follows:

---

48. Cohen, 2016, p. 241.
49. Wilson, A.N. 2017. *Charles Darwin: Victorian Mythmaker*. New York,
    NY: Harper Collins, p. 20.
50. Wilson, 2017, p. 20.
51. Lopez, 2012, p. 50.
52. Lopez, 2012, p. 51.

No one was more influential — or more terrifying, some would say — than Paul R. Ehrlich, a Stanford University biologist. His 1968 book, "The Population Bomb," sold in the millions with a jeremiad that humankind stood on the brink of apocalypse because there were simply too many of us. Dr. Ehrlich's opening statement was the verbal equivalent of a punch to the gut: "The battle to feed all of humanity is over."[53]

Journalist Haberman added that Ehrlich also forecast

that hundreds of millions would starve to death in the 1970s, that 65 million of them would be Americans, that crowded India was essentially doomed, that odds were fair "England will not exist in the year 2000." Dr. Ehrlich was so sure of himself that he warned in 1970 that "sometime in the next 15 years, the end will come." By "the end," he meant "an utter breakdown of the capacity of the planet to support humanity."[54]

The first Director-General of UNESCO, Julian Huxley, in his 1964 *Evolutionary Humanism* book, called for a radical government-enforced world population control policy. Both Huxley and Ehrlich openly encouraged use of birth control and abortion to control the population. They also aggressively opposed the Roman Catholic Church's opposition to birth control and abortion, as well as the churches' opposition to strict governmentally enforced population control.

Summary

Darwin and Wallace relied heavily on the ideas of Thomas Malthus that have proved to be misguided, especially in the

---

53. Haberman, 2015. [Quote from Ehrlich]
54. Haberman, 2015. [Quote from Ehrlich]

last century. Other results include the adoption of the Malthus-inspired eugenics movement in the United States, Nazi Germany, Sweden, and other nations, as well as the widespread support for abortion.

An illustration of the Racism by a University of Michigan Professor of Paleontology. Note the Picture of the African American the Australian are especially distorted.

From Alexander Winchell 1880 *Preadamites*. Chicago: Griggs and Company. Front Peace

Alexander Winchell Picture taken about 1880.

POPULATION CONTROL OR RACE TO OBLIVION?

THE POPULATION BOMB

WHILE YOU ARE READING THESE WORDS
FOUR PEOPLE WILL HAVE DIED FROM
STARVATION. MOST OF THEM CHILDREN.

DR. PAUL R. EHRLICH

THE
POPULATION BOMB
KEEPS TICKING

Foreword by David Brower—
Executive Director, Sierra Club

The Population Bomb, by Stanford University Professor Paul Ehrlich

16

A Book Inspired by Darwinism Triggered Repression Around the World

THE RESULTS OF THE hysteria created by Darwinist Paul Ehrlich's crusade, inspired by Thomas Malthus' prediction of the dire results of overpopulation, caused uncounted numbers of children to be aborted or killed after birth. Ehrlich's predictions of a cataclysmic population increase in a world unable to support it failed for several reasons, including new pest control technology, improved farming methods, and societal trends encouraging couples to have fewer children. This history is a good example of logical theories, that appear to be based on fact, gone woefully wrong based on Darwinist thinking.

In 1968, the "year's most important book," what Greg Garrard[1] called a neo-Malthusian classic, *The Population Bomb*, by

---

1. Garrard, Greg. 2011. *Ecocriticism*, 2nd Edition. New York, NY:

Stanford University Professor Paul Ehrlich, "made dire predictions and triggered a wave of repression around the world."[2] Authored by an evolutionary biologist known for his "groundbreaking studies of the co-evolution of flowering plants and butterflies," it became a best-seller, and turned the author into an international celebrity.[3] The book "would become one of the most influential books of the 20th century."[4]

Ehrlich's conclusion was announced in the first sentence of his book *The Population Bomb*: "The battle to feed all of humanity is over. In the 1970s and 1980s hundreds of millions of people will starve to death in spite of any crash programs embarked upon now. At this late date nothing can prevent a substantial increase in the world death rate."[5] In the end, the book and the movement it birthed "fueled an anti-population-growth crusade that led to human rights abuses around the world."[6] China enacted their one-child policy in 1978, not long after Ehrlich's book became a best seller.

Although Malthusian ideas, such as those presented by Ehrlich, continue to influence scholars today, for several reasons his theory failed in the 1960s and 1970s and has continued to fail today. Inspired by Malthus and a disciple of Malthus named William Vogt, who penned several books in the late 1960s, Ehrlich predicted massive famines as a result of pop-

Routledge, p. 96.

2. Mann, Charles. 2018. Back When the End Was Near. *Smithsonian* 48(9):86-89, January/February.
3. Mann, 2018, p. 86.
4. Mann, 2018, p. 86.
5. Ehrlich, Paul. 1968. *The Population Bomb*. New York, NY: Ballantine Books, Prologue, p. xi.
6. Mann, 2018, p. 86.

ulation increases.[7] Vogt, in his best-selling book *The Road to Survival*, argued in no uncertain terms that current population-increase trends would result in future wars, hunger, disease, and civilization collapses.[8] Likewise, Ehrlich also argued that hundreds of millions would die from the overpopulation crisis that he and other leading biologists expected to occur in the 1970s unless state-mandated birth control and abortion programs were widely applied, or, if necessary, forced on the population.[9]

Ehrlich envisioned that, by 1995, a horrific future awaited humans, including the starvation of millions, or even billions, of people. His many best-selling books in which he endeavored to document this dire future, included, besides *The Population Bomb* (1968), *Population, Resources, Environment: Issues in Human Ecology* (1970, with Anne Ehrlich), *The End of Affluence* (1974, with Anne Ehrlich), and *The Population Explosion* (1990, with Anne Ehrlich).[10]

7. Lopez, Mario. 2012. Hijacking Immigration? *The Human Life Review* 38(4):49-73, Fall. New York, NY: Human Life Foundation, p. 50.

8. Vogt, William. 1948. *The Road to Survival.* New York, NY: W. Sloane Associates.

9. Bergman, Jerry. 2015. Darwinism Used to Justify Abortion. *The Human Life Review* 41(2):53-65, Spring. New York, NY: Human Life Foundation, Inc. See also Bergman, 2012. *Slaughter of the Dissidents: The Shocking Truth About Killing the Careers of Darwin Doubters.* Southworth, WA: Leafcutter Press; 2016. *Silencing the Darwin Skeptics: The War Against Theists.* Southworth, WA: Leafcutter Press; 2018. *Censoring the Darwin Skeptics: How Belief in Evolution is Enforced by Eliminating Dissidents.* Southworth, WA: Leafcutter Press.

10. Ehrlich, Paul (with Ann Ehrlich): 1974. *The End of Affluence: A Blueprint for Your Future.* New York, NY: Ballantine Books; 1970. *Population, Resources, Environment: Issues in Human Ecology.* San Francisco, CA: W.H. Freeman; 1981. *Extinction.* New York, NY: Random House; 1990. *The Population Explosion.* New York, NY: Simon and Schuster.

Ehrlich's Ideas Proliferate

Ehrlich also was able to reach millions via several television appearances, such as in February of 1970, and numerous times afterward, on NBC's "Tonight Show with Johnny Carson."[11] In response to Vogt's and Ehrlich's ideas, the first Director-General of UNESCO, Julian Huxley, in his *Evolutionary Humanism,* called for a radical government-enforced, world population-control policy.[12] Huxley and Ehrlich openly criticized both the communist and the Roman Catholic positions on birth control, and especially on abortion, as well as their skepticism for the need for strict, government-enforced population control to avoid disaster.

Another example of applied Malthusianism is the 1972 book *The Limits to Growth* published by the Club of Rome, and the Global 2000 Report completed for then President of the United States, Jimmy Carter. Science-fiction author Isaac Asimov, reflecting the works of Charles Darwin, Robert Malthus, and Professor Paul Ehrlich, also got on board and issued many appeals for government-mandated, population-control programs.

The negative results from over-population propaganda included policies that required forced or coerced sterilization of millions living "in unsafe conditions, in Mexico, Bolivia, Peru, Indonesia, and Bangladesh."[13] In the end, over "eight million men and women were sterilized in 1975 alone" and soon after "China adopted a 'one child' policy that led to huge numbers—possibly 100 million—of coerced abortions, often in

11. Mann, 2018, p. 87.
12. Huxley, Julian, 1964. Essays of a Humanist, 1st Edition. New York, NY: Harper and Row; New 1992 edition titled *Evolutionary Humanism.* Buffalo, NY: Prometheus Books.
13. Mann, 2018, p. 88.

poor conditions contributing to infections and even death."[14] If parents could only have one child, they wanted it to be a boy, thus many Chinese girls were aborted or killed after they were born.

Ehrlich Proved Wrong

In spite of Ehrlich's predictions, there was no net increase in the death rate around the world due to famine. Actually, according to the U. N. Food and Agricultural Organization, famine has become rarer around the world since the time of his writings, from roughly 1 out of 4 suffering from hunger then, to about 1 out of 10 today. These statistics are more impressive in view of the fact that the world's population has more than doubled since Ehrlich's prediction was made. Although starvation claimed 4 to 5 million lives during the 1970s, "most of the deaths were due to warfare, rather than environmental exhaustion from over-population" as Ehrlich had warned.[15]

All of his predictions have now failed and his work "has been proven spectacularly wrong."[16] In many countries the problem now is population decline. In the United States, the replacement level had been 2.1 lifetime children per woman. More currently, the Centers for Disease Control and Prevention, as of the year ending in September 2017, showed that the total fertility rate is now 1.77 lifetime births per woman.

[From here to the end of page 242, this material was covered verbatim in the previous chapter, pages 229-231]

Why Malthus Proved Wrong

---

14. Mann, 2018, pp. 88-89.
15. Mann, 2018, p. 89.
16. Lopez, 2012, p. 51.

Before Malthus, commentators regarded high fertility as an economic advantage because it increased the number of workers. Malthus, however, convinced most economists that, even though high fertility might increase the gross economic output, it tended to reduce the per capita economic output. Even during Malthus' lifetime, the many major problems with his theory soon became obvious. Malthus had correctly diagnosed

> what economists now call the "Malthusian Trap"— that as population rose, personal income levels decreased. This was true in England, but only until about 1800. When Malthus wrote his *Essay on Population* in 1798, real wages had been stagnant or declining for generations . . . . But after 1800 the facts told a different story. By the . . . early 1830s . . . personal income was increasing even as the population grew.[17]

The reasons why geometric population growth in the 20th century did not result in a Malthusian catastrophe as Malthus expected include greater labor specialization and major capital investment that resulted in large agricultural production improvements. Other improvements included the use of fertilizers and petrochemical pesticides to control crop pests, mechanization (tractors and combines), and the introduction of high-yield farm crop varieties. Humans have also learned how to exploit past solar income — fossil fuels — to greatly increase agricultural production by producing electricity to pump water for irrigation.

One of the most critical innovations was the 1840s discovery by the German Justus von Liebig that nitrogen was a central factor in causing plant growth. Liebig then learned how

17. Snyder, Laura. 2011. *The Philosophical Breakfast Club*. New York, NY: Broadway Books, p. 125.

to synthesize the bio-available form of nitrogen, nitrate, and is thus called the "father" of the fertilizer revolution.[18]

The second critical development was in the early 1900s when chemist Fritz Haber developed a process to synthesize fertilizer by using high temperatures to combine hydrogen derived from methane with atmospheric nitrogen.[19] The energy-intensive Haber-Bosch process is now used throughout the world to fixate atmospheric nitrogen to produce low-cost artificial fertilizers. All of these developments have now largely negated Malthus' major thesis. Even the late editor of the leading science magazine, *Nature*, John Maddox, regarded Malthus as a failed prophet.[20]

As a result, though seemingly logical, the Malthusian premise has been falsified. Zubin, in a chapter titled "The Data That Proves Malthus Wrong," reviews world population growth data plotted against GDP per capita growth, documenting how crop production has historically outstripped population growth. The data also show that

> with the right political and social conditions, men's inventiveness, creativity, collaboration, and innovation actually accelerate the production of food and other resources as population increases, rather than deplete them . . . . Food production in the past few decades has grown exponentially, and . . . new technologies have replaced the need for scarce or outdated resources.[21]

18. Ransom, Cliff. 2015. *100 Inventions that Changed the World*. New York, NY: Time Home Entertainment, p. 59.

19. Ransom, 2015, p. 59.

20. Maddox, John. 1972. *The Doomsday Syndrome: An Assault on Pessimism*. New York, NY: McGraw-Hill.

21. Zubrin, Robert. 2012. *Merchants of Despair: Radical Environmentalists, Criminal Pseudo-Scientists, and the Fatal Cult of Antihumanism*. New York, NY: New Atlantis Books/Encounter Books, p. 16.

An increased supply of labor produced a situation like the story used by Malthus critics: while both the hawk and man eat chickens, the more hawks, the fewer the chickens, but more men usually means *more* chickens.[22] The food situation has actually improved today.[23] Despite the world population doubling between 1960 and 2000, calories produced per day, per capita, have globally increased by 23 percent during this same period.

Ehrlich's Aggressive Opposition to Creationism

Ehrlich critic Benjamin Shapiro entered UCLA at sixteen, graduated summa cum laude in June 2004, and went on to graduate from Harvard University Law School cum laude in 2007. In response to Ehrlich's opinion that "American neoconservatives promote creationism because, as their own statements reveal, they apparently fear an educated population and see the theory of evolution as a threat", Shapiro wondered if it ever occurred to

> Ehrlich that perhaps many neoconservatives believe in the word of God? Probably not, since Ehrlich believes conservatives are out to lynch blacks and enslave the poor. Teaching creation science is foolish, professors believe. "They could just as well talk about Kumulipo," the Hawaiian creation chant, scoffs Professor Pauline Chinn of the University of Hawaii. "Creationism isn't science, it's faith," nods Hawaii Institute of Geophysics and Planetology Professor Gerald Fryer. "The big lie is that there's something to (creationism)," sneers Professor Victor Stenger,

---

22. Zubrin, 2012, p. 5.
23. Lomborg Bjørn. 2001. *The Skeptical Environmentalist: Measuring the Real State of the World.* New York, NY: Cambridge University Press, p. 62.

also of the University of Hawaii.[24]

This indicates the attitude of Ehrlich toward evolution critics. Another example of how negative Ehrlich is toward creationists is the case of Erville Clark, a former student of Ehrlich when he was teaching at Stanford. Professor Clark, in spite of his above-average qualifications that earned him an excellent academic record, was denied his Ph.D. in biology at Stanford University.

He was finally able to complete his doctorate at Oregon State University. The department chair there, in evaluating Clark's admission papers, contacted Stanford and learned that Mr. Clark was denied the Ph.D. because he was a creationist. Professor Ronald Numbers comments that this case reflects the dirty tricks common in academia against creationists. In recounting the bitter incident, Clark expressed the conclusion that much of the reason was Ehrlich's disdain for Clark's anti-evolution views, writing that, early in his Ph.D. program, Clark

> had taken a course on evolution with Paul R. Ehrlich (b. 1932), from whom he received a [grade of] B. Later, when Clark attempted to defend his dissertation *on the ecology of a single county in northern California, Ehrlich zeroed in, quizzing him on ecology around the world, about which the young biologist admittedly knew relatively little.* From what he later learned, four of the five committee members voted to pass him, but the department required a unanimous decision. The next year he retook the examination

---

24. Shapiro, Ben. 2004. *Brainwashed: How Universities Indoctrinate America's Youth.* Nashville, TN: WND Books. Foreword by Attorney David Limbaugh, pp. 89-90.

with the same results, which led to automatic termination.[25]

Numbers continued, adding:

Determined to earn the doctorate his father never possessed, Clark later enrolled in a general science program at Oregon State University, from which he received a Ph.D. in 1971 for a dissertation on radiation biology.[26]

It is clear that one member of his Ph.D. committee made sure that Clark would fail his oral exams. Letters from Stanford about this case in my file expressed open intolerance against creationists, and Clark specifically. In an interview with Dr. Ehrlich about this case, Kevin Wirth reported that Ehrlich claimed the Ph.D. was *not* denied due to Clark's beliefs, but then later Ehrlich exclaimed, well "would *you* grant a Ph.D. to a creationist?"[27]

Summary

The modern "population bomb" ideological movement begun largely by Ehrlich, who relied heavily on the ideas of Thomas Malthus, has proved to be misguided, especially in the last century. The predictions of Ehrlich have, fortunately, largely failed to come to pass. They also proved to be deleterious as a result of large-scale negation of human rights that Ehrlich's ideas promulgated. These programs caused a great deal of harm to society, including millions of abortions, especially of female fetuses in China, and sterilizations in the United States, India,

---

25. Numbers, Ronald L. 2006. *The Creationists*. Cambridge, MA: Harvard University Press, pp.299-271, emphasis added.

26. Numbers, 2006, pp.299-271, emphasis mine.

27. Bergman, 2012, pp 46-47.

China, and many other nations. The full story of the harm of Ehrlich's ideas has yet to be told, but this chapter is a start.

JUDEA PEARL

WINNER OF THE TURING AWARD

AND DANA MACKENZIE

THE

BOOK OF

WHY

THE NEW SCIENCE
OF CAUSE AND EFFECT

A book cover on the Importance of understanding Cause and Effect

17

The Worst Blunder: Rejecting the Law of Cause and Effect in Cosmology

ONE OF THE MOST WIDELY accepted and powerful arguments for the existence of a Creator is the existence of the creation. As a watch requires a watchmaker, likewise a creation requires a creator. This is an example of the Law of Causality [or Causation] which says that, for every effect there must be a cause which is both sufficient and logically deduced from experiment and reason. The Law of Causality is accepted as an axiom and is the basis of science and of our entire society. This argument is used prominently in both the Scriptures and historically. It is today one of the most profound arguments for a theological worldview.

In fact, one of the biggest blunders of Darwinism was the denial of the Law of Causality. At first the evolutionists' argument was that we do not understand the cause of some event, such as the origin of the universe, but more research will surely reveal that it's based on a naturalistic framework. As we will document, the belief is, in the words of Stephen Hawking, from nothing came, eventually, *everything*. One post put it this way:

> Some philosophers and scientists argue that everything has a cause and that nothing can simply exist for no reason. This is known as the principle of causality. Others argue that the universe itself may have no cause and simply exists.... Ultimately, the question of whether everything can simply exist for no reason is one that is still being debated, and different people may have different beliefs and perspectives on the matter.[1]

The idea that everything can exist for no reason is not rational. One of the oldest lines of reasoning and, for many people the most convincing, is the Law of Causality. Isaac Newton's **first law of motion** states that "a body will continue in its state of rest or uniform motion unless an unbalanced force acts upon it." This is an example of the most universally accepted axiom of science, namely that *for everything that exists or occurs there must exist a sufficient cause.* This axiom is the basis of the tremendous effort expended by scientists in trying to find the cause of everything from the common cold to cancer. The view that cancer has a cause, and that cause can be known to researchers, is what drives scientific research in this area. This belief has led to success in science so often that few question the axiom that a cause exists, and most all persons fully believe and act decisively on the conclusion that both a cause for everything exists and that it can be found.

A major *reason* a cause is searched for is because, once

---

1. https://www.quora.com/Can-everything-simply-exist-for-no-reason.

it is understood, the cure or solution is often only one step away. For example, discovery of the cause is often much--or even most--of the battle in curing cancer. When humans have looked for a cause, they have found it so often that we assume that a cause exists for *all* events.

The Law of Causality also argues for the existence of a Creator-God as the un-caused First Cause, and thus the creation model as opposed to the "pure" or atheistic model. As a watch is usually sufficient proof of the existence of a watchmaker, likewise, the act of something moving proves the existence of a mover, and the existence of a *creation* proves the reality of a *creator*. This view concludes that *all events have a cause, except the un-caused First Cause.* In Professor Thompson's words:

> Indisputably, the most universal, and the most certain, of all scientific laws is the law of cause and effect, or as it is commonly known, the law (or principle) of causality. Scientists, and philosophers of science, recognize laws as "reflecting actual regularities in nature."[2]

He added that

> as scientific testing and historical experience can attest, laws know no exceptions. And this is certainly true of the law of causality. This law has been stated in a variety of ways, each of which adequately expresses its ultimate meaning. Kant, in the first edition of his *Critique of Pure Reason*, stated that "everything that happens (begins to be) presupposes something which it follows according to a rule." In the second edition, he strengthened that statement by noting that "all changes take place according

2. Thompson, Bert. 1990. The Bible and the Laws of Science: The Law of Cause and Effect. *Reason and Revelation* 1(3):13-16, March, p. 13.

to the law of connection of cause and effect."[3]

The Law of Causality was the basis of William Paley's famous eighteenth century argument for God from natural theology, the term once used to refer to the study of the natural world.

Paley's Natural Theology

In his famous book, *Natural Theology*, Paley appeals to the cause-effect reasoning as a primary proof for God's existence.[4] His most well-known illustration was that, if one found a stone and was asked how it came to be, one could argue that it came to exist naturally or had been there forever. But if one found a watch on the ground and inquired as to how it happened to be there, one could not argue that it came into existence naturally or that it had been there forever.

Paley argued: Does not the argument that explains the existence of the watch also explain the existence of the stone? Paley answers that "when we come to inspect the watch we perceive that its several parts are framed and put together for a purpose."[5] The watch's complexity and the obvious intent of its design and purpose forces the conclusion that the watch must have had a maker who understood its construction and designed it for a specific use, namely to tell time:

> But suppose I had found a *watch* upon the ground, and it should be inquired how the watch happened to be in that place, I should

3. Thompson, 1990, p. 13.
4. Sprague, Elmer. 1967. "*Paley, William (1743-1805)*." In Edwards, Paul (editor). 1967. *The Encyclopedia of Philosophy,* Volume 6 (of 8):18-20. New York, NY: Macmillan.
5. Paley, William. 1839. *Paley's Natural Theology* (in two volumes). New York, NY: Harper and Brothers, p. 50.

hardly think ... that ... the watch might have always been there. Yet why should not this answer serve for the watch as well as for the stone? Why is it not as admissible in the second case as in the first?[6]

The reason why is that when we examine the

watch, we perceive (what we could not discover in the stone) that its several parts are framed and put together for a purpose, *e.g.*, that they are so formed and adjusted as to produce motion, and that motion so regulated as to point out the hour of the day; that, if the different parts had been differently shaped from what they are, of a different size from what they are, or placed after any other manner, or in any other order than that in which they are placed, either no motion at all would have been carried on in the machine, or none which would have answered the use that is now served by it.[7]

Paley then turns to the design of the human and animal body as evidence of a maker. Much of the rest of his *Natural Theology* is based on this line of reasoning. According to Clark, Paley's argument even influenced Charles Darwin as a young man, who, during his university days

was subjected to two opposed influences epitomizing the forces that were to beat round his head once his theory of evolution had been published. One was that of William Paley, the eminent divine and former Fellow of Christ's [College, Cambridge]. Paley's writings had provided a main argument for those who saw the evidence of heavenly design in nature and for whom

6.   Paley, 1839, p. 50.
7.   Paley, 1839, p. 50.

Darwin's natural selection was to be quite unacceptable.[8]

An example, extending this to the lens of a fish eye, finds that it

> was more spherical than the lens in the eye of land vertebrates because each was adapted to the refractive index of the medium, water or air. "The marks of *design* are too strong to be gotten over," Paley declared. "Design must have had a designer. That designer must have been a person. That person is God."[9]

Paley's *Evidences of Christianity* was compulsory reading for undergraduates at Cambridge when Darwin was a student there. It was also necessary to master Paley's *Evidences of Christianity*, and his *Moral Philosophy*, to pass the B. A. examination at Cambridge. Darwin wrote:

> getting up Paley's Evidences and Moral Phil. thoroughly well as I did, I felt was an admirable training, and everything else bosh.[10]

Darwin's own words eloquently illustrate his high opinion of Paley at the time, though he later attempted to refute the watchmaker worldview. Nonetheless, Darwin mastered Paley so thoroughly that he was convinced that he, Darwin,

> could have written out the whole of the *Evidences* with perfect correctness, but not of course in the clear language of Paley. The logic of this book and, as I may add, of his *Natural Theology*, gave

---

8. Clark, Ronald W. 1984. *The Survival of Charles Darwin: A Biography of a Man and an Idea.* New York, NY: Random House, pp. 12-13.

9. Clark, 1984, pp. 12-13.

10. Clark, 1984, pp. 12-13.

me as much delight as did Euclid. The careful study of these works, without attempting to learn any part by rote, was the only part of the academical course which, as I then felt, and as I still believe, was of the least use to me in the education of my mind. I did not at that time trouble myself about Paley's premises; and taking these on trust, I was charmed and convinced by the long line of argumentation.[11]

Although Darwin later discounted Paley's view, many of his later followers could not dismiss it so easily. The President of the American Museum of Natural History and the most eminent early twentieth century evolutionist, Henry Fairfield Osborn, later noted that the famous evolutionist T.H. Huxley "once told me that Paley's argument for the direct handiwork of the Creator was so logically, so ingeniously and convincingly written that he [Huxley] always kept it at his bedside for last reading at night."[12] Osborn added that as

long as the chance of fortuitous hypothesis of adaptation reigned, Paley's argument for the existence of God was set aside, but our more profound knowledge ... gained by direct observation of Nature, leaves Paley's argument just as strong as it ever was: Paley's 'evidences' may be challenged now no more effectively than it could be challenged in 1858.[13]

A half century later Oxford University Professor Richard Dawkins concluded:

11. Darwin, Francis (editor). 1958. *The Autobiography of Charles Darwin and Selected Letters.* New York, NY: Dover Publications, p. 19.
12. Osborn, Henry Fairfield. 1925. *The Earth Speaks to Bryan.* New York, NY: Scribner's, pp. 64-65.
13. Osborn, 1925, p. 15.

It is almost as if the human brain were specifically designed to misunderstand Darwinism, and to find it hard to believe. ...[The conclusion that] our brains seem predisposed to resist Darwinism stems from our great success as creative designers. Our world is dominated by feats of engineering and works of art. We are entirely accustomed to the idea that complex elegance is an indicator of premeditated, crafted design. *This is probably the most powerful reason for the belief, held by the vast majority of people that have ever lived, in some kind of supernatural deity.*[14]

The realization that the existence of a creation requires a creator, or at least a process that can account for the existence of a creation, requires those who do not believe in an intelligent creator to hypothesize other means to account for the universe's existence. One theory, which was in vogue for a short time partly because of such works as Erich von Däniken's *Chariots of the Gods,* is the idea that life came from another planet and, in essence, was dropped off here via some type of spacecraft. This idea does not solve the problem, but only transfers it to another place and time. We still need to learn *why* and *how* life was created at the place from which it supposedly came.[15]

Evidence for the Law of Causality

The Cause-Effect Law, which is "one of the central operating notions in our ordinary life," is constantly encountered in daily life.[16] When a mother discovers wet mud tracks on the living

14. Dawkins, Richard. 1986. *The Blind Watchmaker.* New York, NY: Norton, pp. xi-xii; emphasis added.

15. Wysong, Randy L. 1976. *The Creation-Evolution Controversy.* East Lansing, MI: Inquiry Press, p. 33.

16. Brand, Myles (editor). 1976. "The Regularity Theory of the Idea of Necessary Connection." Chapter by David Hume in *The Nature of Causation.* Urbana, IL: University of Illinois Press, p. 1.

room floor, she does not need to personally see the culprit to deduce what has occurred. The mud is enough proof to conclude that *someone* has traversed the floor with muddy shoes. Likewise, the existence of the creation is itself sufficient to prove a Creator because the Law of Causality demands that a force made, or created, what exists. This logic is illustrated by the following conversation that Isaac Newton reportedly had with a friend of his who had noticed a recently constructed mechanical model of the Solar System (i.e., an orrery). As Newton sat reading in his study,

> his infidel friend stepped in. Scientist that he [Newton's friend] was, he recognized at a glance what was before him. Stepping up to it, he slowly turned the crank, and with undisguised admiration watched the heavenly bodies all move in their relative speed in their orbits. Standing off a few feet he exclaimed, "My! What an exquisite thing this is! Who made it?" Without looking up from his book, Newton answered, "Nobody!"

> Quickly turning to Newton, the infidel said, "Evidently you did not understand my question. I asked who made this?" Looking up now, Newton solemnly assured him that nobody made it, but that the aggregation of matter [he] so much admired had just happened to assume the form it was in. But the astonished infidel replied with some heat. ... Of course, somebody made it, and he is a genius, and I'd like to know who he is."

> Laying his book aside, Newton rose and laid a hand on his friend's shoulder.

> "This thing is but a puny imitation of a much grander system whose laws you know, and I am not able to convince you that

this mere toy is without a designer and maker; yet you profess to believe that the great original from which the design is taken has come into being without either designer or maker! Now tell me by what sort of reasoning do you reach such an incongruous conclusion?"[17]

In his *Mathematical Principles of Natural Philosophy,* in harmony with Paley, Newton concluded that

it is not to be conceived that mere mechanical causes could give birth to so many regular motions...This most beautiful system of the sun, planets, and comets, could only proceed from the council and dominion of an intelligent and powerful Being. ...This Being governs all things, not as the Lord of the world, but as Lord over all .... for God...is a Being eternal, infinite, absolutely perfect...It is allowed by all that the Supreme God exists necessarily.[18]

Newton also argued that God is not just an orderer and machinist, but sustains the universe directly. Newton's major contribution to science was arguing effectively in his writings for the need for a sufficient cause in explaining the existence of the universe. One indication of Newton's status in the scientific world is the late Isaac Asimov's conclusion that most science historians would agree that Isaac Newton was the greatest scientific mind that ever lived.[19] That the watchmaker argument

---

17. Newton, Isaac. 1957. "Who Made It?" *The Minnesota Technology Center* 38(1):11, October, p. 11.

18. Newton, Sir Isaac. 1952. *Mathematical Principles of Natural Philosophy.* In *Great Books of the Western World,* Volume 34, p. 269. Chicago, IL: Encyclopedia Britannica, Inc.

19. Asimov, Isaac. 1964. *Asimov's Biographical Encyclopedia of Science and Technology.* Garden City, NY: Doubleday.

is still powerful is reflected in the publication of tomes such as *The Blind Watchmaker*:

> Paley drives his point home with beautiful and reverent descriptions of the dissected machinery of life, beginning with the human eye, a favorite example which Darwin was later to use and which will reappear throughout this book. Paley compares the eye with a designed instrument such as a telescope, and concludes that "there is precisely the same proof that the eye was made for vision, as there is that the telescope was made for assisting it." The eye must have had a designer, just as the telescope had.[20]

Use of Reasoning from Effect in the Legal System

The Law of Causality is also critical not only in the exact sciences, such as physics and chemistry, but also in archaeology, history, and even such fields as crime detection (forensics) and paleontology. We often cannot locate (and thus cannot measure or evaluate) the *causer*, but we can examine what was *affected*, and from this examination can interpolate the qualities of the *affecter*.

In the paleontology field, much of what is known about ancient life was deduced from artifacts, such as teeth, bones, animal tracks, dung, and fossil eggs. Tracks and skeletal structures are our main source of knowledge as to how fast dinosaurs walked (or ran), and specifically how they walked, the shape of their feet, as well as the shape of many of their foot bones.[21]

The process of determining guilt in a court of law relies

---

20. Dawkins, 1986, p. 5.
21. Bakker, Robert. 1986. *The Dinosaur Heresies*. New York, NY: William Morrow.

on the *assumption of cause principle*, requiring evidence, such as fingerprints, shoe tracks, clothing threads, or bullets. No judge would accept the claim that the knife that just stabbed the victim did not have a cause (i.e., a knife wielder). An explanation that would be accepted is that the accused obtained a knife from his house and stabbed the victim. This evidence may even be better than the testimony of several reliable persons who observed the offender committing the crime. This same type of evidence is commonly utilized by creationists and the Scriptures to prove the existence of a Creator. For example, Psalms 119:1 in the *Good News Bible* says: "How clearly the sky reveals God's glory! How plainly it shows what He has done!" Rejection of this view is the acceptance of functional atheism because the term *creator* is synonymous with God.

Theism teaches that the First Cause is God who has always existed. The naturalistic worldview, however, teaches the oscillating universe, i. e., an infinite number of 'big bangs' "explains" where each big bang came from. In this view, each big bang is simply the result of the collapse of the previous universe. The present universe will expand to its limit, then will collapse upon itself causing the Big Crunch, which will again explode, producing another big bang.

Thus, the question, "where did the first primordial "egg" that produced the first Big Bang come from", is answered either by assuming that the material universe always existed or that it spontaneously generated itself. Many philosophers and theologians have dealt with the un-caused First Cause by concluding that the Law of Causality applies only to material reality. Thus, God is a spirit who does not obey this law, and un-caused spirit events can cause physical events to occur, not unlike the law of potential and kinetic energy.

Kinetic energy can come from both potential and kinetic energy, but potential energy can come *only* from kinetic energy. Potential energy is not a reality, but only a situation that can produce the reality of kinetic energy. Kinetic energy, on the other hand, can produce a situation in which there is a potential to produce energy, thus called "potential energy".

Our lack of understanding of the spirit world, and our inability to apply reason to things which are not material, or at least not concrete, limits us from speculating about any world other than the material world. We are limited to using analogies and experiences from the material world and we extend these to our perceptions and theories about the non-material reality.

Stephen Hawking's Answer

Stephen Hawking's prominence is indicated by the fact that, as Kip Thorne tells us, Hawking, an atheist, is buried in one of the most hallowed places in the world, Westminster Abbey in London, between creationist Isaac Newton and agnostic Charles Darwin.[22] Hawking's daughter, Lucy, wrote about her father, that he was "dearly loved and respected . . . by millions of people . . . from all around the world," especially by scientists and many educated laymen.[23] He is also "one of the most celebrated and respected personalities of our century . . . the Einstein of our time" and his "theories influenced . . . heads of state, students, scientists, and even the Pope."[24]

---

22. Thorn, Kip. 2018. Introduction to *Brief Answers to the Big Questions*. New York, NY: Bantam, p. xvi.
23. Hawking, Stephen. 2018. *Brief Answers to the Big Questions*. New York, NY: Bantam Books. Introduction by Kip Thorne, p. 214.
24. Lieth, N. 2018. The Death of a Genius and the Life of the Savior. *Midnight Call*, pp 24-25, November, p. 24.

Hawking explains that religion was an early attempt to answer where all matter and life came from until science began developing about 200 years ago. Now, he informs us, science has shown us that religion was wrong. In his words, "science provides better and more consistent answers, but people will always cling to religion, because it gives comfort, and they do not ... understand science."[25]

He ignores the fact that many people both trust and understand science, and still accept the theological explanation. Hawking, a page later, admits that he "*prefers* to think that everything can be explained . . . by the laws of nature," but never attempts to explain the origin of and what sustains these laws.[26] The law of gravity explains empirically that any two masses attract each other with a force equal to the gravitation constant multiplied by the product of the two masses divided by the square of the distance between them. Gravity always works, but *why* and *how* action at a distance works, works, (where an object can be moved, changed, or otherwise affected without being physically touched by another object), Hawking does not even attempt to answer in his book, nor elsewhere.[27] Nor has anyone else explained this, even in a 1,280-page book attempting to answer this question.[28] Hawking claims that the query regarding God's existence "is a valid question for science," but Hawking concluded that it is a science question that has already been rejected by science.[29] C.S. Lewis observed, "The laws of Nature explain everything except the source of

25. Hawking, 2018, p. 25.
26. Hawking, 2018, p. 26.
27. Hawking, Steven and Werner Israel, 1989. *Three Hundred Years of Gravitation.* New York: Cambridge University Press.
28. Thorne, et al., 2018.
29. Hawking, 2018, pp. 27-29.

events."[30]

This entire issue of the origin of the universe was ignored for much of history because it was widely believed by the Greeks, Romans, and other major civilizations that the universe, including time, space, matter, and energy, has *always* existed.[31] As Hawking correctly points out, if the universe has always existed it would have heated up equally everywhere, producing a uniform temperature throughout the universe due to entropy. Furthermore, the night sky would be lit up equally everywhere for the same reason.[32]

The Big Bang

Hawking concluded that the Big Bang is *ultimately* the creation of everything from something called the "primordial egg" which itself appeared from nothing or perhaps from something "smaller than a proton."[33] Then the expansion of the universe occurred and the stars and planets followed. Thus, the Big Bang explains the origin of space, matter, energy, and time from nothing.[34] In other words, thanks to the Big Bang "you can get a whole universe for free" because by the Big Bang "the fantastically enormous universe of space and energy can materialize out of nothing."[35] Thus "the universe itself, in all its mind-boggling vastness and complexity, could simply have popped into existence without violating the known laws of nature . . . [and] we do not need a God to set it up so that the Big

30. Lewis. C. S. "The Laws of Nature" published on April 4, 1945, in *The Coventry Evening Telegraph.*
31. Hawking, 2018, p. 43.
32. Hawking, 2018, p. 45.
33. Hawking, 2018, p. 34.
34. Hawking, 2018, pp. 29-31.
35. Hawking, 2018, pp. 31-32.

Bang could bang."[36] Furthermore before the Big Bang there was no matter, no space, no energy, and no time.[37] Hawking admits that this Big Bang "is hard to grasp, but it's true . . . [and] you don't need a God to create it," because it [the universe] can create itself.[38]

In an attempt to explain the idea that nothing produced everything, and no cause is required, Hawking notes that matter and anti-matter annihilate each other, producing gamma rays. Consequently, the reverse reaction produces matter, ignoring the fact that *energy* in this reaction, namely gamma rays, produces matter, not nothing. This is a major violation of the Law of Causality.

Hawking adds that before the Big Bang there was no time, thus this was the first un-caused cause because there was "no time for a cause to exist in."[39] As is obvious, this entire line of reasoning rapidly degenerates into speculative, often nonsensical circular reasoning by a man who has been given the stature by his peers, and society as a whole, as one of the greatest scientists that has ever lived.

For example, Hawking has exclaimed that "when people ask me if a God created the universe, I tell them the question itself makes no sense... because "Time didn't exist before the Big Bang so there is no time for God to make the universe in."[40] This rings hollow, for if God existed before the Big Bang, He could have created time, then, once time existed, he could have created the universe. Or, instead of the Big Bang somehow do-

---

36. Hawking, 2018, p. 34.
37. Hawking, 2018, p. 37.
38. Hawking, 2018, p. 33.
39. Hawking, 2018, p. 38.
40. Hawking, 2018, p. 38.

ing the creating, God could have created time, space, matter, and energy simultaneously, then created the universe.

The Law of Cause and the Existence of Life

Those who do not believe in a Creator conclude that life originated through spontaneous generation under conditions that *no longer exist today.* They reason that spontaneous generation is not possible *today,* but *was* in the past because it *must* have happened because life is here, and science cannot appeal to a non-naturalistic view. To make the theory of spontaneous generation more palatable, it was believed that life did not spontaneously generate from nothing, nor did inanimate matter change into fully-developed creatures such as flies. Rather, supposedly life spontaneously generated from amino acids that slowly changed into very simple life-forms, and eventually into forms such as viruses and, with more eons, into bacteria and, after many more eons, evolved into humans. However, one problem for evolutionists is that no known simple life forms are known to exist, and viruses are not simple.

Thus, naturalistic evolutionists today in actuality accept a *form* of miraculous spontaneous generation--a theory they attempt to make more plausible by pushing it eons back in time and arguing for very small changes instead of major life productions.

To account for naturalistic evolution, evolutionists usually look to mutations, or changes in the genetic code of the organism caused by damage to the genes from radiation or chemicals. To say that this happened suddenly would be absurd, but this idea becomes reasonable to some persons if it is stretched out over an incredibly long period of time. The cause problem, though, still exists, and is often not helped by adding additional time.

Time, even eons of time, added to an improbable event does not cause it to become more probable. Time increases the chances of rare events happening, but does *not* significantly increase the probability of highly improbable events occurring because the universe is now thought to be both finite and limited. The time span proposed is far too short and the universe's size far too small. Only 10^{80} nucleons and electrons are currently estimated to exist, far too few to explain much by naturalism. *Just because something is statistically probable does not make it logically possible.*

The Need for Adequate Causes

Further, when cause is evaluated, another aspect must be considered. Every effect not only must have a cause, but must have an *adequate* cause.[41] In Thompson's words, "The river did not turn muddy because the frog jumped in; the book did not fall from the table because the fly lighted on it; these are not adequate causes. Whatever effects we observed, we must postulate adequate causes."[42]

An extension from this idea is that, as 4 + 6 cannot equal 12, nor can 4 + 6 equal 7, the effect cannot be either superior or inferior to the cause and, indeed, must be equal to it. Known as the Law of Conservation in chemistry, this law applies not only to the material world, but also to the effects produced by the material world such as energy. Thus, the Law of Conservation of energy (and with mass-energy conversions, the conservation of both) demonstrates that the cause must be of a certain qualitative and, especially, a quantitative level so as to produce a given effect, i.e., the cause-and-effect relationship is conserved.

---

41. Achinstein, 1981.
42. Thompson, 1990, p. 14.

Summary

The existence of a creation requires a Creator or some means of bringing the material creation into existence. If something happened, adequate causal factors must exist to cause it to occur. What accounts for the existence of the creation is the subject matter of the science field called *origins* or *cosmology*.

Research into the origin of life relegates itself to two views, creation by a sufficient Creator or a creation by some means of spontaneous generation--a creation without a Creator. One who accepts the creation hypothesis realizes that gaps exist in this worldview, but this is not unlike the naturalistic evolutionary view which also suffers from many gaps, such as the origin of *new* genetic variety. All origins beliefs are based on probabilities, and acknowledging this fact helps us work from a lower to a higher probability level. This is a road all researchers must travel to find answers, and one which requires filling gaps in knowledge no matter what branch we select.

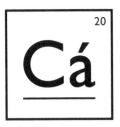

About the Cántaro Institute
Inheriting, Informing, Inspiring

Cántaro Institute is a reformed evangelical organization committed to the advancement of the Christian worldview for the reformation and renewal of the church and culture.

We believe that as the Christian church returns to the fount of Scripture as her ultimate authority for all knowing and living, and wisely applies God's truth to every aspect of life, faithful in spirit to the reformers, her missiological activity will result in not only the renewal of the human person but also the reformation of culture, an inevitable result when the true scope and nature of the gospel is made known and applied.

Milton Keynes UK
Ingram Content Group UK Ltd.
UKHW040630131124
2810UKWH00007B/23